PLANET EARTH

EARTH

— A Journey from Pole to Pole —

Sandcastle Books

Academic consultants
- Dr Mark Hostetler, Department of Wildlife Ecology and Conservation, University of Florida, USA (*Temperate grasslands / Deserts and semi-deserts*)
- Dr Valerie Kapos, Senior Advisor in forest ecology and conservation to the UNEP World Conservation Monitoring Center (*Taiga / Tropical grasslands / Temperate forests / Mountains and highlands*)
- Professor David Mabberley, Honorary Research Associate, Royal Botanic Gardens, Sydney, Australia (*Shrublands / Tropical forests*)
- Dr Barbara Ransom, Research Scientist, Scripps Institution of Oceanography, University of California at San Diego, USA (*Oceans and beaches*)
- Professor Emeritus Robert G. White, Institute of Arctic Biology, University of Alaska Fairbanks, USA (*Arctic tundra and polar deserts*)

Contributors
Michael Allaby, Robert Anderson and Ian Crofton (*Deserts and semi-deserts*); David Burnie (*Shrublands*); Trevor Day (*Oceans and beaches / Taiga*); Ben Hoare (*Temperate grasslands*); Tom Jackson (*Tropical forests*); Ben Morgan (*Tropical grasslands*); Chris Woodford (*Arctic tundra and polar deserts*); John Woodward (*Temperate forests*)

Project Editor: Ben Morgan
Deputy Editor: Dr Rob Houston
Designer: Reg Cox
Cartographers: Mark Walker and Darren Awuah
Picture Researcher: Clare Newman
Managing Editor: Tim Harris
Design Manager: Lynne Ross
Production: Alastair Gourlay
Editorial Director: Lindsey Lowe

The Brown Reference Group plc
First Floor
9-17 St. Albans Place
London
N1 0NX
www.brownreference.com

© 2008 The Brown Reference Group plc

ISBN 978-1-906020-15-6

Published by Sandcastle Books Ltd
The Stables
Sheriffs Lench Court
Sheriffs Lench
Worcs WR11 4SN
UK

This edition published in 2008

Printed in Thailand

Front cover: The Mississippi Delta and the Gulf of Mexico from space.

Title page: Mount Roraima, Venezuela.

The acknowledgments on p. 384 form part of this copyright page.

About this book

Biomes are broad geographical regions with a similar climate and distinctive plants and animals. *Planet Earth* explores the world's biomes in a journey that stretches from pole to pole. The book begins with an introduction to Earth's major biomes, including a world map. Following this are ten sections, each of which considers in detail a particular biome, from Arctic tundra and deserts to mountains and oceans. The sections are largely arranged geographically, starting at the poles and heading toward the equator.

After a two-page introduction, each section details the biome's climate and then its plants and animals. At the end of each section are detailed maps that focus on particular places within each biome, such as the Amazon rainforest or Sahara desert. The map pages are shown in the contents in italics, **like this**. Throughout the book you'll also find boxed stories and fact files that provide fascinating details on particular aspects of a biome, its climate, or its wildlife.

Contents

Biomes of the world

Biologists divide the living world into major zones called biomes. Each biome has its own distinctive climate, plants and animals.

If you were to walk all the way from the north of Canada to the Amazon **rainforest**, you'd notice the wilderness changing dramatically along the way.

Northern Canada is a freezing and barren place without trees, where only tiny brownish-green plants can survive in the icy ground. But trudge south for long enough and you enter a magical world of **conifer** forests, where moose, caribou (reindeer) and wolves live. After several weeks, the conifers disappear, and you reach the grass-covered prairies of the central USA. The further south you go, the drier the land gets and the hotter the sun feels, until you find yourself hiking through a cactus-filled **desert**. But once you reach southern Mexico, the cacti start to disappear, and strange **tropical** trees begin to take their place. Here, the muggy air is filled with the calls of exotic birds and the drone of tropical insects. Finally, in Colombia you cross the Andes mountain range – whose chilly peaks remind you a little of your starting point – and descend into the dense, swampy jungles of the Amazon rainforest.

Desert is the driest biome. There are hot deserts and cold ones.

Taiga is made up of conifer trees that can survive freezing winters.

Scientists have a special name for the different regions – such as desert, tropical rainforest and prairie – that you'd pass through on such a journey. They call them **biomes**. Everywhere on Earth can be classified as being in one biome or another, and the same biome often appears in lots of

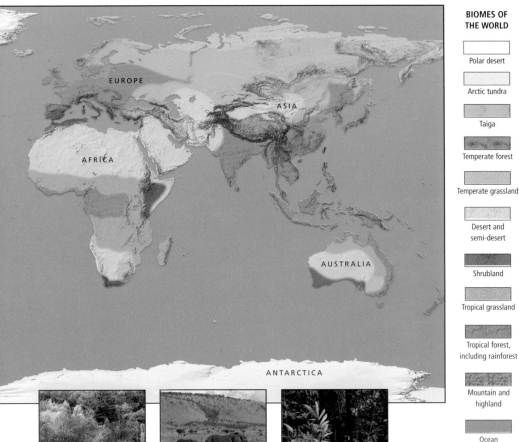

BIOMES OF THE WORLD

EUROPE

ASIA

AFRICA

AUSTRALIA

ANTARCTICA

Polar desert

Arctic tundra

Taiga

Temperate forest

Temperate grassland

Desert and
semi-desert

Shrubland

Tropical grassland

Tropical forest,
including rainforest

Mountain and
highland

Ocean

Temperate forest
includes trees that lose
their leaves in autumn.

Tropical grassland, or
savanna, is home to the
biggest land animals.

Rainforest contains the
richest mix of plants and
animals on the planet.

different places. For instance, there are areas of rainforest as far apart as Brazil, Africa and South-east Asia. Although the plants and animals that inhabit these forests are different, they live in similar ways. Likewise, the prairies of North America are part of the grassland biome, which also occurs in China, Australia and Argentina. Wherever there are grasslands, there are grazing animals that feed on the grass, as well as large carnivores that hunt and kill the grazers.

The map on this page shows how the world's major biomes fit together to make up the biosphere – the zone of life on Earth.

The polar biomes

Next time you open your freezer, think what it would be like to live in an icy cold place. Perhaps you would need a layer of blubbery fat to keep you warm. Or maybe you would have a thick, hairy coat and stand still for long periods.

Polar bears are the only large mammals that can survive on polar deserts.

Biting cold is only one of the problems of living near the poles. But it is the main reason that the Arctic (the region near the North Pole) and the Antarctic (the region near the South Pole) are such challenging places for animals and plants to survive in. The weather is coldest close to the poles, but milder further away. Scientists therefore divide the polar regions into two different biomes: Arctic **tundra** and **polar desert**.

Because the ground is frozen in the far north, trees cannot grow. Between the point where trees stop growing and the coast of the Arctic Ocean lies the tundra. It takes up about a tenth of the Earth's surface and covers the northern-most parts of North America, Europe and Asia. Wild, barren and frozen solid in winter, the tundra bursts into life during summer in a swampy patchwork of colourful plants. Animals as different as

the musk ox and the Arctic hare make this their home. Although there are many lakes and ponds formed from melting ice, much of the tundra gets as little rain as a desert.

Both the northern Arctic and the whole of Antarctica are too cold even for the hardy plants and animals of the tundra. The land

there is either barren or covered with a permanent layer of ice that never thaws. There is even less rain or snow than in the tundra. As a result, this biome is known as polar desert. Very few plants and animals can survive year round in the polar desert. Seabirds nest there, but none are tough enough to survive entirely on land because there is not enough food. Most life in the polar desert is limited to the coast, where the animals can take food from the ocean. But even these areas are cold and harsh, with only short summers bringing relief from the dark and freezing winters.

Polar climate

The pattern of weather that occurs in one region during a typical year is called the region's climate. In the Arctic and the Antarctic, the climate is very cold and dry, and this is why the polar biomes exist.

Have you ever stopped to wonder why there is snow and ice around the polar regions at the top and bottom of our planet, but not around the middle, where there are savannas (**tropical grasslands**) and **tropical forests** instead? The answer lies in the way Earth moves as it travels through space.

Earth travels around the Sun in a giant circle called an orbit, taking a year to complete one orbit. Besides orbiting the Sun, our planet is continually spinning around, making one whole turn each day. It stays roughly upright as it spins, with the poles at the top and bottom. Because the poles never face the Sun directly, the sunlight they receive is spread over a wide area, and this is why the poles are so cold. You'd notice the weak sunlight if you stood on the North Pole in the middle of a sunny day. Even in midsummer the sun would be very low in the sky, and its rays would hardly warm your skin.

Right: This photo shows the sun in several different positions during its path across the sky on a midsummer night in Antarctica. The middle two images of the sun were produced around midnight. On this night, for viewers on the Antarctic Circle, the sun does not set at all, but dips towards the horizon. The sun then continues its wide circle around the sky.

The temperature in Antarctica rarely rises above freezing, even in midsummer. There is hardly any liquid fresh water for plants to absorb.

The Midnight Sun

A strange thing about the polar regions is their unusual pattern of daylight. There is only one day and one night each year at the North and South Poles, each lasting six months. The sun stays just above the horizon for six months of the year, circling through the sky once every 24 hours. It gradually sinks lower, until it disappears altogether for the next six months. Once the sun has set, the pole is plunged into darkness for half a year, and the weather turns bitterly cold.

At the North Pole, the permanently dark winter lasts from 21 September to 21 March, with midwinter on 21 December. The opposite happens at the South Pole, where it is summer from September to March.

The strange days and seasons happen because the poles lie at the ends of Earth's axis – the imaginary line around which our planet spins. While the rest of the planet spins around, turning through day and night every 24 hours, the poles stay in the same place, a bit like the ends of a spinning top. Because Earth's axis is slightly tilted, the poles take turns facing the sun or facing away, and this is why they spend six months in sunlight followed by six months in darkness.

Dark blue indicates high rainfall in these world maps. The polar regions, like desert regions elsewhere,

Arctic Circle

As you travel from the North Pole, the pattern of light and darkness becomes more normal. Once you reach the **Arctic Circle** – an imaginary circle drawn a certain distance around the North Pole – there is only one day each year when the sun does not rise at all, and only one day when it does not set. The same happens at the **Antarctic Circle**.

Six months of continuous daylight might seem like enough to make the poles positively tropical places, but there are some complications. Not only is the sun low in the sky, but the ice and snow at the poles reflect away most of the sunlight. As a result, most of the sun's heat bounces straight back into space, and this makes the poles even more chilly than they would otherwise be.

Poles apart

Many people think the Arctic and Antarctic are much the same, except for being on opposite ends of the world. But there are important differences. For one thing, the Arctic is mostly ocean below its layer of snow and ice, while a huge continent makes up most of the Antarctic. Although the surface of the Arctic Ocean is frozen, the water

are very pale blue in both the January and July maps because they receive so little rain throughout the year.

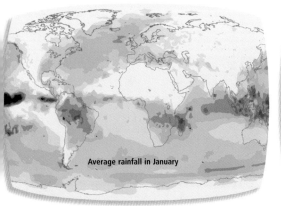

Average rainfall in January

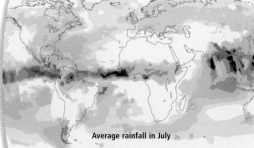

Average rainfall in July

The biting Antarctic wind can sculpt rocks into unusual shapes. Such rocks are called ventifacts.

Windchill factor

Fierce winds blast through both the Arctic and Antarctica. This not only makes the polar regions seem much colder than they really are, but also affects which plants and animals can live there. Based on experiments in Antarctica, the US meteorologist Paul Siple developed a system called windchill factor to show how different wind speeds make it seem colder. Suppose the temperature has reached freezing point (0°C or 32°F). If there is no wind, it will feel freezing. But if a wind of 32 km/h (20 mph) is blowing, the temperature will feel like −16°C (4°F). If the wind picks up to 64 km/h (40 mph), the temperature will feel more like −21°C (−5°F).

Red or orange areas of these maps are hot regions with high temperatures. Blue indicates low temperatures.

The Antarctic region is cold in both July and January, but the Arctic warms to higher temperatures in July.

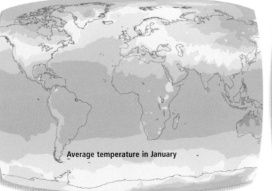

Average temperature in January

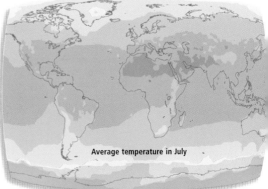

Average temperature in July

below keeps moving. A warm ocean current from the Atlantic keeps the Arctic warmer in winter than it would otherwise be. The surface ice moves and sometimes splits, producing large stretches of open water. Nearby landmasses, such as Alaska and Siberia, also provide some heat. Antarctica, however, is cut off from warm waters by a cold ocean current that flows around the continent. It is also very far from other landmasses, and its surface is much higher than sea level, which makes it even colder.

Average winter temperatures in the Arctic vary greatly across the region, but typically reach lows of about –34°C (–30°F). The average temperature in the Arctic summer is about 10°C (50°F). That is warm enough to thaw the frozen surface in the tundra region, allowing it to burst into life in the brief Arctic summer.

The Arctic is warmer than most people believe. In the early 1990s, a Russian icebreaker forced its way through sea ice to the North Pole with a party of tourists on

Climographs

Each place in the world has its own pattern of weather. The typical pattern of weather that happens in one place during a year is called climate. It is possible to show a place's climate on a climograph, such as the one shown here for St Louis in the USA. The letters along the bottom are the months of the year. The numbers on the left and the small bars show rainfall, and the numbers on the right and the curved line show temperature. You can see at a glance that St Louis is hottest in July, but December is the driest month.

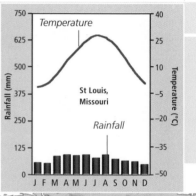

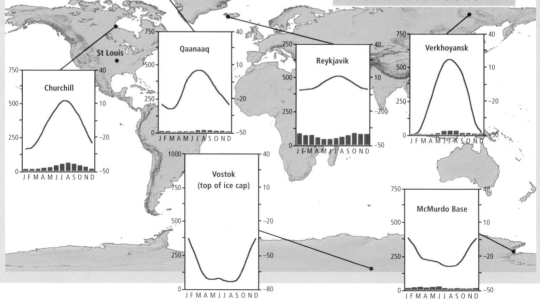

The arid poles

The arid polar climate is caused by cold air sinking over the poles. The air in Earth's atmosphere is continually moving, rising in certain places and sinking in others. When air rises it cools down, and this makes moisture in the air turn to rain or snow, which fall back to Earth. Sinking air comes from high in the atmosphere, so it has already lost its moisture and become dry. As it hits the ground, it spreads outward and stops moister air from moving in. The world's largest deserts and the poles lie in areas where dry air is continually sinking, resulting in clear blue skies and very dry weather.

board. They held a barbecue at the pole, and some of them even went for a chilly swim! Swimming in the Antarctic Ocean is another matter. There, the average winter temperature is −26°C (−15°F), and the average summer temperature is only −3°C (26°F). High on top of the Antarctic ice cap, the conditions are even more extreme: summer temperatures of −32°C (−26°F) drop to an average of −60°C (−76°F) in winter. In other words, summer on the Antarctic **ice cap** is often colder even than an Arctic winter. It is no place for a summer barbecue. If you made a hole in the Antarctic ice and hauled out a small fish, it would freeze solid in minutes.

Water, water, everywhere?

Although there are masses of ice and snow at the poles, the Arctic and Antarctica are among the driest places on Earth. The South Pole receives only a small amount of snow (about 50 mm or 2 inches) each year. Some parts of Antarctica receive less than a tenth of the rainfall or snow of a typical desert. The Dry Valleys of the Transantarctic Mountains are drier than the Sahara.

The Arctic is wetter than Antarctica, though it is still very dry. It typically gets about 200 mm (8 inches) of rain and snow each year, and the tundra tends to retain the water that falls there. There are two reasons for this: underneath the tundra is a layer of permanently frozen soil called **permafrost** through which water cannot seep away; and above the tundra is a layer of cold air. Cold air makes it difficult for water on the ground to **evaporate** (turn to vapour), because air can hold very little moisture when it is cold. Together, the permafrost and the cold air keep water sandwiched inside the tundra. In summer, the water trickles across the flat tundra landscape in small streams and rivers, or it collects in ponds, lakes and marshes.

Alpine cold

The same cold conditions that create tundra landscapes in the Arctic also happen on high mountains elsewhere on Earth. A lot of plants that grow in the Arctic also grow on mountains. Tundra stretches into the Rockies far to the south of the Arctic. The conditions are not the same, though. Outside the Arctic, it is often far wetter, and the strange sequence of very dark winters and bright summers does not exist. The biome on top of high mountains is called alpine tundra, which is covered in more detail in Mountains and Highlands (pages 304–339).

The polar seasons

If you visited the Arctic tundra in summer and winter, you might think you had gone to two completely different places. In summer, when daylight lasts nearly 24 hours, the tundra is a mixture of green, treeless plains, swamps, bogs and lakes. In some places there

Permafrost

If you dig a hole in your garden, you'll probably find nothing but damp brown soil. Try to do the same thing in the tundra, however, and your spade will suddenly scrape against a thick layer of permanently frozen soil: permafrost. Permafrost is so named because it is permanently frosty, even in the middle of summer. It is usually about 50 cm (20 in) below the tundra's surface, though in winter the top layer of soil is frozen, too.

Permafrost plays an important part in the tundra's ecology. It stops water from draining away, and so keeps the tundra wet and marshy in summer, like the tundra on Banks Island, Canada (below). Scientists are worried that climate change is now making permafrost melt in Siberia and other parts of the Arctic, which could harm the tundra.

is more water than land, and travelling can be difficult. For about two months in summer, the tundra comes alive with wildlife. Insects such as mosquitoes and flies, wetland birds and fish, roaming grizzly bears and swooping owls and jaegers are to be found. In winter, the Arctic is another world entirely. The tundra freezes solid, and ice covers the lakes, rivers and sea. Plants vanish beneath the blanket of ice, and most of the animals head south for winter. The nights grow so long that they seem to merge together, and blinding snowstorms can make it almost impossible to see.

If the summer thaw is short in the Arctic, it is almost non-existent in Antarctica. Much of the sea ice around the continent melts, but the land stays frozen solid. Only the coast can support seabirds and other animals briefly in summer, but most of these soon move northwards away from Antarctica before the long winter sets in.

Aurorae (the northern and southern lights) dance around the sky in the polar regions. They are caused by particles from the Sun hitting Earth's atmosphere.

Polar plants

Plants need sunlight and water, as well as soft ground for their roots. But the land near the poles is frozen solid and dark for months on end – and it can be drier than the Sahara. Only the world's toughest plants can survive in this extreme environment.

Imagine what it would be like to live in Greenland. You would need plenty of thick clothes to help keep you warm, including boots and gloves to keep your feet and hands from freezing. In winter, you might want a flashlight for those days when the sun never seems to rise, and in summer, you would need sunglasses to protect your eyes from the dazzling snow and ice.

People can adapt to life in difficult places, but only if they remember to pack the right equipment. Likewise, but over millions of years, plants can adapt to live in the freezing Arctic and Antarctic, but they have to be pretty remarkable plants to survive.

The biggest threats to a polar plant are the freezing cold, the darkness, the icy winds and the lack of sheltered places in which to

Red bearberry leaves brighten this view of tundra plant life in the Yukon Territory, Canada. Like Arctic tundra elsewhere, the Yukon tundra has no trees.

Sun watchers

Although summer days are long in the tundra, sunlight is weak because the sun stays low in the sky. To make the most of the weak light, some plants turn around to track the sun through the sky. The butter-yellow flowers (right) of the Arctic poppy look like satellite dishes as they turn to follow the sun. Just as a satellite dish gathers radio waves and focuses them on an antenna at the centre, so the petals of the Arctic poppy focus warmth onto the centre of the flower, helping the seeds grow quickly. Other plants, such as Arctic avens, use this trick, too.

grow. But polar plants have overcome all of these problems. Just as you would wrap yourself in a jumper to keep warm, so are the stems and leaves of many Arctic plants covered in little furry hairs. Jumpers keep us warm by trapping a layer of air next to our bodies. In the same way, the hairs of Arctic plants trap warmer air around them. One Arctic plant has such a thick woolly coat that it is named the woolly lousewort.

Plants use sunlight to grow through a process called photosynthesis. They trap the energy in light and use it to combine water and **carbon dioxide** (a gas in the air) to make food. Because the poles are dark throughout winter, plants cannot grow. So they either stay inactive under the ice or die after setting seed, and the seeds wait for the next summer. Tundra plants grow quickly in the short summer, making good use of the long days to flower and produce seeds as soon as possible before winter begins again. Many tundra plants don't even bother to flower – instead they grow sideways and split into new individuals, making clones of themselves.

Cold and darkness are not the only problems facing polar plants. There are also gale-force winds and freezing blizzards that would kill many ordinary plants in minutes. For this reason, most polar

Rather than standing tall against the gales, the little Arctic dwarf willow grows along the ground. A coat of downy hairs protects it from the cold.

Why no trees?

One definition of the polar biomes is that they are places where no trees grow. Trees flourish in the taiga biome to the south of the Arctic, but the tundra and polar deserts are tree-less. Why? The most obvious answer is that it is too cold. Yet this cannot be the whole explanation, because the spruce trees that grow along the northern edge of the taiga can survive winter temperatures that are even colder than those on the Arctic coast.

The main reason that trees do not grow is the permafrost, the permanently frozen ground underneath the surface layers of the thin tundra soil. The permafrost makes it impossible for roots to grow any deeper than a few centimetres. Another problem is the lack of shelter from the freezing wind, which stunts growth. And in the polar deserts, there simply isn't enough water for large plants.

in Greenland alone. Conditions are different in Antarctica, though, where only two species of flowering plants exist (*see* page 21).

Of the plants that provide food for the creatures of the Arctic, none are more important than those with berries. Although grizzly bears and polar bears are mainly meat eaters, they are sometimes forced to be vegetarian when prey is in short supply. One of their favourite snacks is the aptly named bearberry. The seeds in bearberries pass through the bear unharmed and sprout if they fall on good ground.

plants tend to grow very near the ground, where the wind is slower and the temperature slightly warmer. Willows grow as shrubs or trees in warmer parts of the world. In the Arctic, the twisted stems of dwarf willows snake across the ground, growing sideways instead of upward. Rarely more than a few inches tall, they escape the worst of the wind and the ice in this way.

Some Arctic plants turn the wind to their advantage, using it to help them spread their seeds further and increase their chances of survival. One of the best-known Arctic plants, cotton grass, has fluffy heads at the top of its thin stems. The heads produce thousands of very small seeds, which are caught by the wind. They swirl into the air and fly far away to grow in new places.

Despite the cruel conditions, as many as 1000 **species** of plants thrive in the Arctic region, and 40 different flowering plants grow

In the polar garden

Gardeners around the world often divide their plots into different areas, such as rock gardens, rose gardens and wildflower meadows. This may seem an original idea, but it is only a copy of what nature does by itself. In the tundra, for example, plants form different types of gardens depending on how much water is available. In marshy areas, mosses form a layer under other plants, such as grass-like plants called sedges. In less soggy places, small shrubs are common. They burst with berries in summer and turn orange or red

Above: The seed heads of cotton grass are a common sight in the tundra in August. Inuit people use the silky white 'cotton' to stuff pillows and mattresses.

Left: In late summer, bears and other tundra creatures feed on tough, black crowberries. People also use these berries to make pies, soups and jam.

The tropical Antarctic

The world's coldest continent is one of the best places to find evidence of past eras, because samples are preserved by the cold and undisturbed by human activity. Even a footprint in the moss of Antarctica can last for decades. Palaeontologists (scientists who study fossils) have found many remains in Antarctica, including dinosaurs and a huge armadillo the size of a Volkswagen Beetle.

Such animals could have lived in Antarctica only if the continent once had much more plant life than it does today. Scientists think Antarctica was joined to Africa, India and Australia about 100 million years ago. Together they formed a vast continent – Gondwana – that was north of the equator and had a tropical climate. Fossils of tropical plants remain in Antarctica to this day, hidden under the ice.

in the autumn. Wildflowers, such as Arctic poppies, tend to grow in the rocky parts of the tundra where it is very dry. The rocks themselves may be covered in lichens and mosses – the true survivors of the polar world.

Polar survivors

Plants do grow in the polar desert of Antarctica, but they are very different from the wildflowers and berries that grow on the tundra. Although life in Antarctica is at its most extreme, algae, lichens and mosses still manage to survive.

By definition, algae are not plants. They are simpler, plant-like organisms that live by photosynthesis, but have no true leaves, stems or roots. In some places, the rocks and ice of Antarctica are turned brilliant red, yellow or green by patches of algae living on the surface.

A lichen is a slightly more sophisticated form of life, made up of a fungus and an alga living together. Lichens are among the hardiest living things on Earth. They can grow on bare rock, and in laboratories they can survive temperatures almost as low as absolute zero (–460°F or –273°C) – the lowest temperature possible. Lichens grow in both Antarctica and the Arctic, colouring

Hidden life

Two Antarctic lakes are thought to contain very different kinds of life. Lake Vanda in the Dry Valleys is permanently frozen over with ice about as thick as the length of a small car. Yet sunlight seeps through, warming the water beneath to a balmy 25°C (77°F) – the temperature of a tropical ocean. In this indoor Antarctic swimming pool, a variety of algae, bacteria and other micro-organisms lead a cosy life.

Lake Vostok is about the same size as Lake Ontario but twice as deep. It is also possibly the world's most remarkable lake, because it is buried under about 4 km (2 miles) of ice. Because it has been cut off from the rest of the world for millions of years, scientists believe it could contain extraordinary new species – or perhaps none at all. Scientists are trying to figure out how to explore the lake with robots, in a way that will not contaminate it and kill off any life that may be there.

almost any surface, from rocks to decayed bones, with blotches of orange and gold. They are especially common on darker rocks, which warm up in sunlight more than pale rocks. Lichens provide the starting point for another type of polar survivor: the mosses.

Reindeer moss is not a moss but a type of lichen, eaten by reindeer. This picture also shows red leaves of a bearberry bush poking through the lichen.

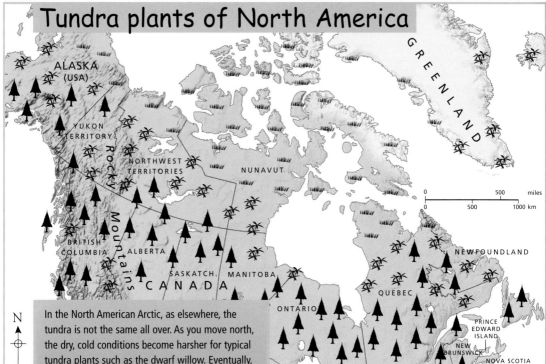

Tundra plants of North America

GREENLAND

ALASKA (USA)

YUKON TERRITORY

NORTHWEST TERRITORIES

NUNAVUT

Rocky

Mountains

BRITISH COLUMBIA   ALBERTA

SASKATCH.   MANITOBA

C A N A D A

ONTARIO

QUEBEC

NEWFOUNDLAND

PRINCE EDWARD ISLAND

NEW BRUNSWICK

NOVA SCOTIA

0   500   miles
0   500   1000 km

N

In the North American Arctic, as elsewhere, the tundra is not the same all over. As you move north, the dry, cold conditions become harsher for typical tundra plants such as the dwarf willow. Eventually, in the far north, only hardy Arctic grasses provide a sparse cover on the ground. In the south, the tundra plants are mixed with the conifer forests of the taiga for many miles. Tundra plants also live much farther south on the high ground of the Rockies.

Conifer trees form the forests of the taiga.

Dwarf willow is a shrub that can grow in tundra but not in polar desert.

Hardy Arctic grasses sparsely cover the ground in dry tundra and polar desert.

By coating rocks with a rough surface, lichens give mosses a foothold in which to grow. Crevices in the moss and lichen trap windblown dirt, forming a thin layer of soil. This soil provides anchorage and nutrients for Antarctica's only two flowering plant species: Antarctic hairgrass and pearlwort (colobanthus). Both live only in the Antarctic Peninsula, where the climate is milder than in the continent's interior.

Below: Mainland Antarctica's only flowering plants, Antarctic hairgrass (upper plant) and pearlwort (lower plant) shelter in a moss-lined rock crevice.

Polar animals

Did you know that the hair on a polar bear can carry sunlight, like tiny fibre-optic cables? Or that seagulls keep their legs much colder than their body to avoid losing heat? These are just two of the ingenious ways in which animals survive the hardships of life at the poles.

The different climates of the Arctic and Antarctic regions mean very different types of plants grow in each place. Likewise, the animals living near the North and South Poles are also different. In the Arctic tundra there are lots of land **mammals**, including grizzly bears, foxes, reindeer, musk oxen and lemmings. In Antarctica, however, there are no native land mammals. Nearly all the animals of Antarctica live near the ocean and must return there to survive the winter or find food. The only animals that live on land permanently are tiny insects and mites.

Polar ecosystems

Just like in any other biome, the organisms of the polar biomes depend on each other to survive. The community of plants, animals and other organisms, together with their physical environment, make up what we call an **ecosystem**. Nearly all Earth's ecosystems are maintained by energy from the sun. Plants or algae use the sun's energy to make food, so they can grow and reproduce. **Herbivores** (plant-eating animals) eat the plants, and **carnivores** (flesh-eating animals) eat the herbivores. So the food made by the plants passes along a **food chain**, from plant to herbivore to carnivore.

The ecosystems of the Arctic and Antarctic are unusual. In Antarctica there are very few land plants, so most animals depend on food from the oceans. The base of the food chain is made up of **phytoplankton** – microscopic, plant-like organisms that live on the surface of the ocean. These are eaten by **zooplankton** – tiny organisms that live in the surface water. The zooplankton are eaten by fish, squid, molluscs and other animals, and these provide food for penguins and seals.

Being a warmer and less extreme place than Antarctica, the Arctic is home to many more species. Just as in Antarctica, there is a marine food chain based on phytoplankton. This food chain is very important for animals that come on land to breed, such as seabirds, seals and walruses. But there is also a land-based food chain. At the bottom of the chain are lichens, algae and land plants. At the top are meat eaters, including wolves, snowy owls, polar bears and people. In between comes everything from bumblebees and wolf spiders to reindeer.

Midget giants

The largest Antarctic animal that lives permanently on land is a wingless relative of insects called a springtail. It grows to only 13 mm (half an inch) long. The continent's biggest native land predator is a mite – a tiny spider-like creature. It weighs less than one ten thousandth of a gram (0.00003 oz).

In Antarctica, there are hardly any land plants. Nearly all the animals that live there, such as these chinstrap penguins, live off food from the ocean, such as fish. These penguins are resting on an unusual iceberg made of blue ice.

Life in the freezer

If you took a monkey from a rainforest and moved it to Antarctica, it would die very quickly. Monkeys are well adapted to the heat and moisture of the tropics, but they cannot survive in a polar desert. All the creatures that live in the polar regions have evolved special characteristics, or adaptations, that help them survive there.

The biggest challenge is staying warm. Many polar animals are **warm-blooded**. Just like people, they keep a constant body temperature, no matter how the temperature of their surroundings varies. Being warm-blooded allows animals to stay active even when their surroundings are freezing cold. In contrast, **cold-blooded** animals, such as lizards and frogs, would become inactive and freeze – so it is not surprising that very few lizards or frogs venture into the Arctic, and none can be found in Antarctica.

Warm-blooded animals need features that stop them from losing heat. Most warm-blooded animals have layers of **insulation** around their body to retain heat. People insulate themselves with clothes, but other

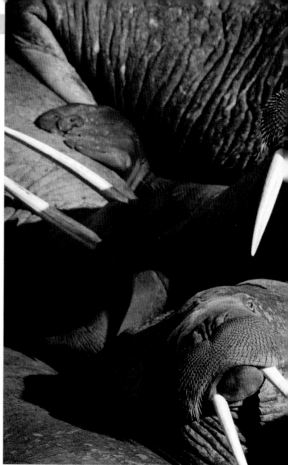

animals, such as polar bears, have a thick fur coat. They also have a layer of fat, or **blubber**. The blubber acts mainly as an energy store for times when food is hard to find, but it also helps keep in the heat. Seals and walruses also have blubber, but unlike land animals, they have an extra insulating feature. By changing their blood flow, they can keep their blubber layer cool while maintaining a warm temperature deep inside their body. Walruses have so much blubber that they risk overheating when they come onto land.

Arctic foxes, like polar bears, have a thick, layered, insulating coat of fur. The fur holds a layer of warm air around the body and acts as a barrier to cold.

24

Walruses rest on land a great deal. This way, they spend less energy keeping their body warm in the cold sea. They can use their tusks as picks during fights.

Although they spend much of their time in the ocean, walruses come ashore to rest and breed in large **colonies** on the Arctic coast. To lose heat, they blush – blood flows through the skin, turning their bodies bright pink.

Walruses use their long whiskers to feel for shellfish on the murky seafloor. With their tusks held out of the way, they grub about for food in the mud, a bit like pigs do. And just as submarines can push their way through sea ice, so a walrus can use its tough head to bash through ice up to 20 cm (8 in) thick.

Cold feet

Keeping their feet warm is a particular problem for polar animals. An animal's warmth is mostly in the centre of its body. Parts that stick out, such as legs, arms, ears and nose, lose heat quickly in the cold. To save precious heat energy, some animals have legs that can be colder than the rest of their body. Seagulls and reindeer are two examples. Eskimos have long known that the lower leg parts of reindeer (or caribou, as they are called in North America) freeze at much lower temperatures than the upper parts. For this reason, Eskimos used the fat from caribou feet to oil the strings of their bows.

Big is better?

A 19th-century scientist named Carl Bergmann claimed that bigger creatures are better off in cold climates than smaller ones, because they don't lose heat so quickly. Why should this be so? The amount of heat an object can hold depends on its volume (the space it takes up), while the speed it loses heat depends on the area (size) of its surface. Small animals have a higher ratio of surface area to volume, so they lose heat faster. Think how slowly a hot potato cools down, compared to a similar volume of peas. The peas have more surface area than the potato, so they turn cold much quicker. But size is not the only answer to surviving at the poles. A large animal must find more food to fuel itself than smaller animals, even in winter, when food is hard to find. In addition, small animals can better avoid the cold by staying in burrows.

Sometimes fur and blubber are not enough to beat the cold. Musk oxen of the Arctic tundra and the penguins of Antarctica may huddle together to help stay warm. Ptarmigan and small birds fly into fluffy snow banks, or dig themselves into the snow of the tundra with their feet. Cold as this may seem, it is still warmer than standing in a blizzard. Some polar animals have a particular size or shape that helps them cope with the cold. Large, bulky animals generally stand up to the cold better than small animals, for example.

Migrating mammals

Rather than endure the dark and freezing tundra winter, most reindeer migrate south at the end of summer. Every year, more than a million of these Arctic deer make a long trek to the forests of the **taiga**, where they find shelter in winter. They return to the tundra on the Arctic coastal plains in spring, when

These reindeer live in Siberia, which has some of the coldest winters the Arctic has to offer. It is no wonder, then, that the reindeer migrate south into the taiga biome, shown here, to find shelter in winter.

they give birth to their calves. Reindeer live throughout the tundra and taiga of North America, Europe and Russia, though they are called caribou in North America. The Peary caribou and the Svalbard reindeer live on Arctic islands, so they can't move south to escape the winter. They must endure the dark and cold, but when desperate, they attempt dangerous crossings over the sea ice.

Another Arctic mammal, the musk ox, does not migrate far, but shifts only a few miles between its summer and winter grazing grounds. In summer, musk oxen eat sedges and willows on low-lying tundra; in winter, they move to ground free of deep snow to eat grasses exposed by the Arctic winds. The severe climate is seldom a problem for musk oxen, because their shaggy coats are eight times warmer than sheep's fur and protect them well against harsh blizzards. The most severe blizzards can last for several days, though, and prevent musk oxen from feeding. At such times, they lie down together to deflect the wind. One way musk oxen lower their need for food in winter is to spend little time moving. The less energy they use for movement, the more energy they have to maintain their body temperature.

Hibernating mammals

The musk ox's method of saving its energy is halfway between staying active for the winter and hibernating completely. To hibernate fully, animals seek shelter, reduce their body temperature and become inactive, or **dormant**, usually until the winter has passed. During **hibernation**, their heart beats more slowly and they breathe much less often than they do normally. Although they don't eat, their body survives on reserves of stored fat.

Right: On the tree-less tundra, there is nowhere for Arctic ground squirrels to hide. This one is keeping a lookout for predators while others in its group feed.

Grizzly bears hibernate in large dens that they build out of snow in the autumn. With its entrance tunnel, small living room and air hole, a bear's den can be a cosy place to spend the winter. The snow keeps out the cold, and the bear's body heat (and that of its cubs) keeps the den warm. A bear also prepares for hibernation by building up the fat on its body. The fat provides water as well as food for the long winter months.

The grizzly bear is one of the largest hibernating mammals in the Arctic. Much smaller mammals hibernate, too, including the Arctic ground squirrel, which spends two thirds of every year in hibernation.

Arctic ground squirrels don't live in trees (there aren't any) but in underground burrows. These provide shelter from **predators** as well as from the cold climate. Lots of animals prey on the ground squirrel – snowy owls hunt them from above, and polar bears try to claw the squirrels out of their holes. The ground squirrel's hibernation is made up of short periods. During a period, it curls into a ball and allows its body temperature to fall to that of its burrow. If its burrow gets very cold, the squirrel's body might freeze solid, so its brain stays awake and keeps its body temperature above the freezing point.

South polar skuas are vicious predators. Their favourite food is penguin chick, but they also eat other seabirds and sometimes even other skuas' chicks.

A flight of snow geese might be a familiar sight as far south as Mexico, but their destination is the Arctic tundra, where they raise their chicks in summer.

All mammals need sleep, so after two weeks or so, the squirrel warms itself to normal body temperature, relaxes and falls asleep for some hours, before entering its next period of wakeful hibernation.

Migrating birds

Just as some people fly to warmer places for winter, so birds use their wings to escape the worst of the weather. Most Arctic birds spend only their breeding season in the tundra, and fly vast distances south once they have raised their young. Some sandpipers, for example, fly 9500 km (6000 miles) south from their Arctic nesting grounds in less than a month, often flying over 150 km (100 miles) a day. The bird with the most spectacular migration pattern is the Arctic tern. It spends the

Goodbye, great auk

When European ships started to visit the Arctic, one of the first casualties was the great auk. Similar to a penguin, this flightless bird was very common on islands off Newfoundland. From the 16th century onwards, sailors began to kill the great auk because it was a quick and easy source of food, oil and feathers. Numbers of the birds plummeted. By the 18th century, the Newfoundland government was trying to halt the massive slaughter. But it was already too late. In June 1844, collectors clubbed the last two great auks to death for their eggs, and the bird became extinct.

winter in the ocean around Antarctica. In summer, it flies all the way to its breeding grounds in the Arctic tundra.

About fifty species of birds thrive south of the Antarctic Circle, including terns, petrels, fulmars, gulls, shearwaters and albatrosses. In Antarctica, the birds live along the coast because they depend on the sea for food. Most Antarctic birds eat shrimp-like animals called krill, fish or squid, but some eat other birds or even seals. Petrels loiter around seabird colonies, hoping to gobble up a penguin chick or feast on a dead seal. But even petrels live in fear of skuas – aggressive

Early summer in the Russian Arctic is time for red-breasted geese to arrive and begin nesting.

🐧 Penguin points

▲ Penguins live in the Antarctic but not the Arctic.

▲ Penguins can't fly. They use their wings as flippers for swimming.

▲ Penguins have no need to fly because there are no large land predators in the Antarctic.

▲ Fossils found in New Zealand reveal that some prehistoric penguins were as tall as people.

▲ The only penguins to nest on the Antarctic mainland are Adélie penguins (below) and emperor penguins.

birds that terrorize seabird colonies and readily attack people when threatened.

More birds live in the Arctic than Antarctica. There are several reasons for this: the Arctic tundra is nearer to other areas of land; the climate is less harsh; and there are more varied habitats for breeding and feeding. Even so, most birds fly south for the winter and spend just a few months breeding in the Arctic each summer. There are only a few hardy year-round residents, including the ptarmigan, the snowy owl and the raven.

During the breeding season, predators are common in the Arctic, both in the air and on the ground. Airborne predators include eagles and skuas, while land predators include foxes, wolves, bears and **ermines** (short-tailed Arctic weasels).

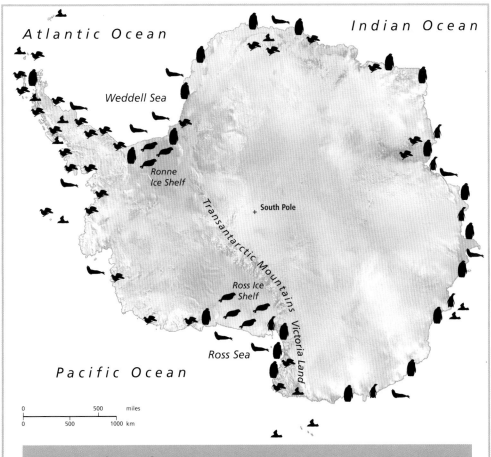

Atlantic Ocean

Indian Ocean

Weddell Sea

Ronne
Ice Shelf

+ South Pole

Transantarctic Mountains

Ross Ice
Shelf

Victoria Land

Ross Sea

Pacific Ocean

| 0 | | 500 | miles |
| 0 | 500 | 1000 | km |

Animals of Antarctica

Most of Antarctica is covered with a high dome of ice. Nothing can live on top – it is much too cold and too far from the nearest source of food: the ocean. All Antarctic animals live within reach of the ocean. Large colonies of Adélie and emperor penguins roost on rocky coasts and islands around Antarctica. In winter, though, male emperor penguins travel far from the open sea across the ice to incubate their eggs in safety. Predatory birds such as petrels and skuas hunt and scavenge near the coastal penguins, but some fly inland to nest in dry valleys and on outcrops of rock. Ross seals live deep in fields of sea ice, but Weddell seals live even further from the open sea, on the permanently frozen ice shelves. They reach the sea by cutting down through the ice with their teeth.

Adélie
penguin

Emperor
penguin

Ross
seal

Weddell
seal

South polar
skua

Snow
petrel

Because there are lots of predators, Arctic birds need effective defences. Fulmars vomit on their attackers. Arctic swans trample, bite, batter and hiss at anything that threatens them. And many birds nest together in large colonies, from ducks to guillemots. With so many eyes and ears on the alert in a colony, the risk of being caught unawares by an attacker is much lower.

For migrating birds, timing is everything. They must carefully time their transglobal journeys so they arrive at their breeding grounds at exactly the right time of year. Timing is important in other ways, too. Skuas lay their eggs so the chicks hatch at the same time as those of penguins. This ensures there will be plenty of food around for the hungry young skuas.

Toughest of the tough

Although some polar creatures shy away from winter by migrating or hibernating, others remain where they are, using a variety of different tricks to survive. Unable to fly away from Antarctica, penguins huddle together to keep warm. The ptarmigan is one of the few Arctic birds that doesn't fly south for the winter. It also holds the record for the bird that spends winter closest to the North Pole. When winter approaches, the ptarmigan changes from brown to white and sprouts fluffy feathers on its feet. Its uses its feathered feet to dig tunnels in the snow, where it is much warmer than in the air outside.

Lemmings endure the Arctic winter by digging a complicated network of tunnels in the snow. As they dig down to the ground

Starvation wages

After a female emperor penguin lays her egg, she leaves it to the male to care for. Balancing the egg on his feet, the male tucks a flap of bare skin over the egg to keep it warm. He spends more than three months of the bitter Antarctic winter without eating while he looks after the egg. By huddling together (below), the male penguins can limit their heat loss during this time. Even so, they lose half their body weight in these months.

White in winter

Many polar creatures are white, including polar bears, Dall's sheep, Peary caribou and some gyrfalcons. Others turn white only when the winter comes. These include Arctic hares (left and right), ermines, lemmings, Arctic foxes and birds such as the ptarmigan. Being white helps animals hide in snow or ice, and so reduces the chance of being spotted by a predator. It also helps predators sneak up on victims without being seen. Some scientists think that white fur is warmer than other colours. White materials reflect heat more than dark materials, so a coat of white fur reflects body heat back towards the skin. The white hairs also contain air spaces that make them even warmer.

surface, they eat whatever plants they find. Similar to hamsters, they have short legs and ears, and lots of brown fur. But in winter they turn white, like many Arctic creatures. Lemmings breed very quickly – females give birth to up to nine young at a time, only three weeks after mating. Sometimes the population of lemmings grows so much that many are forced to leave their burrows and migrate elsewhere. The mass migrations happen every few years, when hundreds of lemmings can be seen scampering across the tundra. Occasionally, some fall off cliffs or drown in ponds or the sea by accident, but lemmings do not do this deliberately, as some people think.

Like any other biome, the Arctic tundra has scavengers – animals that live off the spoils of others. The Arctic fox, for instance, follows polar bears for the remains of their kills. Well-adapted to life in the cold, it has a short nose and small ears that reduce heat

Lemmings survive the Arctic winter by gnawing plants, which they find beneath the snow.

loss. Its fur is luxurious and even covers the undersides of its feet to keep out the cold. The polar bears it follows are also expert Arctic survivors, equally at home on land, on sea ice or swimming in the chilly ocean. Polar bears prey on seals and young walruses and also scavenge from dead whales. If food is in short supply, they venture inland for berries, grass or whatever they can find. Some polar bears even enter towns to sniff out morsels of food in rubbish.

Polar warriors

Suppose you had to design an animal to survive life at the North Pole. Could you come up with anything better than a polar bear? A typical polar bear is about 2.1 m (7 ft) tall and 540 kg (1200 lbs) in weight – as much as five heavyweight boxers.

A lot of this weight is fat. Underneath the skin, polar bears have a blanket of blubber several centimetres deep. It is thickest on the back of the legs and the hind quarters, where the animal is most exposed to the wind. Although blubber is helpful for keeping the bear warm as it plods over the ice, it is even more important when the bear is paddling through the water. Polar

bears are excellent swimmers – they can swim 100 km (60 miles) across open water to reach the ice floes where they hunt.

Blubber is only one layer of the bear's clothing. Next comes a cosy layer of wool. And on the outside, there is a thick fur coat made up of long, hard guard hairs. Each guard hair works like one of the glass fibres in a fibre-optic cable. Sunlight is carried down the hair to the bear's body, helping to warm the skin. With blubber, wool and a sun-heated fur coat, polar bears are so well-insulated that they hardly show up on infrared (heat-sensitive) cameras.

No way in

Creatures that develop ways of defending themselves against their hunters are more likely to thrive. When musk oxen are attacked, they huddle together in a circle, rump-to-rump, protecting their calves between them. That leaves just their heads and their horns exposed, which makes it much easier to defend themselves against predators such as wolves.

Small is beautiful

Cold conditions may favour large creatures, but the polar regions are also home to many small forms of life. One of the Arctic's most ferocious little creatures is a shrimp-like animal called an **amphipod**, which lives in the ocean. When a young Eskimo fell through the ice and drowned in the Canadian Arctic some years ago, rescuers were shocked when they discovered his dead body. Although his clothes were intact, amphipods had picked off and eaten all the flesh from his bones in less than a day.

Lots of insects and spiders live in the Arctic tundra. They spend the winter in a resting form, usually as eggs, which are not killed by freezing. As soon as it is warm enough, the insects burst into activity. Mosquitoes hatch from tundra pools and swarm in their millions. There are so many mosquitoes that this may be one of the reasons why reindeer migrate north to give birth. The insects live both in the taiga, where reindeer spend their winters, and in the tundra, where reindeer calve. But they appear a whole month later in the tundra. This extra month gives the reindeer time to calve and raise their young before the mosquitoes start biting. The multitude of other Arctic insects includes butterflies, crane flies and bumblebees.

Plants and insects must rush to take advantage of the brief Arctic summer. This crane fly is soaking up some sunshine on an Arctic poppy.

North American Arctic

The tundra and polar deserts of Canada and Alaska are the emptiest parts of North America. The animals and people who live here have to endure long, dark, freezing winters, when temperatures can plunge to –50°C (–58°F).

Bering Str
Arctic Ocean
1
2 Arctic National Wildlife Refuge
ALSAKA (USA)
Brooks Range
▲ Mount Chamberlain
Mount ▲ McKinley
● Anchorage
3
Great Bear Lake
YUKON TERRITORY
4
NORTHWEST TERRITORIES
Kenai Peninsula
Pacific Ocean
Yellowknife ●
Great Slave Lake
Canadian Rockies
BRITISH COLUMBIA
ALBERTA
SASKATCHEWA
● Edmonton
Vancouver ●
CANADA
USA

Fact file

▲ About 12,000 years ago, Canada was covered with ice and much of the USA was tundra. Tundra animals included mammoths, sabre-toothed cats, lions, camels and bison.

▲ The tundra is still home to some remarkable creatures, including musk oxen, lemmings, polar bears and caribou.

▲ The USA bought Alaska from Russia in 1867 for just $7.2 million – that's roughly £55 million in today's terms, or £36 per square km (£93 per square mile). In real terms, Alaska's vast oil and mineral deposits make it worth many as much.

Dall sheep live in the rugged mountains of Alaska, where Inupiat people hunt them by snowmobile.

GREENLAND

North Magnetic Pole

Ellesmere Island

8

6

Devon Island

9

11

Baffin Island

NORTH AMERICA

EUROPE

ASIA

AFRICA

SOUTH AMERICA

AUSTRALIA

ANTARCTICA

NUNAVUT

Iqaluit

Great Plain of the Koukdjuak

Atlantic Ocean

10

Hudson Bay

MANITOBA

miles km

1000

500

500

Hudson Bay Lowlands

7

NEWFOUNDLAND

QUEBEC

0 0

Lake Winnipeg

St John's

ONTARIO

PRINCE EDWARD ISLAND

Winnipeg

NEW BRUNSWICK

Quebec

NOVA SCOTIA

N

Lake Superior

Montreal

1. Bering Strait
A narrow gap between Alaska and Siberia, about 64 km (40 miles) across.

2. Arctic National Wildlife Refuge
A protected area of Alaskan tundra that contains important breeding grounds for polar bears and caribou.

3. Brooks Range
A mountain range in Alaska. The highest point, Mount Chamberlain, is about a third of the height of Mount Everest.

4. Great Bear Lake
A large freshwater lake – the largest entirely within Canada.

5. Arctic Ocean
The world's smallest ocean. During winter, most of the Arctic is covered with sea ice.

6. North Magnetic Pole
The place to which compasses point. The magnetic pole is about 1600 km (1000 miles) from the North Pole. It changes location slowly over the years.

7. Hudson Bay Lowlands
A vast area of swampy tundra and wetlands.

8. Ellesmere Island
Cape Columbia, at the top of the island, is the northern-most part of North America.

9. Devon Island
Parts of this rocky desert island look just like Mars. NASA uses the island to test Martian probes and buggies.

10. Great Plain of the Koukdjuak
A wetland area with many rivers, ponds and streams.

11. Baffin Island
Baffin Island is the world's fifth largest island. No trees grow there, but there are many lakes. The east coast contains high mountain peaks.

Across the Bering bridge

Between Alaska and Siberia is a narrow passage of water called the Bering Strait, but this has not always been there. During Earth's ice ages, the sea level fell as water turned to ice. As a result, the land between Alaska and Siberia emerged above sea level, forming a land bridge.

The land bridge across the Bering Strait allowed animals to walk across. Ancient species of horses and camels wandered west from Alaska to Asia and evolved into the zebras and camels we know today. Some animals moved east, including caribou (below), lemmings, foxes and wolves. The Native Americans, who were the first people to settle in North America, also probably crossed the Bering bridge.

Antarctica

Antarctica is the coldest, driest, windiest, darkest and highest continent on Earth. Nowhere on the planet is less hospitable to life.

Fact file

▲ Antarctica has 70 per cent of Earth's fresh water but is actually a desert.

▲ In winter, Antarctica doubles in size as the sea freezes around it.

▲ On average, Antarctica is three times higher than other continents because of all the ice. The weight of the ice has squashed the land to below sea level in some places.

▲ Antarctica's ice is slowly moving. It takes about 50,000 years for a snowflake at the South Pole to get to the ocean.

Most of Antarctica is covered by ice so thick that only mountaintops show through it.

The dry valleys

It's strange to think that a continent with as much ice as Antarctica could also contain a rocky desert, yet the Dry Valleys have been free of ice for millions of years. They are dry because the nearby mountains hold back glaciers, and because strong winds blow away what little snow falls.

Despite the name, the Dry Valleys contain Antarctica's only river – the Onyx – which flows only in summer and contains beautifully clear water. There are also a few lakes, though these are permanently frozen over.

You might think the Dry Valleys would be devoid of life, but they aren't. The rocks contain microscopic organisms called cyanobacteria, which can lie dormant for hundreds of years. When enough snow falls to make the rocks damp, the cyanobacteria spring back to life, using the sun's energy to make food.

1. Lambert Glacier
A vast glacier that flows slowly off the mainland and into Amery Ice Shelf.

2. Vostok
This Russian base is officially the coldest place on Earth. The world's lowest ever temperature (−89.2°C or −128.6°F) was recorded there.

3. South Magnetic Pole
The place on Earth's surface that compasses point away from. The magnetic poles slowly change position over time.

4. Dry Valleys
Ice-free, rocky valleys near the Transantarctic Mountains.

5. McMurdo Station
This US base on Ross Island is Antarctica's biggest community, with a summer population of 1200 and a winter population of 200.

6. Mount Erebus
A gigantic active volcano on Ross Island, at the edge of the Ross Ice Shelf.

7. Transantarctic Mountains
This vast mountain range forms the dividing line between Greater and Lesser Antarctica.

8. South Pole
The most southerly point on Earth.

9. Ross Ice Shelf
A vast shelf of permanent sea ice that ends in towering cliffs.

10. Vinson Massif
Antarctica's tallest mountain, at 5140 m (16,864 ft) – a popular destination for climbers.

11. Antarctic Peninsula
The northern-most point of Antarctica. The Peninsula contains many islands and volcanoes, some of which are active.

Indian Ocean

Mawson (Australia)

Amery Ice Shelf

Lambert Glacier

1

2

● Vostok (Russia)

+ South magnetic pole **3**

Greater
Antarctica
(East Antarctica)

Dry Valleys **4**

McMurdo (USA) **5**

6

▲ Mount Erebus

Ross Sea

Transantarctic Mountains

7

Ross
Ice Shelf

8 South Pole +

9

Pacific
Ocean

Lesser
Antarctica
(West Antarctica)

Weddell
Sea

Ronne
Ice Shelf

Atlantic
Ocean

▲ Vinson Massif

10

Antarctic Peninsula

11

South Orkney
Islands

South Shetland Islands

0   500   miles
0   500   1000 km

AUSTRALIA

AFRICA

ANTARCTICA

SOUTH
AMERICA

39

The taiga biome

Taiga forests occupy a larger area than all the tropical rainforests. They grow in a region of extreme weather encircling the northern hemisphere from Alaska to Japan.

The slopes of Grouse Mountain, Vancouver, are covered in taiga forest, in which mostly coniferous trees grow.

Taiga occupies about one-tenth of the Earth's land surface, and as a land biome it is second in size only to deserts. The forests that grow in the taiga biome are filled with mainly conifer trees. Conifer trees keep their leaves all year round and produce cones rather than flowers. Often, only two or three conifer **species**, such as spruces, pines or firs, cover large areas of the forest.

Most of the taiga grows in icy land near the Arctic Circle – the coldest place in which full-size trees can grow. This sort of taiga is called boreal forest. Some taiga forest grows along the north-west coast of North America. There is so much rainfall there that the taiga is described as rainforest. Despite this name, these forests are filled mainly with conifers and are more similar to boreal forests than to the tropical rainforests around the **equator**.

The word *taiga* comes from the Russian word for 'marshy pine forest', which is a very apt description. Boreal forest is named for *Boreas*, the Greek god of the north wind.

Beyond the northern limit of taiga, the temperatures are too low for full-size trees to grow, and **tundra** – a biome with plants no larger than shrubs – replaces taiga. At its southern limit, taiga gives way to forests of broad-leaved trees and **temperate** grasslands. In between, vast areas of the taiga form dense, almost impenetrable forest. However, the landscape sometimes creates a jigsaw puzzle of forests, wetlands and lakes.

Taiga covers much of Alaska and Canada and extends as far south as New England. Scotland has a few patches of taiga forest, but from there forests form an almost unbroken swathe from Scandinavia to Japan. Taiga-like forests also hug the slopes of high mountains well to the south of boreal taiga.

Taiga is the world's largest source of softwood for timber and papermaking. The biome also holds important reserves of fossil fuels. However, due to its enormous size and harsh weather, the taiga is sparsely populated by people and has largely been allowed to remain a pristine wilderness.

Taiga climate

For most of the year, taiga is dark, cold and covered in snow and ice. During the short periods of warmth in spring and summer, the days get longer, the ice and snow melt and the forest comes to life.

The climate of taiga forest is very harsh, with snow and ice covering the ground for much of the year. The plant life is shrouded in water, but this water is in a frozen form that plants cannot use. During the long winter, plants endure a water shortage as severe as that in deserts. However, with the spring thaw, the reverse is true, and there is an abundance of liquid water. Now, plants have to cope with soils that are very damp or have had all the **nutrients** washed out of them. Despite all these difficulties, conifer trees thrive in taiga forests.

Around the world

As with other land biomes, taiga exists because the particular combination of **climate** and soil favours certain kinds of plants. The long, cool winters and short, warm summers of this biome occur in lowlands in the far

A thick layer of snow weighs down conifer trees in a foggy forest in Norway. Taiga forests are covered in snow for most of the year.

north of North America, Europe and Asia. Similar conditions also exist further south on the slopes of tall mountains, and taiga-like forests grow there, too. No taiga forest grows in the southern **hemisphere**. This is because the area where taiga would grow is mainly covered by ocean.

Taiga develops where the growing season for plants is at least three months, and where the average daily temperature in the warmest month of the year is about 10°C (50°F). In winter, temperatures in some taiga forests can be even lower than in the Arctic tundra to the north. In fact, northern Siberia is one of the coldest places on Earth – chillier than anywhere, except for Antarctica. In much of Siberia, differences between summer and winter temperatures are also among the largest anywhere. In winter, temperatures can plunge to as low as –68°C (–90°F), while in

summer they soar to 30°C (86°F) – a temperature range approaching a phenomenal 100°C (180°F).

The taiga may be cold for much of the year, but the presence of snow can benefit plants. Snow acts like a fluffy, air-filled jacket, insulating trees and soil from the bitterly cold air. In winter, the soil at a depth of 50 cm (20 in) can be 20°C (36°F) warmer than the air above. At these depths, tree roots are still able to take in life-giving water, even though the temperatures above ground are well below freezing.

Hardy trees
Conifers dominate the taiga. Few broad-leaved, **deciduous** trees, which shed their leaves each year, survive in the biome. Because taiga areas have such short growing seasons, deciduous trees are at a disadvantage.

Right: Needles of a white pine tree dripping with meltwater. When the snow and ice melt, taiga forests become very wet indeed.

Mountainside Forests

Well beyond the southern limit of lowland boreal taiga, conifer forests grow on mountain slopes where temperatures are much cooler than surrounding low-lying areas. The trees in these high-altitude (high above sea level) forests are very similar to those that live in areas of boreal taiga. For example, the highland forests of the Alps and Pyrenees mountains in Europe contain the same species of pine and fir tree that grow in the taiga forests in the far north of Europe.

The Earth is warmer near the equator than at the poles. Therefore, as a rule, the mountains that are nearer the equator, and further from true taiga, have taiga-like conditions higher up and are home to more non-taiga trees. Near the northern end of the Rocky Mountains in North America (below), conifer forests grow to a treeline (the upper limit of tree growth) at an altitude of only 1500 metres (4900 ft). In the warmer, more southerly Rockies of Colorado, the belt of conifer forest begins at an altitude of about 2130 metres (6900 ft) and the treeline reaches to about 3200 metres (9900 ft) above sea level.

Plants **photosynthesize** (make food from sunlight) with their leaves. Each spring, deciduous trees must grow a new set of leaves, which they then shed when the weather gets cooler in the autumn. This is very wasteful if the growing season is only short. Coniferous evergreens keep their needle-like leaves for several years. They are, therefore, ready to photosynthesize and grow as soon as spring begins.

Humid summers

The conifer trees of the taiga are well suited to coping with cold and dampness, but they cannot tolerate warmth coupled with dryness. When plant enthusiasts grow taiga trees in botanical gardens and give them plenty of water in summer, the trees still fare poorly if the air is dry. They lose water through their needles and grow to only a fraction of the size they would reach in their normal habitat. Spruces cultivated in warm climates grow to half their natural height.

Waterlogged soil

The layered soil of taiga forest is called podzol, from the Russian word for ash, which describes the colour of one of the soil's layers. Podzol forms because taiga climates are so cold, and because the pine needles shed by conifers are broken down very slowly by decomposers in the soil. As a result, the ground becomes covered in a thick layer of pine needles and other debris shed by trees. These layers eventually form podzol.

The combination of cold and wet conditions, plus slowly decaying plant matter, makes the upper region of the soil acidic. Over the year, the amount of water falling as snow, rain or hail is much greater than that rising into the air by **evaporation**. The extra water sinks into the ground and is turned acidic by the soil. This acid-rich

In the short summer, taiga forest is bathed in warm sunshine during very long days. At the northern limit of the taiga, the sun sets for only a few hours a day.

The world's largest trees

On North America's Pacific coast, running from Alaska and Canada in the north to California in the south, coniferous forests clothe the western mountain ranges. Here, winters are milder and wetter than in other northern forests, but the plant life is similar to boreal taiga: pine, fir, spruce, hemlock and larch.

The forests receive an enormous amount of rain – over 4 metres (13 ft) every year, and they are called rainforests because of this. The coastal mountains trap the wind blowing in from the ocean, and this moist wind releases its rain as it rises up the mountainside. The western slopes get all the rain, while the region to the east of the mountains is much drier.

The mountains also protect the rainforests from the icy air that travels down from the Arctic. On the coast, the temperature rarely drops below freezing, while on the eastern side of the mountains, the forests must cope with much colder weather.

Being so wet, the forests have an almost tropical luxuriance, with an undergrowth of ferns, and thick mosses and lichens. In north California and south-west Oregon, the forests are infiltrated by giant redwoods (above), the largest trees on Earth. The Redwood National Park of northern California is home to the biggest tree in the world – a 112-metre (367-ft) coast redwood, which has bark 30 cm (1 ft) thick.

Climographs

Each place in the world has its own pattern of weather. The typical pattern of weather that happens in one place during a year is called climate. We can sum up a place's climate on a climograph, such as the one shown here for St Louis in the USA. The letters along the bottom are the months of the year. The numbers on the left and the small bars show rainfall, and the numbers on the right and the curvy line show temperature. You can see at a glance that St Louis is hottest in July, but December is the driest month.

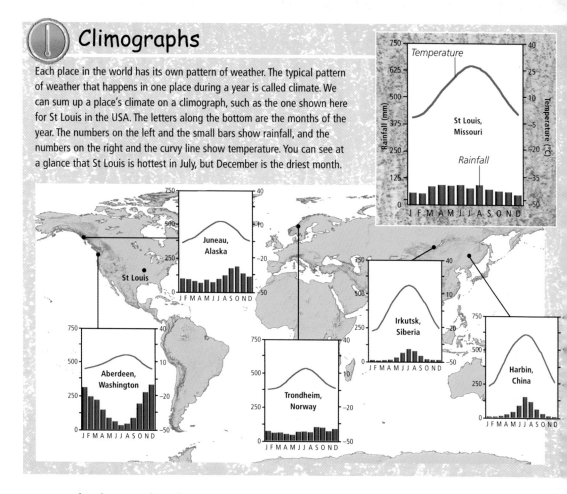

water dissolves metals such as iron and aluminium from the soil and deposits them deeper down. Sometimes, iron-rich layers called iron pans develop. Iron pans stop water from draining deeper into the ground. As a result, the soil above the iron pan becomes completely filled with water and this water drives all the air out of the soil.

In these conditions, plant material decomposes even more slowly. Over many hundreds of years, it accumulates to form **peat** – a brown mass of partially decayed vegetation. Dried peat can be burned as fuel. When peat is burned, the sunlight energy trapped by plants hundreds or thousands of years ago is released as heat.

History of soil

Scientists can unlock the ancient history of the taiga from its peat. **Pollen** grains – the microscopic capsules that contain the male sex cells of trees and other plants – are as recognizable as the flowers from which they come. But while flowers are fragile, pollen grains are armour-plated. They can survive preserved in peat for thousands of years.

The deeper the layer of peat, the older it is. Scientists collect the pollen grains from different layers and identify and count the grains under the microscope. This tells them which trees grew nearby thousands of years ago. It also tells them something about the climate at the time, and how this has changed over the years. Changes in climate produce changes in plant life. The record of buried pollen charts the comings and goings of different plant species through time.

Permafrost

In parts of northern Canada and much of Siberia, the taiga grows above a solid layer of frozen ground. This permanently frosty soil is called **permafrost**. About 1 metre (3 ft) below the surface, the soil is rock-solid ice. Tree roots cannot penetrate this icy barrier and spread sideways to collect water.

The permafrost stops water from draining away, so the soil above becomes saturated with water. The trees themselves help create

Black spruce trees growing in open taiga in Labrador, Canada. The trees grow thickly in sheltered areas but are more scattered in exposed places.

the permafrost because they absorb the sun's heat, preventing it from reaching the icy ground. In parts of Siberia, the permafrost extends to more than 1250 metres (about 4000 ft) deep. Seeds buried in permafrost can be held in suspended animation for thousands of years. Most of the preserved seeds die, but just occasionally, a seed survives.

Open and closed taiga

At the northern edge of the taiga, the temperatures are almost too cold for trees to survive. Further to the north, the trees give way to open tundra, while to the south of this boundary, open taiga grows. Because of the cold, the trees growing in open taiga are generally small and lean and more widely spaced than the trees growing further south. In North America, open taiga is dominated

by black spruce. Between the widely spaced trees, plenty of sunlight reaches the ground. Lichens, shrubs and small ground-level plants flourish in these clearings.

In the warmer southern areas of taiga, liquid water is available to plants for longer periods of the year. Because of this, the trees grow more densely, producing closed taiga forest. The tree cover is often so thick that only a little light reaches the forest floor. Shrubs and other small plants have limited opportunity to survive here, except where natural clearings are created by fires, fallen trees or areas of marshy ground.

From bogs to forests

Low-lying hollows and depressions in the forest collect water from surrounding areas, and the soil becomes so wet that trees cannot grow at all. In these boggy, airless conditions, the **bacteria** that normally breaks down dead material cannot thrive, so pine needles and other debris that accumulate in the hollow decay very slowly. This creates good conditions for mosses, such as sphagnum. Such mosses change the character of the soil. Over decades, the mosses die away and become sediments that gradually fill the hollows. Eventually, the hollows become dry enough for trees to grow there.

Taiga plants

Trees dominate the taiga, but taiga forests do not have the lush diversity of tropical forests. Taiga plants have to live in extreme conditions, and only a few species are strong enough to survive.

About 2000 different species of conifer, flowering plants, ferns and mosses live in the world's taiga forests. This is far fewer than the number of species living in forests in warmer parts of the world. The majority of taiga trees belong to a mere dozen or so species, most of which are **evergreen** conifers with needle-like leaves.

Since the end of the last **ice age**, some 10,000 years ago, **glaciers** have slowly retreated from today's taiga regions. Glaciers still flow through some taiga forests, such as those in parts of Alaska and Norway. Because of the harsh conditions only a few species have evolved to survive there. The present taiga plants and animals only moved in once the ice had retreated.

Only a few hardy plants live in the taiga. Huge areas might be covered by a few species of trees.

The needles of a silver fir tree. These waxy spikes stay on the tree all year round and can withstand ice, snow and high winds.

Life in the cold

In many parts of the taiga, tree roots cannot penetrate very far into the soil before they reach the rock-solid permafrost. They have to get all their water and nutrients from the top 1 metre (3 ft) or so of soil. During the freezing winters, when liquid water is in very short supply, taiga plants need to hold onto all the water they can get.

The conifers' needle-like leaves have a thick, waxy coating that stops water from leaking out. The coating also acts like a suit of armour, giving the leaf strength. Like the leaves of most large plants, conifer needles absorb the gases they need and get rid of waste gases through tiny holes called stomata. Conifer stomata are often sunken into grooves, which avoids their losing too much water while taking in and giving out gases.

Dense taiga forests create their own cushioned environment. The sheltered, shaded conditions trap moist air, reduce wind speeds and keep temperature changes to a minimum. Most conifers are evergreen – they keep their leaves all year around. They can photosynthesize (trap sunlight to make food)

and grow whenever the sun is shining, although most growing occurs during the short, warm summers. The trees' needles are angled so they can collect sunlight coming from all directions.

Larches survive in the coldest conditions of all. Although they are conifers, they shed their leaves in winter to reduce water loss and frost damage. They have shallow, widespread roots that capture whatever water is available and also anchor the trees in the ground to withstand gales.

Fact file

▲ In 1915, a fire in Siberia burned an area roughly five times the size of Spain and Portugal.

▲ Trembling and quaking aspens get their name from the quivering effect of the leaves in the breeze.

▲ Many conifer trees are cone-shaped. Heavy snow slides off the downwards-sloping branches, so it does not weigh down and damage the tree.

Hidden partnership

Beneath the forest floor is a complex network of **fungi**, whose thread-like feeding tubes, or **hyphae**, permeate the soil. Hyphae are the underground parts of fungi. We notice the presence of fungi only when they produce mushrooms and toadstools above the surface.

Many fungal hyphae form partnerships with tree roots, entwining around them or even growing inside them. Such partnerships are called **mycorrhizae**. The hyphae in mycorrhizae digest dead matter in the soil, releasing nutrients for both themselves and the tree. Besides providing nutrients, mycorrhizae protect trees from disease and harmful soil bacteria, by producing

A rain-covered mushroom sits among spruce saplings. Fungi play a very important role in the life of taiga trees.

antibiotics (bacteria-killing substances). In return, trees create the right conditions for mycorrhizae to flourish. They shed dead needles for the fungi to feed on, and their roots provide a supply of sugar. All in all, the partnership works well for both. Without the mycorrhizae, conifer forests would not grow as thickly as they do. Smaller taiga plants, including wild flowers such as orchids, rely on mycorrhizae to survive on the forest floor.

Trees dominate

For a small plant, it is a tough life trying to grow on the floor of a thick conifer forest. The trees cut out the sunlight, they take water and nutrients from the soil and they

This pine drop plant is an unusual species that grows in North American taiga. Pine drops do not photosynthesize but get food by breaking down fallen pine needles.

shed twigs and needles that can smother a growing plant. Worse than that, the needles contain toxic substances that stop other plants from growing nearby. Few plants can thrive under a dense forest **canopy**. But if a clearing forms when a tree falls over or burns down, smaller plants have a chance to gain a foothold. They grow quickly and spread their seeds before a new tree takes over the space. Their seeds lie in the soil waiting for another clearing to open up.

Layer upon layer

A few shrubs, such as junipers, wild roses and alders, do grow below the conifer canopy. The shrubs' fruits provide food for forest animals, which may also shelter among the plants' tangled branches.

Lower down at ground level, cowberry, bilberry and twinflower plants grow in scattered patches, particularly where the tree cover is sparse. Where the soil is damp, lichens and mosses hug the ground. Higher up, other lichens grow on branches and tree trunks wherever the air is clean. Their absence is a sign that the air is polluted.

The plants of the forest floor grow in dim light. In fact, were they to be placed in bright sunlight most would shrivel and die. Some forest-floor plants bear nectar-rich flowers to attract insects to pollinate them. Generally, these plants – cowberries, wintergreens and starflowers, among them – have white flowers. These are bold signals to attract bees and butterflies in the forest gloom.

Nature's larder

The seeds and fruits of trees and shrubs are the main food source for many of the taiga's animals, including squirrels, chipmunks and birds such as nutcrackers and crossbills. Although this seems like bad news for the plants, they, too, can benefit. For example, nutcrackers and crossbills eat the seeds of Swiss stone pine. At least some of the seeds pass through the birds' digestive systems unharmed. When they land on the ground, the birds' droppings provide a helpful dollop of natural fertilizer. Brown bears and capercaillies perform a similar service in spreading juniper and bilberry seeds.

Animals also disperse seeds and fruits without having to eat them. The tiny, spiny fruit of the twinflower catches on the fur of small mammals and the feathers of birds. The animals may travel far and wide before the fruit drops to the ground.

In death, life

The thick layer of pine needles on the forest floor takes time to break down. Gradually, the poisons inside the needles are washed out by rain, and the needles become brittle and vulnerable to attack. Armies of small animals, such as springtail insects, soil mites, woodlice and earthworms, eat the needles and other buried debris. As the plant matter is broken down into smaller and smaller

What is a cone?

Most mature conifers produce scaly structures called cones. A cone is a conifer's equivalent to a flower. Male cones tend to be smaller and mature earlier than female cones. They produce pollen grains, which are released into the air when the cone's scales open up (right). The pollen is carried on the wind and caught in open female cones. The male and female sex cells fuse inside the female cone and produce seeds. The female cones then close up, and the scales do not open again until the seeds are ripe. The ripe seeds fall out of the cones and drop to the ground or travel on the wind, until they land in a suitable place to grow. The entire breeding process, from the growth of cones to the release of the seeds, takes about fifteen months.

chunks, fungi and bacteria finish off the decaying process that the animals began. The chemicals locked up in the dead plant material are gradually returned to the soil.

Do-it-yourself

Plants do not always rely on animals to transport pollen, or to scatter fruits and seeds. Many plants are able to produce seeds without having to receive pollen from another plant. For example, the common wood sorrel and May lily produce white flowers to attract insects, but they can pollinate themselves if necessary. They can also produce new plants by growing underground stems that establish independent roots and shoots nearby.

Mosses and lichens

Mosses carpet the tree trunks and ground in damp taiga. They photosynthesize, but unlike seed-producing plants such as trees and wild flowers, they have no true leaves. Mosses also take up water and nutrients from the soil, but they do not have proper roots. They can reproduce sexually, but they release

The silver fronds growing among this cowberry bush are lichens, confusingly named reindeer moss.

sperm into water, rather than producing pollen grains. The sperm swim to other plants and fertilize their female sex cells. Mosses are simple, miniature plants, but they have some major advantages over larger plants. They can withstand drying out. Some types can lose three-quarters of their water – becoming leathery tufts – but swell up and spring back to life again when water returns. And mosses can absorb water and dissolved minerals directly from snow and rain. They do not need to have roots in the soil.

Lichens are even hardier than mosses. They are a partnership between fungi and **algae** (simple plant-like organisms). The algae photosynthesize and provide food, while the fungi absorb water and minerals from the rain and snow. The fungi also form protective sheaths around the fragile algae. These sheaths shrink and close in dry conditions when water could be lost, and open again when moisture returns. Lichens thrive on moist bark and fallen wood. Beautifully sculpted lichens, such as the fine

Fire in the taiga

Fire in taiga forests sounds like bad news, but many of the trees can cope with heat and flames. Larches and pines have thick bark that offers good protection against fire damage. (Spruces and firs, however, tend to have thinner bark and shallow roots that are damaged by fire.) The cones of jack pines release their seeds only after a fire. The heat makes the cones explode, releasing the seeds, which then have a good

chance of germinating in the ash-covered clearing created by the fire. Flames and searing heat also sterilize the forest floor and kill off disease-causing organisms and parasites. Fires clear space for new trees to grow (below), and the ash adds nutrients to the soil. Following a fire, a rich variety of small ground plants grow, until the hardy coniferous trees and other taiga plants gradually take over once again.

strands of one species called old man's beard, cover branches. Some lichens growing on trees produce acids that have antibiotic properties. They may even protect their host trees from attacks by wood-destroying fungi.

Dark conifers

The dark conifers – the spruces and firs – are so-called because their leaves are very dark green. When seen from an aircraft, these trees darken large areas of forest. In European taiga, Norway spruce is the most common species. In Asia, the Siberian spruce is the dominant dark conifer.

Taiga plants of North America

The trees that grow in the North American taiga are typical of taiga around the world. Hardy larches survive in the far north. Spruces and firs cover the main parts of the region, while deciduous trees, such as birches, become more common further south. The coastal forests of giant redwood trees, however, are unique. No other taiga gets so much rain, and these forests are lusher than in other areas.

Larch trees live at the northern edge of taiga.

Black spruces grow in cold conditions.

Douglas firs are common in mountain forest.

Paper birches are deciduous trees that live in southern taiga.

Redwoods, the world's largest trees, grow in forests along the Pacific North-west coast.

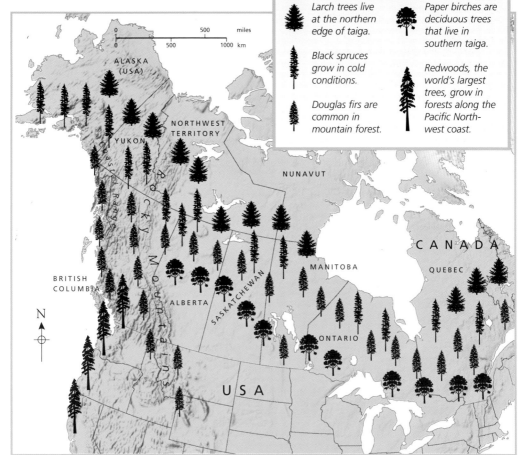

57

Mosses grow best in damp places. In the Hoh Rainforest in Washington State in the USA, mosses almost completely cover the trees, thanks to the high rainfall.

Spruces grow slowly and need damp soil all year around. In winter, these trees look particularly attractive because the pale snow contrasts heavily with their dark foliage. Spruce forests have a place in Nordic folklore, which says that they are home to mischievous gnomes, goblins and trolls.

In North America, the black (or bog) spruce is a common dark conifer. These trees are generally small and hardy and grow in very cold and boggy conditions. The white spruce is a taller dark conifer that grows in warmer, better-drained soil in the region.

Fir trees do not grow as far north as spruces. They require milder conditions and more fertile soils. The Douglas fir of North America is one of the world's largest trees, growing 100 metres (330 ft) tall, with a trunk 5 metres (16 ft) across. They form forests in the Rocky Mountains and grow in mixed forests close to the Pacific North-west coast.

Christmas trees

In Europe and North America, people buy conifers to decorate their homes at Christmas. Different species are chosen in different countries, depending on availability and local preferences. In North America, for example, the Douglas fir is popular; in parts of Europe, Norway spruce is the favourite.

The link between conifers and Christmas goes back more than 1000 years. According to tradition, St Boniface, an English missionary in Germany in the 8th century AD, stumbled across people worshipping an oak tree dedicated to the god Thor. In anger, Boniface cut down the tree, and a fir tree began to grow in its place. Since then, fir trees have been linked with Christian worship.

Light conifers
Light conifers have paler leaves and include most pines and larches. They are more widely distributed than dark conifers because they can tolerate a broader range of conditions. The Scotch pine is the most common light conifer, covering much of the European and Asian taiga. In North America, jack pine

This patch of southern forest taiga has both evergreen and deciduous trees. The deciduous aspen trees have shed their leaves, while the conifers (rear) keep their needles.

takes the lead. Larches are light conifers that shed their leaves. They can resist extreme cold and grow further north than any other type of tree.

Deciduous trees
A few deciduous trees, which shed leaves in winter, grow in taiga. Birches, aspens and poplars grow in warmer, southern regions. European white birch and trembling aspen grow in Europe and Asia, and white birch and quaking aspen live in North America.

Taiga animals

Despite the long months of snow and ice, a wide variety of animals eke out an existence in taiga forests, including some of the largest land animals in the world. Most live alone among the forest trees, rarely crossing each other's path.

The long, hard winter of the taiga presents a great challenge for most animals living there. Thick snow makes it difficult for larger animals to move about, and the snow covers food on the ground.

Most of the large animals of the taiga feed on plant material, such as leaves, fruit and seeds. In the long winter, deer have to exist on tree bark, mosses and lichens. Chipmunks, woodmice and squirrels rely on hidden stores of seeds and summer fruits.

As for the smallest creatures, such as insects and other invertebrates, many live underneath tree bark, among the leaf litter and buried in the soil. In the cold season, they hide away in a **dormant** (inactive) state or they overwinter as eggs or young. Some of these animals have natural antifreeze in their

In summer, taiga forests are filled with biting insects. The insects spend the winter as dormant pupae and develop into adults as the warm weather begins.

Canadian moose are at home in shallow water (right), where they feed on soft aquatic plants. In winter these large deer eat less, surviving mainly on bark.

body fluids. This substance stops them from freezing to death. Most taiga invertebrates feed on detritus – the dead remains of plants and animals. Others feed on the heartwood of trees, deep inside their trunks.

Because the taiga is so cold, and conifer needles contain many waxy and toxic substances, dead plant matter takes a long time to break down. In summer, an army of slugs, millipedes, woodlice and beetles feeds on the decomposing plant matter. As they break it down, they release nutrients and return them to the soil.

Eaten alive
At the height of the short summer, taiga forests are filled with flying insects, many of which bite larger animals. The air is alive with millions of mosquitoes and blackflies feasting on the blood of **mammals** – including

Wolves spend the winter living in packs. They hunt as a team, travelling large distances in pursuit of prey. In summer the packs disband and wolves may hunt alone.

people. Only the female flies feed on blood – to provide enough energy to produce their eggs. The males eat flower nectar and plant sap. Mosquitoes lay their eggs in water, where their larvae hatch and grow. If the summer is particularly dry, there will be far fewer mosquitoes than usual. A warm, wet summer, however, is good for mosquitoes.

Deer

Elk and reindeer are the taiga's largest plant eaters. Reindeer, which are called caribou in North America, migrate from tundra to taiga in winter, but elk – called moose in North America, where another deer is called the elk – tend to remain in the taiga all year round.

The elk is lord of the taiga and the world's largest species of deer. Males are more than 1.8 metres (6 ft) tall at the shoulder and can weigh 500 kg (1100 lbs). Despite their large size, elk are shy and peaceful animals. With keen senses of smell and hearing, they generally disappear into the forest when disturbed. Nevertheless, if confronted, an elk can defend itself well. Using antlers reaching up to 2 metres (79 in) across, and kicking with its sharp hooves, a healthy adult male can fend off all but the worst wolf attacks. However, the males use their antlers more often in ritual fights with rivals over access to female mates.

Elk prefer to graze on the leaves and fruit of small plants at the edges of the forest and in clearings. They have a large appetite and can eat around 15 kg (33 lbs) of food a day in winter and an incredible 35 kg (77 lbs) daily in summer.

These deer spend long periods close to ponds and rivers, because there are plenty of edible plants in the water and along the banks. In summer, they sometimes submerge themselves for hours on end to avoid the swarms of biting insects. The water is also a haven from marauding wolves. In winter,

with food very scarce, elk eat strips of tree bark. A large population of elk can devastate forests this way.

Wood bison live in the southern parts of the North American taiga. These very rare animals are not deer but are closely related to other cattle-like bison that once lived in the open prairies to the south.

Pack hunters

Unlike all other taiga **predators**, grey wolves hunt co-operatively. In deep winter, when food is scarce, they gather together to track down and overpower even the largest deer. In summer, they are more likely to hunt separately, going after much smaller prey, such as squirrels and marmots.

 # A pale shadow

Thick fur or feathers keep many taiga animals warm in winter. Some of the taiga's mammals – the snow-shoe hare and the stoat, for instance – turn white in winter. This change of colour serves as camouflage in a snow-covered landscape, allowing the hare (below) to hide from predators more easily, and the stoat to sneak up on its victims. Pale fur may offer better insulation than dark fur. Some scientists believe that dark pigment (coloured chemical) thickens the hair. Pale fur is thinner, leaving more space between the hairs to trap warm air, and this improves insulation.

The female capercaillie is smaller and less conspicuous than the male. The males use their distinctive plumage in complex displays to attract mates.

The wolf pack – a family group of eight to twelve wolves led by a single male and female pair – tracks its quarry by smell. Wolves can smell their prey from almost 2 km (over 1 mile) away. Once they pick up a scent, they cluster together – like American football players in a huddle – before setting off in pursuit. What messages they pass to one another at this time – by growls, a flick of the ear, a shake of the head – are still a mystery.

Once the wolves get close to their prey, they begin the attack. The onslaught is triggered by the victim fleeing in fright. The wolves take turns jumping onto the head, rump, back or flanks of the prey, inflicting bites that injure and gradually weaken it. Little by little, the panic-stricken animal is overpowered and then torn to pieces. Each wolf gobbles down as much meat as it can manage. Adult wolves can gorge 9 kg (20 lbs) at a single sitting.

Despite their reputation and bloodthirsty hunting techniques, wolves are really timid creatures. There are few, if any, properly documented examples of wolves attacking and killing people. In fact, people are a much

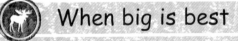

When big is best

In a cold environment, large size can be an advantage. Larger creatures have smaller body surface areas compared to their weights than smaller creatures, helping large animals conserve heat better. This is why male stoats from northern Canada weigh about three times as much as their cousins in milder forests in the USA. It also helps explain why many taiga animals are record breakers: the elk is the world's largest deer, the wolverine the largest weasel and bears (right) are the largest land predators.

and on the ground. Many birds nest in taiga forest trees, raise their young and then fly south to spend the winter in warmer areas.

Taiga fighter

Few birds remain in the taiga all year round. Among those that do are woodpeckers, crossbills, nuthatches and, biggest of all, the capercaillie. This bulky bird, a type of grouse weighing up to 6 kg (13 lbs), feeds on wild fruits in summer and autumn and resorts to a diet of pine needles in winter. In the cold season, capercaillies stay in trees during the

bigger danger to wolves than the other way around. Hunters shooting wolves over the last 200 years have massively reduced wolf numbers around the world.

Summer visitors

The arrival of spring in the taiga fills the air with birdsong. Many of the taiga's birds, such as Siberian rubythroats, are summer visitors. They fly north to take advantage of the abundant insect life on the trees, in the air

A black woodpecker mother feeds two hungry chicks. This large species of woodpecker lives right across Europe and Asia, including northern Japan.

day and bury themselves in snow to pass the night. In the summer, a male capercaillie stridently defends his territory against other males. When a resident male spots another male approaching, he gives a call that sounds a little like a cork being pulled from a bottle. If the call has no effect, the defending male drops to the ground and prepares to fight the invader. The fight begins as a ritual in which the birds pretend to bite each other. If one does not back down, the confrontation can degenerate into a brawl, with one bird clasping the neck of the other. If the males are well matched, they fight until one is seriously injured or dead. The winner controls the territory and has access to females.

Head-bangers

The black woodpecker is the largest and loudest woodpecker in Europe and Asia. It uses its chisel-like beak to excavate holes in tree trunks and pry off bark to reveal hidden

A Clark's nutcracker perches on top of a conifer tree. This species lives in the conifer forests of the Rocky Mountains, where it feeds on seeds and insects.

Hunting in the snow

In winter, much of the taiga is covered in snow around 1 metre (3 ft) deep, and temperatures plunge to −40°C (−40°F). The small forest predators hunt beneath the snow. There, weasels and stoats pursue shrews and rodents, such as squirrels. Shrews, in turn, hunt insects, while the rodents search for pine cones.

Large animals have difficulty moving through the deep snow. The exceptions are wolverines, which have broad feet that act like snowshoes. The wolverine's dense, long fur is another aid in icy weather. It does not freeze, even when wet.

The wolverine (below) – known also as a glutton in Europe and Asia – belongs to the weasel family. It has a remarkable reputation for strength and aggressiveness, out of all proportion to its size. Although it grows to only 27 kg (60 lbs) in weight, a wolverine can take on a reindeer or an elk floundering in deep snow. Sometimes a wolverine stumbles through a camper's tent, wrecking the contents along the way.

Wolverines are solitary animals, except during the brief breeding season. They eat small rodents, eggs, young birds and insects, supplemented with wild fruits and pine seeds. They also eat carrion, sometimes following wolf packs to scavenge for scraps left behind. Wolverines have even been known to drive bears from their kills.

People rarely see wolverines because they are so secretive. Females give birth to two or three cubs in mid to late winter, safe within a den under snow and often beneath a fallen tree. The young can hunt for themselves by the end of their first summer.

European taiga animals

Fewer large animals live in taiga than in other biomes. Many of these animals spend long periods without seeing another member of their own species. Despite being small in number, these species are spread over a wide area. Many, such as wolves and bears, live in all parts of the biome and also reside south of the taiga belt. Elk and bears spend the summer in barren tundra to the north of the taiga.

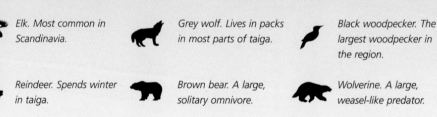

Elk. Most common in Scandinavia.

Grey wolf. Lives in packs in most parts of taiga.

Black woodpecker. The largest woodpecker in the region.

Reindeer. Spends winter in taiga.

Brown bear. A large, solitary omnivore.

Wolverine. A large, weasel-like predator.

insects. It is not unusual for these voracious birds to eat a thousand ants or beetle larvae (young) during a single meal.

The holes these woodpeckers make provide homes for other creatures, from owls to red squirrels and, by breaking up rotten wood, the birds speed up the recycling of nutrients. The black woodpecker has a remarkable tongue that extends over 5 cm (2 in) beyond its bill. It is pointed and covered in hook-like barbs that stick into food.

Like other woodpeckers, these birds' brains are cushioned by a sac of fluid enclosed within a thick skull. These structures absorb the thousands of blows delivered by the bird's bill each day. The sound of a woodpecker's drilling can be heard over a kilometre away.

Nutcrackers and crossbills

Some birds are highly dependent on the seeds of conifer trees. Nutcrackers use their powerful beaks to crush and batter pine and spruce cones, releasing the seeds. Crossbills are more delicate – they pry open the cones to extract the seeds. Different species of crossbill have beaks suited to particular types of cone. In Siberia, the parrot crossbill uses a robust, rounded beak to extract seeds from tough pine cones, while the two-barred crossbill, with a much thinner bill, goes for the more delicate cones of the larch.

Crossbills are the only taiga birds that breed during winter. They can extract seeds from cones throughout the winter, providing a year-round supply of food. Nutcrackers breed in spring. In autumn, they bury supplies of seeds under the snow to see them through the hard times ahead.

Voles

Forest voles are tiny rodents, with adults weighing only about 40 g (1.5 oz). They avoid the worst of the winter by digging tunnels in snow; the air-filled snow is a good insulator against the cold weather outside. Under the snow, voles search for buried nuts and soft fruits. In summer, their diet is much more varied, including seeds, leaves, mushrooms, soft fruits, lichens, bark and insects. Like most rodents, they can breed quickly when conditions are favourable, producing up to five litters a year.

Squirrels

Squirrels and chipmunks eat pine nuts and bury cones in a winter food store. Red squirrels use their sharp incisor teeth to gnaw the scales off spruce and pine cones to get at the seeds. They are active almost all year round and keep moving during summer, searching for fresh cones. In winter, they rely on food they have buried. A red squirrel may bury 200 cones in a day. Uneaten seeds begin growing into trees the following spring.

Crossbills are so called because the tips of their bills cross over like a pair of scissors. This helps them snip into cones to get at the seeds inside.

Miniature carnivores

Stoats and weasels are the small predators of the taiga – long, sleek and agile, they are rarely more than 24 cm (9 in) from head to tail and weigh less than 200 g (7 oz). The stoat – with its pale, thick winter coat – was a favourite quarry of trappers. The pale winter fur, called ermine, was used for making ceremonial robes. In 1937, Canada exported 50,000 ermine pelts to the UK for the coronation of King George VI. Some 300 pelts were needed to make a single gown.

Stoats mate during the summer, but the babies do not develop inside the females' womb until many months later. This delays pregnancy and so ensures that young are born the following spring, after the thaw, when food is easier to find.

Silent but deadly

The great grey owl of the Russian taiga looks much larger than its true body size because of its thick downy feathers. These are good for keeping out the cold, but they also dampen any sounds during flight. The owl hunts by listening for the delicate scratchings of its

A hoary marmot keeps a lookout for danger in an Alaskan forest clearing. These large rodents give a range of alarm calls when they spot predators.

Bear feast

Fast, cold rivers flow through the taiga of Europe and North America. In some of these rivers, once a year a miraculous fishing event takes place. Salmon, fresh from the sea where they have been fattening themselves for several years, fight their way upriver to spawn (lay eggs). They battle to overcome all obstacles in their path – including waterfalls and fishing nets – in their desire to reach the spawning grounds. Salmon return to the very same stretches of river where they themselves hatched from eggs many years before. Predators, especially bears, relish this annual bonanza.

In the taiga forests of Canada and Russia, brown bears wait in the shallows at the base of rapids (below left). Here, salmon gather before their fight upstream. The fish sometimes pack so densely that the bears just have to scoop their paws through the water to catch one.

For the chinook salmon of Alaska and northern Canada, spawning ends in the exhausted adults' death. Their decaying bodies fertilize the river water, encouraging plankton and plants to grow, and in turn small freshwater animals, such as insect larvae. The newly hatched salmon feed on these creatures.

prey – generally voles. Once located, the owl hovers above and then drops onto its prey, which may be deep below the snow. The owl plunges through the snow, seizes the victim in its talons and kills it with a bite to the back of the neck.

Coping with winter

Many taiga animals spend the cold winter inside warm nests in an inactive state. They eat as much as they can during the short summer and put on fat reserves to last them through winter. Nevertheless, many rely on food stores during the cold season. The Siberian chipmunk, for example, often leaves its nest to feast on its seed store.

Only a few taiga animals, such as the squirrel-like marmot, **hibernate**. They become dormant for long periods, their pulse and breathing rates drop to a fraction of their normal level and they do not feed. Even so, they wake every few weeks to get rid of urine, and they stir during the coldest spells to avoid freezing to death. Contrary to popular belief, bears are not true hibernators. They do not sleep right through the winter, but wake up at intervals. A mother brown bear, for example, wakes regularly to suckle her cubs.

North-eastern American taiga

The eastern belt of taiga in North America sprawls across ancient mountains and wet lowlands. The region's landscape, including the immense Hudson Bay, was created by massive glaciers.

The beauty of this lake in Ontario is typical of the hundreds that are scattered through the region. Some of the lakes are popular holiday destinations.

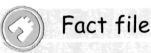

Fact file

▲ More than half of Canada's electricity comes from hydroelectric power stations in the taiga.

▲ Michigan is known as the Wolverine State. Trappers would bring wolverine furs and those of other taiga animals to trading posts in the state.

▲ Half of Canada's population is clustered in towns and cities around the St Lawrence River. Farmers have cleared most of the forests along the river.

1. Lake Superior
The world's largest surface area of fresh water. It covers almost the same area as Ireland.

2. Ouimet Canyon
A gorge 152 metres (500 ft) wide and 107 metres (350 ft) deep.

3. Hudson Bay
This massive bay is ice-locked from November to July.

4. Canadian Shield
A flat area that was once a towering range of mountains.

5. Adirondack Mountains
An area of taiga wilderness popular with hikers.

6. Charlevoix Reserve
A protected region of taiga, broad-leaved forests and wetlands. The area contains also the 700-metre (2200-ft) Hautes-Gorges, which are the deepest in eastern Canada.

7. Réservoir Manicouagan
A vast asteroid crater that has been made into the world's sixth-largest reservoir.

8. Acadia National Park
Reserve protecting America's most southerly taiga forest.

9. Labrador
A large peninsula in north-eastern Canada. Its rugged coast of fiords and islands was formed by glaciers.

10. Newfoundland
The main island in the larger province of the same name, visited by Viking explorers 500 years before Columbus's first voyage to America.

Hudson Bay

Churchill

3

marshy lowlands

MANITOBA

James Bay

Canadian

4

Shield

ONTARIO

Lake Nipigon

Ouimet Canyon

2

1

Lake Superior

WISCONSIN

Lake Michigan

MICHIGAN

Lake Huron

Lake Erie

Chicago

ILLINOIS   INDIANA   OHIO

U S A

CANADA

QUEBEC

Réservoir Manicouagan

7

Charlevoix Reserve

6

Quebec

St Lawrence River

Ottawa

Montreal

5

Adirondack Mountains

Toronto

Lake Ontario

NEW YORK

PENNSYLVANIA

Labrador Sea

9

NEWFOUNDLAND

10

St John's

Gulf of St Lawrence

NEW BRUNSWICK

PRINCE EDWARD I.

NOVA SCOTIA

Halifax

MAINE

8

Acadia National Park

Boston

Atlantic Ocean

N

NORTH AMERICA   EUROPE   ASIA

AFRICA

SOUTH AMERICA

AUSTRALIA

ANTARCTICA

0   250   miles
0   250   500 km

Developing the wilderness

In the last 30 years, Canada's national and provincial governments have had to decide how to best protect the taiga wilderness while providing energy and raw materials for the country's expanding population. Between 1975 and 1990, the Cree and Inuit people around the southern part of Hudson Bay lost 15,500 square kilometres (6000 sq miles) of their land to dams (right) and generating stations to provide power for Quebec and Ontario. Since then, plans to further develop the wilderness have been subject to stricter controls.

Siberian taiga

The Siberian taiga is the world's largest forest – it covers an area twice that of the Amazon rainforest. It is crossed by some of the world's biggest rivers, down which timber companies float felled logs to sawmills and factories.

A village in western Siberia. Millions of Russians have moved into the taiga in the last 300 years.

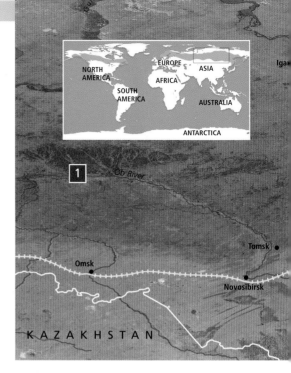

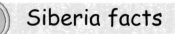

Siberia facts

▲ The Ural Mountains stop rain clouds from reaching western Siberia. To the east of the mountains the climate tends to be dry with bitterly cold winters and hot summers.

▲ The Trans-Siberian Railway crosses seven different time zones.

▲ The Siberian taiga is bordered by the Arctic tundra in the north and the Kazakh and Mongolian steppes (grasslands) in the south.

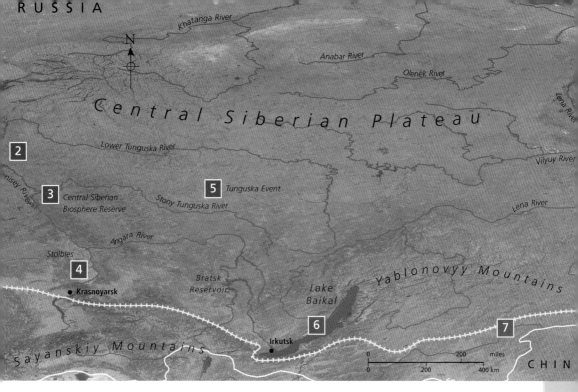

RUSSIA

Khatanga River

N

Anabar River

Olenëk River

Central Siberian Plateau

2

Lower Tunguska River

Vilyuy River

Lena River

Yenisey River

3 Central Siberian
Biosphere Reserve

Stony Tunguska River

5 Tunguska Event

Lena River

Angara River

Stolbies

4

Krasnoyarsk

Bratsk
Reservoir

Lake
Baikal

Yablonovyy Mountains

6

Irkutsk

Sayanskiy Mountains

7

0   200   miles
0   200   400 km

CHIN

1. Ob River
At 5410 km (3362 miles) long, the Ob is Russia's longest river. It flows from the Altai Mountains close to the Mongolian border to the Gulf of Ob in the Arctic.

2. Yenisey River
This river is an important Siberian transport route. Timber is shipped around the world from Igarka. Some believe North America's earliest peoples came from this region.

3. Central Siberian Biosphere Reserve
A large taiga reserve in the homeland of the Evenki people, who carry on their traditional way of life.

4. Stolbies
Unique volcanic-rock formations created by wind and rain. Many stolbies are contained in a taiga nature reserve beside the Yenisey River. The tallest reaches 120 metres (366 ft) high.

5. Tunguska Event
On 30 June 1908, a huge meteorite smashed into the ground near the Stony Tunguska River. More than 2150 sq km (830 sq miles) of forest was destroyed, and, hundreds of miles away, trains were derailed by the impact.

6. Lake Baikal
Lake Baikal covers one and a half times the area of Wales. The lake holds the largest volume of fresh water of any lake in the world. In places, it is almost 2 km (over a mile) deep. More like a sea than a lake, it harbours 1500 unique plants and animals, including freshwater seals.

7. Trans-Siberian Railway
The world's longest railway. Along its 9299-km (5778-mile) route, from Moscow to Vladivostok, it crosses desert, mountain and forest. Express trains take seven days to travel the entire length.

Hidden wealth

7

Much of Russia's wealth lies beneath the taiga of Siberia. Most of Russia's petroleum oil and gas is drilled in western Siberia, while eastern Siberia sits upon huge coal deposits. Siberia's wood and coal are transported long distances to reach industrial centres in European Russia. Most of Siberia's rivers run into the Arctic Ocean and are often blocked by ice. The Trans-Siberian Railway (right), completed in 1904, is the main transport link for Siberia's produce.

Temperate forests of the world

Every year, temperate forests around the world blaze with colour as the leaves begin to die. The spectacular display is a sign that life in the forest is dominated by the seasons.

The tropical rainforest flanking the Amazon River in South America is a paradise for plants and animals. It is always warm and wet, and sun shines all year round.

Further north, in the eastern USA, life is different. For part of the year the forest is lush and teems with life, but as the months pass, the days get shorter and colder. Starved of energy and water, the plants stop growing. Eventually, most of the soft-stemmed plants seem to die away, while many trees lose their leaves and become bare skeletons. With nothing to eat, most of the animals leave or go underground. Nothing stirs. Yet the plants are not dead; they are just waiting. Eventually, the days will get longer and warmer, and life will start over.

The parts of the world that have this cycle of the seasons – from warm summer to cool winter and back again – are called **temperate**.

A temperate forest in the Appalachian Mountains of northwestern USA. In the autumn, seasonal forests turn gold, red and yellow as leaves die before falling to the ground.

Together, the forests that grow in temperate countries make up the world's temperate forest biome. The summers are never as hot there as in tropical forests, but the winters are never as cold as they are near the poles.

Most temperate forest grows in eastern North America, Europe and eastern Asia.

In these places, winter frost stops most trees from growing all year round, so the trees shed their leaves and shut down over winter. Such forests are called temperate **deciduous** forests.

In some temperate countries there may be no winter frost. If there is enough rain, the trees keep their leaves and continue growing through winter. The result is temperate **evergreen** rainforest, of the kind that grows in New Zealand and Tasmania. Where there is less rain, there may be long summer droughts, best survived by evergreen trees with leathery leaves. This type of evergreen temperate forest grows in south-east Australia.

Temperate climates

Earth's temperate forests lie roughly midway between the tropics and the poles. The weather here changes with the seasons. The broad leaves of the trees may turn and fall as winter sets in, but it never gets too dry or too cold for the temperate forest wildlife.

The **temperate climate** is mild – neither extremely hot nor extremely cold. Summers can be hot and dry, but they are rarely so parched that the plants shrivel up or the soil turns to dust. Winters are often cold and snowy, but never as harsh or long-lasting as in the **taiga** forests of Canada, northern Europe or Siberia. So while the temperate climate is changeable, it is fairly comfortable for much of the year.

The ideal climate for a tree is sunny, warm and wet, throughout the year, as it is in a tropical **rainforest**. But for trees outside the steamy equatorial rainforest, the temperate zone is the next best place to be.

Southern complications

If the Earth was a smooth ball, dotted all over with continents and seas, there would be two bands of temperate forest extending around the globe to the north and south of the tropics. The world is not like that, though. Most of the land is concentrated in the north, and the southern **hemisphere** is mostly ocean.

The southern tip of Africa, for example, might support temperate forest if it extended a little further south. As it is, the temperate zone there makes a fine habitat for fish.

South America extends further south, so you might expect a temperate forest to develop in Argentina, between the tropical zone and the chilly wastes of Antarctica. Instead, most of Argentina is taken up either by dry grassland, called the pampas, or by a cool desert called Patagonia. The reason lies in the west of the continent, where the high Andes mountains form a long barrier between the Argentinian plains and the Pacific Ocean. The wind usually blows from the Pacific in this part of South America, so it has to cross the mountains before it reaches Argentina. As the air rises to pass over the Andes, the moisture it picked up from the ocean cools down and turns to rain, falling on the mountains.

 ## Microclimates

According to world maps of climate, vast areas enjoy exactly the same conditions. It doesn't really work like that, though. A high mountain in the temperate zone can have a virtually Arctic climate and Arctic-type plants at its peak. Even a steep hill may have a completely different type of climate on each flank, depending on which side faces the sun. One sheltered valley may be a warm refuge from cold winds, while another may be a frost hollow that regularly fills with heavy, freezing air. These local differences are called microclimates, and they explain why some parts of the temperate forest biome are a patchwork of different trees, while other parts have no trees at all.

In South America, only a small fragment of land, in Chile, has the mild conditions needed by temperate forest. Forests of southern beech trees grow here, and provide a rare and valuable habitat for a unique wildlife.

Ice age extinctions

Every 100,000 years or so, the world enters the grip of an ice age. The climate gets colder everywhere, and the ice sheets that cover the poles spread out, engulfing vast areas of land and sea. The last ice age probably ended about 11,000 years ago. At its peak, ice sheets spread well into what are now the USA and northern Europe. The temperate forests were wiped from these regions by the ice, but in North America most of the temperate plant species survived by moving south. In Europe, the plants couldn't move south because the mountain barriers of the Alps and Pyrenees cut off their retreat. Hemmed in by ice to the north and mountains to the south, many European plant species were wiped out altogether – which is why Europe now has fewer species of temperate forest plants than North America.

By the time the moving air reaches the other side of the Andes, it has lost its moisture, so Argentina does not get enough rain to support a forest. Instead, the plains of Argentina are grassland or desert. There is a patch of temperate forest on the western side of the Andes, in Chile, but it is small because it is crammed between the ocean and the barren heights of the mountains.

On the other side of the Pacific, New Zealand and Tasmania have no such problem. Lying in the warm temperate zone, they are swept by oceanic winds that bring plenty of rain – often more than 1000 mm (40 in) each year. The nearby ocean keeps the weather mild all year, with no dry season and no frost. As a result, the islands are clothed in temperate evergreen rainforest.

A few patches of temperate rainforest also grow in south-eastern Australia, but only on the oceanic side of the mountain chain, the Great Dividing Range, that extends down the eastern side of the continent. Like the Andes, these mountains catch all the rain swept in

from the ocean on the wind, and the landscape in the temperate zone to the west of the Great Dividing Range is dry grassland. So the area of temperate forest in Australia is only about the same as that of New Zealand, and including Tasmania the total area is smaller than Sweden and Norway combined.

The continental north

The northern hemisphere is totally unlike the southern. Instead of vast expanses of ocean, it has great continental landmasses. In the far north these form an almost continuous ring around the planet, mantled with icy **tundra** and the dark taiga forests of Scandinavia, northern Russia, Siberia, Alaska and Canada.

South of the taiga lies the temperate zone. Unlike that of the southern hemisphere, the northern temperate zone extends over an immense area of land, covering most of the USA, southern Canada, central and eastern Asia and Europe. As in the southern hemisphere, however, the terrain and climate make a lot of the area unsuitable for forest.

In western North America, the mountains extending along the Pacific fringe of the continent act as a rain-catching barrier, stripping moisture from the air blowing off the ocean. So the terrain to the east of the mountains is starved of rain. Much of it is desert, extending far north in the **rain shadow** of the Coastal Ranges and the Cascades. This region, known as the Great Basin, is cut off to the east by yet more mountains – the Rockies – so it is also isolated from any moist air from the Gulf of Mexico.

East of the Rockies, desert grades into the dry temperate grasslands of the prairies. Here, as on the pampas of Argentina, there is not enough rainfall to overcome the drying effects of the wind and sun, especially in summer, so forest trees cannot get enough water. A typical temperate forest needs at least 300 mm (12 in) of rain a year, and the

New Zealand's climate is not tropical, but some parts receive more than twice as much rain as many tropical rainforests. The rain encourages a lush growth of ferns and evergreen trees, forming temperate rainforest.

Temperate forest covers the Great Smoky Mountains National Park in the Appalachian Mountains. Frost destroys the delicate leaves of these trees (inset), so the trees are deciduous – they shed their leaves every year. As autumn wears on, the leaves turn red and golden before falling to the ground.

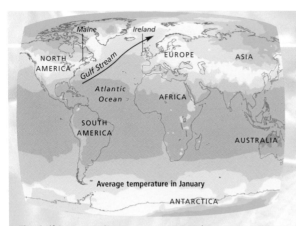

The Gulf Stream carries warm water across the ocean to western Europe. This gives Europe a mild climate, shown orange on this map, while North America and Asia remain cold and blue.

Hot flush

The US state of Maine is famed for its awesomely cold winters, where a 'white Christmas' is guaranteed. Yet on the other side of the Atlantic Ocean, western Ireland is further north than Maine, and it hardly ever snows. Why?

An ocean current called the Gulf Stream carries warm water north-east from Florida to Europe. As it swirls around the west coasts of Europe, it warms the air and gives European countries a far milder climate than you might expect. This is why the temperate forest zone in Europe is so much farther north than the same zone in America.

prairies can get a lot less than this. From a point roughly halfway between the Rockies and the east coast, moist air from the Atlantic brings just enough rain to give trees the edge over grass, and the forest begins.

The temperate forest once covered virtually the whole of the eastern USA as well as parts of south-eastern Canada. In the south-eastern USA the climate is warm, wet and almost frost-free, so the forest has an almost tropical feel. Further north, the winter frosts get increasingly severe, so most of the forest trees are the deciduous type that grow fast in summer and lose their leaves in winter. Deciduous trees need to grow for at least four months of the year, but in the far north the summers are so short that this becomes impossible. So, north of the Canadian border, the deciduous trees gradually fade out, the northern evergreens take over and the temperate forest gives way to taiga.

Atlantic rain

Across the Atlantic, Europe has no spine of mountains acting as a barrier to moist ocean winds, so the climate is wet enough for temperate forest to grow almost all over the region. In Ireland and western Scotland there is enough rain throughout the year to support a temperate rainforest, but these countries lie

Deciduous trees look lifeless in winter, but the growing season in the temperate climate is long, and they will have time to re-grow their leaves in spring.

83

Climographs

Each place in the world has its own pattern of weather. The typical pattern of weather that happens in one place during a year is called climate. We can sum up a place's climate on a climograph, such as the one shown here for St Louis in the USA. The letters along the bottom are the months of the year. The numbers on the left and the small bars show rainfall, and the numbers on the right and the curvy line show temperature. You can see at a glance that St Louis is hottest in July, but December is the driest month.

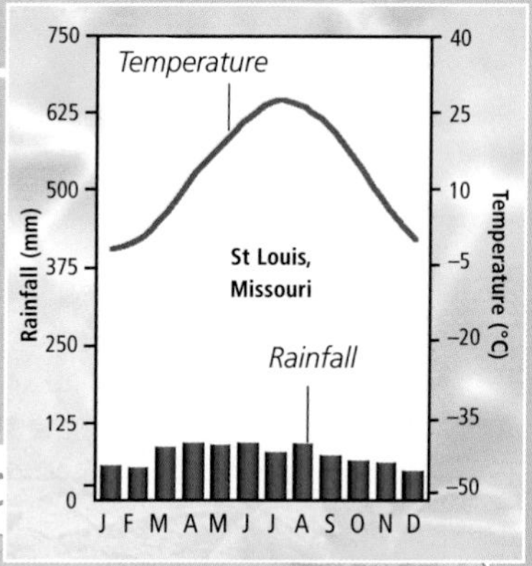

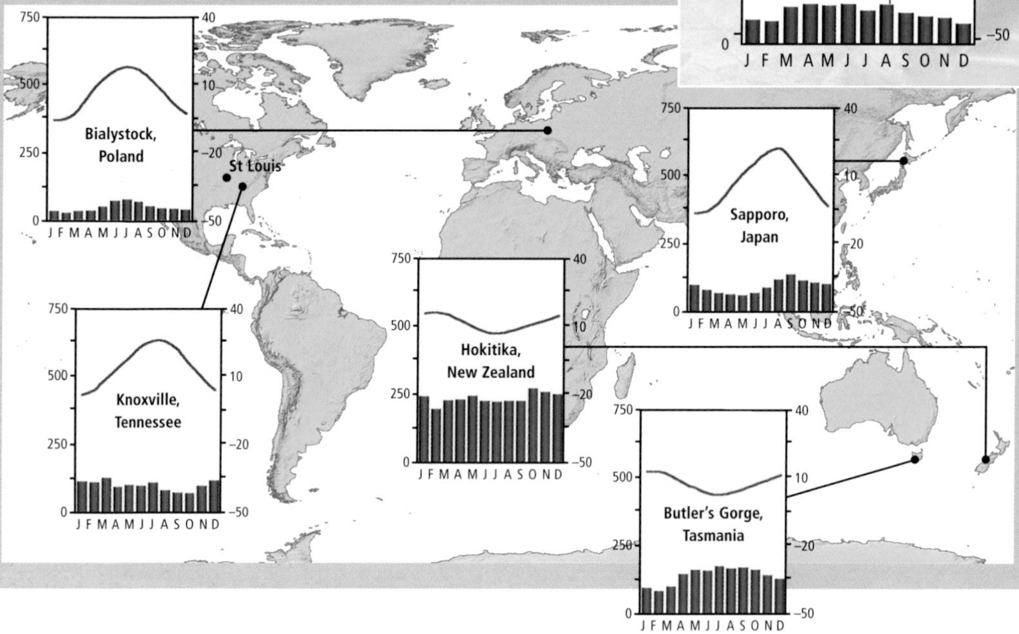

so far north that temperate evergreen trees cannot survive. Instead, the cool soils become waterlogged, which starves the ground of air and so stops dead plants from rotting away. The dead plants build up into masses of dead matter called peat bogs. Formed over thousands of years, these bogs once extended across large areas of Ireland and Scotland.

Further east, where the rainfall is lighter but still reliable throughout the year, much of the land from Ireland to central Russia was originally covered in temperate deciduous forest, like the forests of New England. In the north this temperate forest grades into taiga, just as in Canada. To the south, around the Mediterranean, most of the rain falls in winter, and it may not rain at all in summer. This type of climate favours trees with tough, leathery evergreen leaves that can function in winter and resist drying out in summer. Where there is enough rain, these hardy trees sometimes form forests and woodlands, but most of the Mediterranean landscape is **shrubland**.

The heart of Asia
Just beyond the Volga River, on the eastern fringes of Europe, the influence of the Atlantic Ocean finally fades. Denied the regular rainfall it needs, the temperate forest fizzles out in a

scatter of trees and dry temperate grassland. This Asian equivalent of the North American prairie is known as steppe, and it extends across the heart of Asia to central China. To the north is the taiga forest, growing on land that, because of the long, dark winters, never really dries out. To the south is desert, much of it lying on the dry side of the Himalayas and the high plateau of Tibet. Far away from the gentle influence of the ocean, this northern desert and steppe is scorched in summer, bitterly cold in winter. It is among the last wildernesses on the Earth.

To the **nomads** who still roam the central Asian heartlands, the steppe and desert must seem endless. But further east the icy highlands of Tibet give way to the peaks and valleys of the central Chinese hill ranges, and the temperate zone comes under the influence of winds blowing off the Pacific Ocean. The climate is milder, with more reliable rainfall, and the forest can grow again.

This east Asian temperate forest region extends in a broad swathe up to the Siberian border, and through Korea to Japan. On its southern fringes it is semi-tropical, while further north the frosty winters favour deciduous trees, which shed their leaves in winter, mixed with evergreen conifers on poorer soils. But over the centuries, generations of farmers have stripped most of the trees from the Chinese lowlands. Today, the most extensive eastern temperate forests survive in the Siberian far east, Korea and Japan. There, the rich colours of the deciduous trees in the autumn recall those of New England, on the other side of the world.

The limestone pinnacles of southern China might make stunning scenery, but they don't make good farmland. So, they remain clothed in the temperate forest that covered much of China thousands of years ago.

Plants of the forest

Trees like oaks, beeches and maples dominate the world's biggest temperate forests. They are deciduous – they cope with winter by shedding their leaves in autumn and growing new leaves in spring. The plants of the forest floor survive as roots, bulbs or seeds, ready to shoot up from the ground in spring.

As it hurtles through space, taking spectacular photographs of the universe, the giant Hubble Space Telescope gets its power from the sun. Solar panels soak up the light and convert it into electricity to drive the telescope's cameras and transmitters. Its batteries are always charged up because all its energy is supplied by the sun.

Hundreds of miles below, on Earth, life also gets all its energy from the sun. The chocolate bar that you eat to give you energy is made from cocoa beans and sugar, which come from plants. The plants make the sugar and the beans from simple chemicals that they absorb from the air and draw up through their roots. Like cooking, this process needs energy, and the plants get it by spreading their own solar panels – their leaves – in the sunlight.

The more light a leaf can collect, the better; so the best shape for the job is broad and flat. Besides absorbing energy, leaves have another function. Each leaf is peppered with tiny holes, or pores, that let water **evaporate** (turn to vapour) and drift away. The process of evaporation makes the leaf suck in more water through its stalk. This, in turn, pulls water from the tree's twigs and branches, and up through its trunk from the

roots – water that carries vital chemicals the tree needs for making food. So leaves are not only energy-collecting solar panels; they also power the pumps that allow trees to collect chemicals from the ground.

Leaves for the job

Around the **equator**, where it is always warm and wet, a leaf can do its job all year round. And since leaves are complicated structures, most tropical trees try to make them last as long as possible. Each leaf is thick and strong, and usually keeps working for a full year.

The trees that carry this type of leaf are called broad-leaved evergreens, which sums them up quite neatly.

Many trees and smaller plants that live in other parts of the world use the same tactic, even though their leaves may be doing nothing for part of the year. In warmer temperate regions, like southern Australia and around the Mediterranean, the hot, dry summers are a problem for plants. If a plant

Evergreen rhododendrons dominate the foreground of this view of the Blue Ridge Parkway in the Appalachian Mountains. Behind is a mixture of broad-leaved trees, typical of temperate forests, and a few needle-leaved trees.

Unlike the temperate forest trees of Europe and North America, Australian eucalyptus trees keep their leaves throughout the year.

In **temperate** regions with harsh winters, such as the eastern USA, frost is the enemy. All plants contain a lot of water, and soft-stemmed plants keep themselves upright by filling their veins with water. This is why pot plants collapse if you forget to water them. They get into a far worse state if they are frozen, though.

When water turns into ice it expands and takes up more room. A lot of the water in a plant is inside tiny packages called cells – if it freezes and expands it can burst the cells and turn the plant tissue to mush. If you've ever put a fresh strawberry in the freezer, you'll know all about it.

Getting frozen like this can be deadly, but the plants of colder temperate forests have ways of defending themselves. One way is to grow strong, woody stems and extra-tough leaves that can survive being frozen. A few broad-leaved evergreen trees and shrubs, such as rhododendron and holly, use this method.

Holly leaves are thick, tough and waterproof, like those of drought-resistant trees, and they live in the same warm, dry regions. But they are also tough enough to withstand freezing, and this allows holly to live in places with frosty winters. The leaves stay green all winter, which makes them a juicy target for browsing animals when there is not much else to eat. Holly trees protect themselves from being eaten with lower leaves that bristle with sharp spines.

Other evergreen trees have narrow, waxy leaves like needles or scales. These work well in droughts, which explains why needle-leaved conifers are common in dry places like the mountains of Nevada and California. They are also frost-proof, so they are perfect for trees growing in the far north, where the

keeps losing water from its leaves when there is no more in the soil to be sucked up by the roots, it will wilt and die.

Plants such as eucalyptus trees grow tough evergreen leaves with fewer pores than usual, so they lose far less water. The leaves are often waterproofed with wax, and they dangle or are held on edge instead of facing the full sun. They don't work too well at catching light, but if there is a summer rainstorm they are ready to gather energy and pump water.

long winters favour trees such as pines and spruces. You can find out more about this type of forest in Taiga (pages 40–75).

Shutdown

Tough-leaved evergreen trees like hollies and pines grow in all temperate forests, but they are not as successful as another group of trees that have developed a completely different way of dealing with winter. Instead of carrying small, thick, waterproof leaves that work relatively well all the time, the deciduous trees have broad, thin, delicate leaves that work very well for just some of the time. It's a gamble, but in a temperate climate it pays off.

Every spring, each deciduous tree grows a new set of these super-efficient leaves, and all summer they gather energy and pump water and **nutrients** to fuel the tree's chemical factories. They do their job so well that

Fire!

Every summer, ferocious wildfires sweep through vast areas of the world's temperate forests. Temperate forests in warmer places like south-east Australia are most at risk. In 1983, a forest fire destroyed more than 2600 square km (1000 square miles) of forest, an area the size of Gloucestershire, in the Australian state of Victoria.

An enormous fire like that is a disaster, but many of the trees in warm temperate forests need the occasional fire. Protected from the flames by their bark, the big trees survive while the blaze clears the ground of dead leaves and undergrowth. As the heat rises, it makes the cones and pods of the trees pop open, so their seeds fall out and drift down to the newly cleared ground – a perfect recipe for a brand-new crop of young trees.

These hazel twigs, although encased in ice, already have frost-proof leaf buds. Leaves will unfurl from the buds as soon as the ice melts in spring.

Spreading seed

An oak tree can produce 90,000 acorns each year, but if these just fell straight to the ground they would have little chance of growing in their parent's shade. Even if they did grow, the saplings would steal food and water from their parent. So trees have found ways of scattering their seeds over wider areas, giving them a better chance to find a patch of sunlight in the forest.

Tiny birch seeds blow on the wind, while heavier maple seeds (right) have papery vanes that spin like the rotors of a helicopter to keep them airborne. Oaks make use of forest animals such as squirrels, jays and chipmunks, which carry off the acorns for food, bury them and then forget some. Other trees, such as hawthorns and cherries, have bright fruits that attract

birds. The birds swallow the fruits and digest the flesh, but the undamaged seeds pass through the birds, to be dumped on the other side of the forest.

a deciduous tree can grow much more efficiently than its evergreen neighbours. In most temperate forests, deciduous trees like oaks, beeches, maples and aspens generally overwhelm the evergreens and crowd them out. The evergreens hang on in areas with bad soil, where deciduous trees have trouble getting enough plant food to make their new leaves each year.

The broad-leaved deciduous trees make the most of the summer sun by growing, flowering and producing their seeds. As summer moves into winter, though, the failing light means that their leaves can make less and less food. If the weather gets really

Maple leaves burst from their buds in spring. At first tightly folded up, they soon flatten out and present their broad surfaces to the sun.

cold, it doesn't rain but it snows, and the snow sits on the ground instead of soaking in. So in winter, the trees suffer as if there was a drought. The evergreens stick it out, but the deciduous trees shut down, dump all their leaves and don't grow again until spring.

Autumn

Every leaf that a tree makes costs it energy. When a tree drops all its leaves at the end of the season, it throws away a big investment. To be sure of surviving – and doing better than the neighbourhood evergreens – it must cut its losses. One of the most expensive substances in a leaf is **chlorophyll** – the green chemical that captures sunlight and uses it to make sugar. Rather than lose all the valuable chlorophyll in its

American forest trees

The temperate forest biome in North America is not the same all over. In the north, in Quebec and Ontario, temperate forest gradually merges with the northern coniferous forest, or taiga. In the south, the temperate forest changes into exotic kinds of subtropical forest, where the evergreen trees have needle-shaped leaves to survive summer droughts, or have stilt roots to cope with living in swamps.

Maple; a typical broad-leaved deciduous tree of the temperate forest.

Red spruce; a typical needle-leaved, evergreen conifer tree of the taiga.

Loblolly pine; a needle-leaved, evergreen conifer of subtropical America.

leaves, a deciduous tree sucks it back into the twigs to be used again. As the green chemical drains from the leaves, they change colour. In Europe most of the oaks, elms, beeches, chestnuts and other trees turn brown or yellow, but in New England and Japan the forests are flushed with colour as the maples turn bright gold and red.

When all the chlorophyll and **sap** has drained from each leaf, its stalk develops a thin layer of crumbly cork where it joins the twig. This is so brittle that a breath of wind is enough to snap the leaf away and send it fluttering to the ground. Within a few weeks,

Above: The leaves of deciduous trees, such as these maple leaves, turn different colours because they no longer contain the chlorophyll that made them green.

the forest is stripped bare, and the ground is hidden beneath a thick, multicoloured carpet of shed leaves.

Without their leaves, the trees cannot make food. Trees have to save all their energy for spring, when they must somehow sprout a whole new set of leaves before they can start up the factory again. But they get a head start. Before autumn, each tree has already made its spring leaves, keeping them tightly packaged in frost-proof buds on every live twig. When the warm weather returns, the buds only have to pop open to allow the new leaves to unfurl and start working.

Dieback

The deciduous trees are the biggest, most noticeable plants in the temperate forest, but they are vastly outnumbered by the plants of the undergrowth. Most of these do not have tough, woody stems like the trees, and when winter arrives the frost destroys them.

Hearts of oak

Trees like this mighty oak can grow to immense size because their trunks and branches are strengthened with tough, springy wood. Even in a live tree, most of this wood is dead, but it includes a thin living layer just below the bark. The living layer adds new sapwood to the trunk. Sapwood is a soft type of wood with veins that carry watery sap up from the tree's roots.

As the tree grows, it converts its inner sapwood to much harder, stronger heartwood, which supports the tree like a skeleton. The living tissue also produces another layer on its outside, which carries sugary sap down from the tree's leaves. Overlying this layer is the bark: a tough, corky sheath that protects the tree from frost, fire and hungry animals.

Or at least, the plants seem to be destroyed. Their leaves and stems shrivel, collapse and rot away.

But the plants are not dead. Like the deciduous trees, they are just shutting down for a while. As long as their roots are in good shape, they can survive having their foliage frozen and killed. They prepare for spring by building up food in bulbs, fleshy roots or fat buds on the living parts just below ground level. The trees can help here as well, because a thick layer of fallen leaves on the forest floor acts like a blanket against the freezing air temperatures. When spring arrives, new green shoots sprout through the fallen leaves, and the plants that appeared dead are back in business.

Below: In North America, trilliums grow on the forest floor and can live there for many years. Like trees, their underground bulbs lay down a ring of growth every year.

Plants that die back in winter but survive underground are known as herbaceous perennials. **Herbaceous plants** die down to ground level each winter, and **perennial** plants keep going year after year. Herbaceous perennials do both. They are particularly common in temperate deciduous forests, because when the trees are still without leaves in early spring, the forest floor is flooded with light. This gives small plants a chance to grow, flower and spread beneath the trees – but only if they are ready and waiting to sprout from just below the surface.

This spring surge of growth creates some of the most spectacular flower shows on Earth. In the deciduous woods of Virginia and North Carolina, great drifts of violets, blue delphiniums and white trillium lilies burst into bloom, soaking up the sun so they can make their seeds before they are shaded by the new tree foliage. In Europe, and especially in England, the woods are carpeted with a magical haze of bluebells, along with wood anemones, daffodils and primroses. You can see wood anemones drinking in the energy of the light, as each flower tracks the movement of the sun through the sky like a tiny dish antenna.

Living in the shade

The spring flowers have to race to set their seeds, because by early summer the sunlight is blocked out by the spreading canopy of leaves on the forest trees. The trilliums and bluebells soon vanish beneath a dense growth of nettles, ferns and other plants that flourish in shade. These have broad leaves that are well suited to gathering as much light as possible, so the plants can make food. But there is another way a plant can get food while living in the shade: it can steal it.

One of the plants that grows in European forests is a delicate-looking flower called cow wheat. Although it has slender leaves, which capture only a little sunlight to make food, it can live in deep shade. It survives because it attaches its roots to those of other plants and steals their sugary sap. It lives off others in the same way that bloodsucking animals such as ticks and lice do. These freeloading animals

 # Tree rings

When a tree is growing fast in spring and early summer, it adds a thick layer of wood to its trunk. In late summer, it grows much more slowly, adding a thinner, harder layer, then stops altogether. In spring it starts up again, adding another thick layer. So by simply counting the layers, which show as rings on the cut end of a felled tree, you can see how old the tree is.

The layers also record the weather during the tree's lifetime. A good summer creates an unusually thick layer, while a cold summer results in a thin one. In very old trees, these varying layers can show what the weather was like each summer for more than a thousand years.

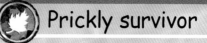

Prickly survivor

The first seed-producing trees appeared on Earth about 300 million years ago. They were primitive, scaly versions of modern conifers like pines and spruces, and they dominated the forests for about a hundred million years until the ancestors of today's broad-leaved trees started taking over.

Amazingly, a few of these primitive types of trees still grow in temperate forests. The most spectacular is the monkey puzzle or Chile pine (left), which has sharp scales instead of leaves, and grows up to 30 metres (100 ft) tall on the slopes of volcanoes in the southern Andes mountains. Barely changed in 200 million years, it probably developed its spiny defences to discourage hungry dinosaurs!

Left: Fungi get their food in an amazing range of ways, but in a temperate forest you can often find them feeding on dead wood.

and plants alike are called parasites. Weird-looking parasitic plants called broomrapes go further than cow wheat, and get all their food from the roots of other plants. Since they make no food of their own, they do not need chlorophyll. So instead of being green, they are almost colourless. Some orchids live in a similar way, and can survive in virtual darkness. Yet the real experts at getting food without light are the strange organisms we call fungi. A **fungus** is not a plant. It is mostly made of chitin, which is the material that forms the

Below: Mushrooms and toadstools come in different shapes and colours. A few, such as these fly agaric toadstools, are brightly coloured. The colour may warn animals that the fungus is poisonous.

hard outer casing of insects. Instead of making its own food from raw chemicals, as green plants do, a fungus eats ready-made food, like dead plants or animals. A fungus can dissolve wood and turn it into sugar, which it then uses to make its own structure. And like broomrape, some fungi are parasites that eat live food. (Broomrape feeds on tomatoes.)

The fungi most of us know about are the various sorts of mushrooms that pop up overnight from the forest floor, but these are just the fruits of much bigger organisms that live hidden in the soil. Their thread-like stems form tangled mats that gather food from decaying leaves or rotting timber. These often cover huge areas – scientists investigating a honey fungus growing in a temperate forest in Michigan, USA, found that it extended over 125,000 square metres (150,000 sq yds) – the size of a small airfield.

The threads of some fungi also entwine the roots of living plants and steal some of their sap. Yet the plants can survive this, because some fungi repay the plants by supplying certain substances that plants cannot get from the soil by themselves. Many of the plants in temperate forests rely on these partnerships for survival – if their seedlings are planted in soil that does not contain the right sort of fungus, they keel over and die.

Windows of opportunity

Although the forest plants put a lot of effort into producing seeds, most of them never get a chance to grow. The ground is too crowded, and there is often not enough light for tiny seedlings to get a good start. They need a break, and they get one if a big tree is blown over in a storm. This makes a clearing in the forest, letting in the light. It gives the seeds

the chance that they have been waiting for. First to start growing are the fast-breeding plants like foxglove and willowherb. Within a few weeks, the bare ground is thick with them, and for a year or two their flowers form a bright splash of sunlit colour in the forest. Meanwhile, other seeds have been blown in on the wind, such as those of birch trees. These also sprout in the sunlit clearing, and after a few years the young birch trees shade out the earlier arrivals and grow into a small birch thicket.

Birches do not live long, though. Eventually they give way to trees such as oaks, maples and tulip trees. And so, after many years, the wound in the forest heals over.

The ghost orchid of European temperate forests is white because it doesn't need chlorophyll to make its own food. Like a fungus, it feeds on dead leaves.

Animals of the forest

Temperate forests teem with animals, from leaf-nibbling insects to wolves and bears. But when the trees lose their leaves in winter, food is hard to find and life becomes tough. To survive, animals must make the most of the changing seasons.

If you stand under an oak tree on a warm day in early summer and look up, you might think it's raining. The air is full of drops of moisture, falling on your face. But the drops are not water. They are honeydew: a sticky, sugary fluid ejected by sap-sucking bugs feeding high in the tree. These bugs swarm over the leaves in the thousands, filling their tiny bodies with sweet sap. Every now and then, each bug produces a tiny bead of surplus sugar and water and lets it fall. There are so many bugs in the tree that the honeydew falls like continuous light rain. The whole tree is literally crawling with life.

A single European oak can provide food for more than 1000 different types of insects, including 45 sorts of sap-sucking bugs and more than 200 varieties of caterpillars. They drink the sap, munch through the leaves and nibble the buds. Tough-jawed beetle grubs gnaw into the bark and timber, and long-nosed weevils drill into acorns to lay their eggs. All these insects are hunted by an army of wasps and spiders, and these, in turn, are snapped up by small birds that nest in the branches.

Chipmunks are good climbers, but they spend most of their time on the ground searching for food. They bury secret stores of nuts and seeds around the forest to eat in winter.

Treecreepers (right) spiral up tree trunks, using their tweezer bills to pick out small insects. Meanwhile, heavy-billed woodpeckers drill for wood-boring grubs, like that of the stag beetle (inset), which grows to 10 cm (4 in) long.

Bigger birds, like pigeons and crows, raid the tree for acorns, and when the ripe acorns fall they are eagerly gathered up by mice, squirrels and deer.

And that's just one tree. A small wood contains hundreds of such trees, and a forest has thousands. Growing up to 30 metres (100 ft) tall, they form a huge, living, three-dimensional home for countless wild animals. But there is a catch, and it happens every year: winter.

Hard times

In the tropical rainforest, there is no winter. Rainforest animals can feed and breed all year round, and flourish in such colossal numbers that they probably outweigh all the other animals on land. But temperate forests are not like that. However lush and green the trees are in summer, winter transforms them into dead-looking skeletons.

They are not usually dead, of course, and there is food to be had if you know where to look, but not enough to feed the teeming populations of animals that live in the rainforest. So any animal that wants to enjoy summer in the temperate forest has to find a way of coping with winter.

99

Eurasian lynx once lived throughout the temperate forests of Europe and Asia, but today they are more common in the taiga, where there are fewer people to hunt and kill them. People are now releasing lynx into the temperate forests of countries like France, Germany and the Czech Republic to re-establish them there. Lynx prey on small animals such as mice, rabbits and birds, as well as the occasional deer.

To survive in a temperate forest, an animal has to change its way of life with the seasons. It cannot develop a specialty like eating ants, because ants are simply not available for half the year. That's why there are no dedicated anteaters in temperate forests.

Take fruit. In tropical forests, trees can bear fruit at any time of year. Whole flocks of fruit bats spend their time searching for these trees, and when they finish feeding in one tree, they look for another. They can carry on like that all year. But in the temperate forest, all the trees that bear fruit do it at the end of summer. For a few weeks, there is plenty of fruit for all, but then it's gone. An animal that eats fruit and nothing else would be in big trouble; unsurprisingly, there are no fruit bats in the temperate forests.

Instead, the fruit is eaten by generalists – animals that eat lots of different things. An American black bear, for example, may spend up to twenty hours a day feasting on berries and apples in autumn, along with acorns, beech nuts, insects, dead meat and any small animals it can catch. The fruit comes in very handy, because it is full of energy that the bear can store as fat to keep it going through the winter. Badgers do much the same, gorging themselves in a race to put on as much weight as possible before the food runs out. Squirrels, chipmunks and jays gather nuts and seeds with feverish speed and hide them in secret stores to eat later. Throughout the forest, the fruit and nut season is a time of urgent activity, because the animals know that hard times are on the way.

The big sleep

A black bear has a simple way of getting through the winter. Having stuffed itself with so much food that it puts on a 13-cm (5-in) layer of fat around its body, it looks for a snug den in a cave or hollow tree. When it finds one, it goes to sleep.

It sleeps much more deeply than normal, though. All its body processes – its heart rate, breathing, digestion and body chemistry (**metabolism**) – slow down. Its temperature also falls a little, from 38°C (100°F) to maybe 31°C (88°F). In this state, the bear's body uses less energy than when it is active, so its store of fat lasts longer. In the long, cold

Acorn transport

Jays are clever birds. Instead of just hoping to find enough food to see them through the winter, they gather acorns from oak trees all over the forest and bury them in secret stores. When they feel hungry, they can just dig up some acorns and have a feast.

The only problem is remembering exactly where the food is buried. Most jays remember well enough, but they also ignore some stores. The acorns may then sprout and become new oak saplings, growing far away from their parent trees. Since this is good for the oak trees, it seems likely that their acorns are specially designed to be perfect food for jays. So maybe it's the oaks that are clever, and not the jays.

winters of northern Minnesota, black bears may have to survive like this for more than six months, so every little bit helps.

Squirrels and badgers sleep through the winter in much the same way, although since squirrels cannot put on so much fat, they often wake up to raid their stores of nuts. They are lucky, because nuts keep well through the winter. Other small animals are not so fortunate. Unless they can escape winter altogether by flying away to somewhere warm, they have to survive the long, cold months without any food. They do this by falling into a much deeper kind of sleep called **hibernation**.

A European hedgehog, for example, eats mainly worms, insects, slugs and similar small animals, but such prey is extremely hard to find in winter. So, like the black bear, it stuffs itself with food before the cold weather arrives. Then it curls up and goes to sleep, often in a pile of fallen leaves on the forest floor. Sleep is hardly the right word, though, because its body almost shuts down altogether. Its temperature can fall to near freezing, and its heart rate and breathing slow to the point where it seems to be dead. In this state, its body uses so little energy that a well-fed hedgehog can get through winter without eating at all – although it will be very thin by the time it wakes up in spring.

Chilling out

Animals such as frogs, snakes and butterflies have no option but to hibernate, because they rely on the sun to keep them warm. They are often called 'cold-blooded', but this is confusing because in summer their blood is as warm as ours, and maybe warmer. When they are warm their muscles work well and they can digest food properly. But when winter arrives, they are forced to slow down, switch off and chill out.

Frogs often hibernate on the bottoms of forest pools beneath the ice; provided the water doesn't freeze solid, the frogs survive. Forest snakes go underground, hiding in burrows or cavities beneath tree roots. Sometimes several hundred American garter snakes hibernate in a single den, knotted together in an effort to keep out the worst

🐿 Drumbeat

In spring, the temperate forests ring with birdsong, but one sort of song is quite unlike the others. It's a mechanical, drumming rattle that sounds like a miniature road drill: the song of a woodpecker.

Woodpeckers are equipped with strong, sharp bills for hammering at timber, to get at wood-boring insect grubs and to excavate nest holes. In spring, they make the most of this pecking power by drumming on dead branches to attract mates. Every bird takes care to select a drum with good ringing tone, and each type of woodpecker has its own special drumming style.

Beware the bear

A sleeping black bear might look like a big, cuddly toy, but it certainly isn't. Even in the middle of winter, a bear can wake up from a deep sleep in just a few moments, and although black bears don't eat people, they really hate being disturbed. Startled bears quickly become angry bears, and an angry bear is something you don't want to meet. It might just smack you with a paw before it lumbers off into the forest, but even a quick swipe of those tin-opener claws is enough to do considerable damage. You don't mess with bears.

The great escape

Most seed-eating birds can find enough food in the temperate forest to see them through the winter, but for insect eaters and nectar feeders, life becomes impossible. The little ruby-throated hummingbird (right), for example, breeds throughout the forests of the eastern USA in summer. Like all hummingbirds, it feeds mainly on nectar, hovering on whirring wings to sip from its favourite red flowers. It also eats a few insects. Both nectar and insects are impossible to find in winter, so the hummingbird flies south to Central America. To get there, it crosses the Gulf of Mexico in a nonstop flight of 800 km (500 miles) – an amazing feat for a tiny bird.

The same crossing is made by larger red-eyed vireos and scarlet tanagers. These insect- and fruit-eating birds of the north-eastern temperate forests fly all the way to South America for the winter, travelling up to 10,000 km (6000 miles) in total. In Europe, the little willow warbler may migrate the same distance from English woodland to southern Africa, and return to exactly the same woods the following spring.

of the cold. Even so, if the temperature in the den drops below freezing point, the snakes can freeze, too. This is usually fatal, but not always. A garter snake can survive freezing for a few hours, even if nearly half its body fluids turn to ice.

Some cold-blooded animals have an antifreeze chemical in their bodies that stops water from turning into ice. These include many butterflies that spend the winter as pupae – the transition stage when a caterpillar turns into an adult. The pupae attach themselves to trees and sit tight,

European dormice hibernate for about seven months in a nest of dead leaves underground. While hibernating, they become as cold as their surroundings.

Porcupines don't hibernate, but their long quills and fur keep out the worst of the cold. In winter, they chew tree trunks to feed on the soft tissue under the bark.

surviving temperatures that plunge well below freezing. In spring, they hatch as winged adults, none the worse for their deep-freeze experience.

Other forest insects have a more radical approach to winter. They let it kill them. To a tiny insect, a single summer is a long time – certainly long enough for it to find a mate and produce some eggs. Protected by their shells, the eggs are much tougher than the insects that laid them, and are able to withstand hard frosts. They hatch in spring, producing an army of grubs and caterpillars just as the forest trees sprout their new leaves. In summer, these infant insects turn into adults, which mate, lay eggs and die in autumn, completing the cycle.

Most forest animals try to live longer than a single summer. If they can't avoid winter by hibernating, they have another option – they can go somewhere warmer. When spring arrives and the forest bursts back into life, the animals return. This regular movement with the seasons is called **migration**, and the most seasoned travellers are birds.

Cold comfort

In autumn, millions of birds migrate south to find food in the tropics. Meanwhile, the northern temperate forest is gripped by winter. Most of the shrubs and trees are bare, but their buds – and the insect eggs that often lie inside them – make good eating for the small birds that stay behind.

Below them, the fallen leaves lie in deep layers, because the cold weather slows the activity of the tiny animals and fungi that will eventually eat the leaves and convert them into soil. This is good news for mice and voles. They tunnel beneath the

Tiny terrors

The scariest animals of the temperate forest are not bears, or even wolves. They are tiny animals called ticks, which climb onto your skin and suck your blood. You might think this is no big deal, and in a way you'd be right – no tick can steal more than a pea-sized drop of blood. But what they give you in return for the meal can be deadly.

Ticks carry more nasty micro-organisms than any other type of bug, and the micro-organisms cause horrible, sometimes lethal, diseases. Among the diseases spread by ticks are Rocky Mountain spotted fever, Colorado tick fever, Lyme disease, Siberian tick typhus and tsutsugamushi disease. In the 1880s, in Montana, a variety of Colorado tick fever killed 80 per cent of the people who caught it, making it more deadly than the bubonic plague.

insulating blanket of leaves and snow to nibble at scattered seeds and nuts, and never need to emerge into the cold winter air.

Larger animals must endure the cold, however. As they burn energy trying to keep warm, they get hungrier than ever. In European forests, wild boar grub among the leaves looking for acorns and roots. Birds follow them to snatch up any worms or insects that get unearthed. Deer and bison kick the snow aside in search of greenery, but often resort to eating twigs and bark. In the misty forests of China, giant pandas may abandon their usual diet of bamboo shoots to scavenge the carcasses of animals that have died from cold and starvation.

All the while, there is danger. Agile forest hawks, like the European sparrowhawk and American sharp-shinned hawk, swoop and swerve through the bare branches to seize small birds in midair. These are hunted in turn by more powerful killers, like the northern goshawk. At night, owls listen for mice scurrying through the leaf litter, then glide down on soundless wings to snatch them up in their talons. Red foxes and even wolves prowl the forest in search of prey or dead meat, while beneath the snow, slender weasels chase voles through their runs and burrows. Deeper still, moles tunnel in the soil, devouring worms and fat beetle grubs.

Hungry hordes

As the days get longer in spring, the buds on the trees swell and burst, and new leaves unfurl in the sun. At the same time, all the insect eggs that have weathered the winter in buds and bark crevices hatch out, and swarms of caterpillars and other grubs emerge to nibble the tender young foliage.

Roe deer are common in European forests. Always on the lookout for danger, they bark like dogs when alarmed. The males re-grow their antlers every spring.

Long haul

Butterflies look too fragile to go on long migrations, but some do exactly that. The most travelled are the monarch butterflies that spend summer in the temperate forests around North America's Great Lakes. Rather than risk freezing in the northern winter, many fly south-west on an awesome 3200-km (2000-mile) journey to Mexico. There they roost in their millions in a few trees that have been used by their ancestors for centuries (right). They rest until spring, then start flying north again, all the way back to the Great Lakes.

Sometimes insects attack a tree in such numbers that they strip all its leaves. Unable to make food, the tree stops growing, and may even die if insects attack it year after year. The most notorious of these hungry hordes are caterpillars of the gypsy moth, which attack oaks, aspens and similar trees. In its native Europe, birds and predatory insects keep the gypsy moth in check. In the 1860s, however, people accidentally released the gypsy moth in North America, where it had no natural enemies. It has spread throughout the north-eastern USA and regularly destroys huge areas of forest.

Normally, as the insects feed and grow fat, they attract insect-eating birds. Many birds will have stayed in the forest all winter, but they are soon joined by migrants returning to feast on the insects and raise their families. The forest bursts into song as the male birds stake their claims to desirable nesting sites, warn off rivals and try to attract females.

Once their eggs hatch, the birds face the challenge of feeding the hungry youngsters. Baby birds need high-**protein** food if they are

to grow properly, so even seed-eating birds like finches feed their nestlings on caterpillars and other insects. Meanwhile, bigger birds, such as hawks and crows, are feeding their young too. With the forest full of eggs and nestlings, they enjoy rich pickings. Luckily, if small birds lose their first family to predators, they normally have enough time to start a second one.

Birds are not the only animals feasting on the insects. In the forests of south-eastern Australia and Tasmania, sap-eating animals called sugar gliders switch their attention to caterpillars, beetles and small spiders in the spring. The protein-rich diet helps them build up strength for the breeding season.

In spring, scarlet tanagers fly from the rainforests of South America to eastern North America to raise families. Their favourite nesting sites are oak trees.

Sugar gliders are also known as flying possums. They make their way from tree to tree by leaping across open spaces, high above the forest floor, and gliding on furry webs of skin stretched between their outspread legs. They can travel up to 100 metres (330 ft) like this, saving them the trouble – and risk – of coming down to the ground. They are only active at night, and have huge eyes that gather the dim light and pick out their target trees in the gloom.

While gliders find their way in the dark by sight, insect-eating bats orient by sound. As it hunts, a bat emits a rapid stream of squeaks. These spread out through the air like ripples on a pond, and bounce off trees, leaves and airborne insects. The bat's sensitive ears pick up these echoes and convert them into a stream of electrical nerve signals, rather like the signals that pour down a cable TV line. The bat's brain then

A sugar glider uses its bushy tail as a rudder while gliding between trees. It has sharp claws and a pincer-like grip for holding on when it lands.

Bamboo bear

Bears are basically meat eaters that have developed a taste for eating fruit, nuts, sugary sap and other vegetable foods. But one bear goes even further, and lives almost entirely on bamboo, a sort of giant grass. It's called the giant panda.

Giant pandas live in the mountain forests of central China, on the fringes of Tibet. There, the tall trees rise above a dense undergrowth of bamboo, which grows so thick that the panda never has to look far for a meal. It's hardly ideal food, though, so an average panda has to eat about 8 kg (18 lbs) of it every day. That's like eating about sixteen big packets of breakfast cereal!

Even so, the energy from the bamboo is barely enough to cover the giant panda's daily needs. So, unlike a black bear, the panda can't put on enough weight to sleep through the winter. It has to stay awake – and keep eating.

The damp forest floor makes a perfect home for newts and salamanders, which need to stay moist. They come out at night to hunt for worms, slugs and insects.

builds up an image from the signals, just like the TV, so the bat can see in the dark. This way of 'seeing' is called echolocation.

Most forest bats hunt flying insects such as moths and beetles, using echolocation to capture them as they flit and drone through the night air. But a European long-eared bat has such sensitive hearing that it can hear the faint footsteps made by prey crawling and fluttering over leaves and branches. Flying with amazing precision, it weaves its way slowly through the foliage, scanning for juicy prey lurking among the leaves. When it detects a suitable victim, it hovers, pinpoints the source of the sound and then seizes the insect – and all in complete darkness.

Return flight

As summer wears on, the leaves on the trees get darker, tougher and less edible. Most of the insect grubs have turned into moths, wasps and flies, so the feeding frenzy slows down. Many adult insects do not eat at all but live just long enough to mate and lay eggs. Their job done, they run out of energy and are picked off by birds and bats, or simply fall exhausted to the forest floor.

With fewer insects to catch, many of the birds that flew north from the tropics in spring get ready to fly back again. To be sure of making the trip, they eat ravenously in late summer to build up big stores of energy-rich fat, making the most of the insects while they last. Some migrant birds may leave the northern temperate forests as early as August. In more southerly forests, they hang on as late as October. Eventually, all the summer visitors disappear, and as the leaves start falling from the trees, the animals that are left behind prepare for another winter.

The long-eared bat's sensitive ears can hear the tiniest rustle among the leaves of an oak tree. After snatching its meal, the bat returns to a perch to feed at leisure.

109

Eastern North America

Temperate forests once covered the eastern USA and parts of Canada, from the swamps of the deep south to the Great Lakes and beyond into Quebec. Most of these forests are gone, but the surviving ones are world-famous for their glorious leaf colour in autumn.

1. Mount Katahdin, Maine
The northern end of the Appalachian Trail, where temperate deciduous forest becomes mixed with evergreen taiga.

2. Adirondack Park
3200 km (2000 miles) of trails lead visitors through the sugar maples and paper birches of this reserve.

Forest facts

▲ Much of the eastern USA is taken up by the Appalachian Mountains. A broad band of lowlands loops around the south of the mountains from the prairies to the east coast.

▲ The North American temperate forest is rich in different species of animals and plants. There are more than 27 species of salamanders within the Great Smoky Mountains National Park alone, compared to 360 species worldwide.

▲ The southern Appalachian Mountains support more than 130 species of trees (the whole of Europe has just 85) and more than 1500 species of wildflowers.

Left: The autumn colours of maple trees are typical of American temperate forest in the north. In the south, though, there is subtropical forest formed by trees that don't lose their leaves.

NORTH AMERICA
EUROPE
ASIA
AFRICA
SOUTH AMERICA
AUSTRALIA
ANTARCTICA

SASKATCHEWAN
MANITO
MONTANA
NORTH DAKO
SOUTH DAKOT
KANSAS
COLORADO
U
OK
NEW MEXICO
TEXAS
MEXICO

Lake
Winnipeg

CANADA

QUÉBEC

ONTARIO

Lake Superior

Mount
Katahdin

1

MINNESOTA

Montreal
Ottawa

Green
Mtns.

NEW BRUNSWICK

White
Mtns.

Lake Huron

WISCONSIN

Toronto

Lake
Michigan

MICHIGAN

Adirondack
Mtns.

Lake
Ontario

NY

Catskill
Mtns.

Plymouth

3

IOWA

Missouri River

Chicago

Detroit

Niagara
Falls

Lake Erie

RI

Cleveland

5

4

New York City

INDIANA

OHIO

Philadelphia

ILLINOIS

Indianapolis

Ohio River

Washington, DC

6

Kansas City

S

A

7

Shenandoah
Mountains

8

KENTUCKY

VIRGINIA

MISSOURI

NORTH CAROLINA

TN

Knoxville

Mount Mitchell

Memphis

Mississippi River

9

Great Smoky
Mtns.

Blue Ridge
Parkway

Atlantic

Springer
Mountain

ARKANSAS

Atlanta

SOUTH
CAROLINA

Ocean

ALABAMA

10

Red River

Dallas

11

Delta
National Forest

GEORGIA

LOUISIANA

Houston

New Orleans

FLORIDA

N

Gulf of Mexico

BAHAMAS

0   250   miles

Miami

0   250   500 km

3. Plymouth, Massachusetts
The site where the Pilgrims landed in 1620 and started clearing the forest to grow crops.

4. New York City
This city is the centre of the biggest US urban region, in which 17 million people live.

5. Appalachian Mountains
Extend from Newfoundland, Canada, south to Atlanta, Georgia.

6. Kansas City, Missouri
Here, the original temperate forest faded into dry prairie grassland.

7. Ohio River
When early settlers from Europe crossed the Ohio River they discovered rich farmland.

8. Shenandoah National Park
Created in 1936, this reserve is said to have more black bears per square km than anywhere else in America.

9. Great Smoky Mountains National Park
The warm, flower-strewn forests of the Smoky Mountains are among the world's most beautiful.

10. Atlanta, Georgia
City known as the gateway of the Old South, near the southern end of the Appalachian Trail.

11. Delta National Forest, Mississippi
The temperate forest biome extends south to the southern Mississippi flood plain.

The Appalachian Trail

If you think you need a little exercise, you could try hiking most of the length of the American temperate forest biome along the Appalachian Trail. Officially opened in 1937, the trail is the longest footpath in the world. It extends more than 3360 km (2100 miles) from Springer Mountain in Georgia to Mount Katahdin in Maine. That's the same as the distance across the Atlantic from South America to Africa. If you manage to hike the whole trail you'll become an expert on temperate forest wildlife – and you'll get to see a great many trees.

111

Forests of Europe

IRELAND

PORTUGAL

First settled by farmers in the Stone Age, about 9000 years ago, the temperate deciduous forests of Europe have been cut and managed for millenia. Only fragments of the original wild forest remain, but the landscape is dotted with half-wild forests and small woodlands.

Forest facts

▲ Crowded countries like the United Kingdom have lost most of their forest, but larger fragments of forest survive in the more thinly populated regions of the east, in countries like Romania. Even in France, forest still covers a quarter of the land.

▲ Before the last ice age, the forests of Europe and China may have formed a continuous belt.

▲ Forests in eastern Europe are dying because of acid rain. The acid rain comes from pollution emitted from factories and power stations.

Bialowieza national park

Perched on the border between Poland and Belarus, the Bialowieza Forest is a unique area of wilderness. It is part of the original untamed forest that once covered Europe from the Atlantic Ocean to the Ural Mountains. First protected as long ago as 1541, when it was a royal hunting ground, the forest is now protected by the United Nations as a Biosphere Reserve.

Bialowieza is famous as a wild refuge for the European bison, which was reintroduced after the last truly wild bison in the forest was shot by a poacher in 1919. Today there are more than 250 European bison roaming the forest, along with elk, beavers, lynx and wolves.

(Map of Europe with numbered locations 1–10 marked. Labels on the map include:)

NORWAY · SWEDEN · FINLAND · Oslo · Stockholm · Helsinki · Lake Ladoga · St Petersburg · RUSSIA · Vänern · Vättern · Baltic Sea · DENMARK · ESTONIA · LATVIA · LITHUANIA · RUSSIA · BELARUS · Minsk · Copenhagen · Hamburg · Poznan · Warsaw · Bialowieza Forest · Belavezhskaja Pushcha Nature Reserve · North Sea · UNITED KINGDOM · London · New Forest · NETHERLANDS · GERMANY · Berlin · POLAND · Kiev · Kharkiv · Rhine River · BELGIUM · Harz Mtns. · Erzgebirge forest · UKRAINE · Dnieper River · Paris · Ardennes · Taunus forest · Black Forest · CZECH REPUBLIC · Sumava forest · Tatra Mtns · Carpathians · Dnipropetrovsk · Donetsk · Fontainebleau Forest · Seine River · Vosges forest · Munich · SLOVAKIA · MOLDAVIA · Rostov-na-Do... · Loire River · Jura Mtns. · AUSTRIA · Budapest · HUNGARY · ROMANIA · Odesa · FRANCE · Alps · SWITZERLAND · SLOVENIA · CROATIA · Belgrade · Transylvanian Alps · Bucharest · Massif Central · Mont Blanc · Milan · Apennines · BOSNIA AND HERZ. · YUGOSLAVIA · Danube River · Black Sea · Cauca... · Pyrenees · Rhone River · Corsica · Abruzzo National Park · BULGARIA · Sofia · SPAIN · Barcelona · Rome · ITALY · ALBANIA · MACEDONIA · Madrid · Mediterranean Sea · Sardinia · Sicily · GREECE · Athens · Istanbul · TURKEY · Caspian...

Scale: 0 – 250 miles · 0 – 250 km

N

1. Atlantic Ocean
The warm currents of the north Atlantic create the mild climate of western Europe. Temperate forest thrives in southern Sweden – that's as far north as southern Alaska.

2. The Pyrenees
This mountain barrier divides the deciduous temperate forests of central Europe from the hot, dry Mediterranean shrublands of Spain and Portugal.

3. Fontainebleau
One of the earliest nature reserves in Europe, this former hunting forest was protected in 1848.

4. Paris
The capital of France is a great European city built with wealth created by farming the land after the ancient forest was cleared.

5. Oberharz Nature Reserve
Centred in the Harz Mountains, Oberharz is a relic of the dense forests that once covered central Germany. Many of its trees are damaged by acid rain.

6. The Alps
The soaring peaks and ridges of the Alps prevented plants spreading south in the last ice age, so many types became extinct.

7. Bialowieza Forest
The largest surviving fragment of Europe's original wild forest, never cut or managed, except as a hunting ground.

8. Transylvanian Alps
These wild mountains are among the last haunts of European wolves.

9. Moscow
The Russian capital lies on the northern edge of the temperate forest zone, where the taiga forest starts.

10. Volga River
East of the mighty Volga, the forest fades into the steppes of central Asia.

In early summer, before the forest trees have fully opened their leaves, bluebells carpet the ground in many British woodlands.

Temperate grasslands of the world

Picture yourself standing alone in the middle of a massive field. Grass surrounds you on all sides. Now imagine the field has no fences or hedges and it goes on and on as far as the eye can see. That is grassland.

A prairie dog forages for food in a dry Arizona grassland. Temperate grasslands such as the North American prairies are home to many small mammals such as prairie dogs.

In natural, unaltered **temperate grasslands**, grass stretches to the horizon in every direction, a sea of green that melts into the blue sky. In the shimmering heat haze it is difficult to tell where the grass ends and the sky begins. The landscape seems empty, and the only sounds are the hum of countless insects and the swishing of grass as it bends this way and that in the constant wind.

This is what grasslands are like in summer. The grasslands of the American West, called prairies, are big, flat and open. At first, they can appear empty and lifeless, like a green desert. But this is an illusion – there is much more to prairies than meets the eye. Prairie is just one type of grassland. In South America there are huge expanses of lush pasture called the **pampas**. **Veld** is the name for the grasslands that cover southern Africa, while the grassy plains of south-eastern Australia are known as **rangeland**. Stretching across central Asia are the **steppes**, grasslands so vast they are clearly visible from space.

All these grasslands belong to the temperate grassland biome. The word **temperate** describes their weather, which features warm summers and chilly winters. In summer it can get very hot, and in winter it may be freezing for days on end. However, temperate parts of the world are, on average, seldom as hot as the tropics or as cold as polar regions, but somewhere in between.

Temperate grasslands are one of the world's most important biomes. But, as this book explains, plants, animals and people have to be tough to survive there. Life in temperate grasslands can be very hard indeed.

Grassland climate

Temperate grasslands grow where there is not enough rain for forests but too much for a desert. With changeable weather and little shelter from the elements, they can be challenging places to live.

On a bright summer's day, anyone would think a temperate grassland is an easy place for plants and animals to live. It's likely to be pleasantly warm – not too hot, but just right. Often there is hardly a cloud in the sky and you can see for miles.

But this is not the whole story. Wide open spaces like grasslands are in fact harsh environments with a punishing **climate**. Climate means all the different types of weather that an area gets each year. In temperate grasslands the climate is dominated by non-stop change.

Fierce storms can break out at any time in grasslands, and when the weather changes for the worse, there's very little shelter to be found. Howling winds tear across the land, whipping up powerful dust storms in summer

The cloudless skies of the grassland summer may be suddenly disturbed by violent storm fronts that sweep past, unleashing thunder and lightning.

and raging **blizzards** in winter. Without a doubt, grasslands can be very unfriendly places indeed.

Great seas of grasses spread across the plains and rolling hills of every continent except Antarctica, where it is far too cold. This is a clue to where you find temperate grasslands – climate controls their location, as it does for most biomes. You normally find temperate grasslands in the centre of continents far from the sea. They are temperate because they occur in the world's moderate, temperate zone – between the heat of the tropics and the cold of the poles.

Rain control

More than anything else, it is rain that shapes the temperate grassland biome. The amount of rain that falls in a particular spot each year – the rainfall – decides which plants grow there. All plants need water to grow, and the wettest parts of the world have the greatest variety of plant life.

Lots of rain, or a high rainfall, allows trees and dense vegetation to thrive. Forests cover areas of high rainfall. If there is little rain, or a low rainfall, it is harder for plants to grow and trees cannot survive. Deserts occur in areas with the lowest rainfall. In places with more rain than deserts but less than forests, grasslands naturally take hold.

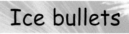

Ice bullets

Ferocious hailstorms batter the American prairies, spraying the ground like gunfire. Hail is frozen rain that forms inside supercooled clouds, but unlike snow it falls during the warmer months of the year. The heaviest hailstone ever reported in the USA crashed into Coffeyville, Kansas, on 3 September 1970. The giant lump of ice weighed 757 g (1.7 lbs) and measured 19 cm (7.5 in) across.

Changing seasons

It is not only the amount of rain that determines where grasslands exist – the timing of the rain also matters. In prairies and other temperate grasslands, some times of the year are wetter than others. The rainiest seasons are late spring and early summer. Torrential downpours lash the ground, creating temporary pools and turning gentle streams into foaming white water. As much as 250 mm (10 in) of water may cascade down in the space of a few hours. However, the rains don't last long, and soon the water soaks into the soil or drains away.

In late summer, the opposite happens. It drizzles but might not rain properly for several weeks or more. During the summer drought, the sun's rays bake the earth and many streams dry up. There are occasional violent thunderstorms, but these are short lived. The remote steppes of inland Asia suffer the most devastating droughts of all. Sometimes, hardly a drop of rain falls for long periods, transforming the green and pleasant land into a dry and dusty world.

Grass grows quickly and green in the spring rains, but by midsummer the tops are scorched by the sun and starved of water, turning to dry, yellow straw.

Lands of extremes

Wild swings in temperature are another crucial feature of temperate grasslands. On the steppes of Mongolia, for example, daytime temperatures soar to more than 40°C (104°F) in midsummer and dive to –20°C (–4°F) or lower in winter.

Just like the spring rainstorms, the cold spells often arrive without warning. Grassy plains may vanish under a thick blanket of snow for miles around. On other occasions the snows melt almost as quickly as they came. During the summer months, frequent heatwaves scorch the land. Such dramatic changes in the weather test the endurance of plants, animals and people to the limit.

Blowing in the wind

Strong winds make life difficult on grasslands, blasting everything in sight. The wind blows harder and longer in the prairies than anywhere else in the USA. It is almost always windy in temperate grasslands because the country is so flat and exposed. There are not enough trees to stop the wind from gathering speed and racing along.

Wind has a big impact on the biome. It makes fires hotter and faster-moving, and in winter it sweeps snow into deep drifts. It dries out the land by speeding water **evaporation**,

Border wars

Grassland boundaries are vague and ever-changing, not fixed lines drawn on a map. In rainy years, young trees take root along the edges of a grassland, and the grassy areas slowly turn into woodland. In dry years, grasses creep back into the wooded areas, which retreat, so the grassland expands. If it is exceptionally dry, however, the grasses start to die off, and the grassland becomes desert.

in the same way as a hairdryer works. The wind drops from time to time, but there is always a breeze – it is never entirely still.

Two of a kind

In hot countries there is another grassland biome: **tropical grassland**. Hot weather is not the only difference between tropical and temperate grassland – there is also much more rain in the tropics. A temperate grassland gets 250–750 mm (10–30 in) of rain a year, while a tropical grassland can get 1250 mm (50 in) or more. The hot, wet climate makes tropical grassland a very different place from temperate grassland. The grass grows much faster and taller, and there are many more trees and bushes.

Africa is the best part of the world to compare the two grassland biomes. Vast areas of the continent are covered with savanna – tropical grassland dotted with trees and patches of woodland. Further south, where it rains less and the winters are considerably cooler, temperate grassland takes over. In southern Africa, the main type of temperate grassland is called veld.

Tornado Alley

Every year, 700 tornadoes sweep across the USA's Tornado Alley, a region running from North Dakota and Minnesota to Texas and Louisiana – and some places here are hit three or four times. A tornado is a violently spinning column of air that bursts out of a storm cloud and swoops to the ground. Inside the vortex, air rotates at awesome speeds of up to 800 km/h (500 mph). Tornadoes are usually born when warm, moist air from the Gulf of Mexico meets cold Canadian air and dry air blowing off the Rockies. The airflows crash into one another with explosive force. Tornadoes can come from any direction, but most travel from south-west to north-east, or west to east.

Tornadoes, or twisters, unleash utter chaos. One of the worst recent outbreaks was on 3 May 1999, when a series of deadly tornadoes swept through Kansas, Oklahoma and northern Texas, killing forty people and causing £770 million worth of damage. On 18 March 1925, a single mighty twister killed 689 people in Missouri and Illinois.

Illinois
Kansas
Oklahoma
Texas

Tornadoes per
130 km (50 miles) square
  less than 1 a year
● 1–2 a year
● 2–3 a year
● 3–4 a year

Endless variety

Temperate grasslands all share the same basic climate, but each has its own unique conditions. For example, the pampas of South America has milder winters and cooler summers than North America's prairies. Ground frosts are rare in the pampas and deep snow is virtually unheard of.

High ground also gets different weather from lowland regions. In the USA, the Black Hills of South Dakota and the Ozark Plateau of Missouri are like islands in the prairie. They host a very different mix of plants and animals to the surrounding plains. Here trees such as ponderosa pine and spruce may grow.

Below: Up on the Black Hills of South Dakota, extra moisture allows a unique mix of prairie plants to flourish, including big bluestem grasses and even trees.

White out

If summers in grasslands can be hot and dry enough to turn the grass to straw, winters can be very severe indeed. Not only is the weather icy cold, but there is usually a thick blanket of snow over much of the land. But this is not the worst of it. Frequently, snowstorms are whipped up into blizzards by the ferocious winds that can tear across the open grassland. When a blizzard occurs, strong winds combine with low temperatures to blow fine, dry snow off the ground, creating an icy maelstrom that cuts visibility to just a few hundred metres and makes movement almost impossible. The worst blizzards can bury animals, cars and houses – or people venturing outside – in deep drifts of snow. Typically, there are two or three

Trails of fire

Huge grassland fires often break out in late summer and autumn. Lightning usually sets them off, but nowadays people also start fires, sometimes by accident and sometimes on purpose. The masses of dead grass stalks burn easily and provide abundant fuel. Winds fan the flames until they are as high as houses and push the blazing infernos over the dry land. The fires can burn for days, travelling hundreds of miles. Fire is vital to the grasslands. Without fire, tallgrass prairie soon changes to oak-hickory scrub.

Climographs

Everywhere in the world has its own pattern of weather. The typical pattern of weather that happens in one place during a year is called climate. We can sum up a place's climate on a climograph, such as the one shown here for St Louis in the USA. The letters along the bottom are the months of the year. The numbers on the left and the small bars show rainfall, and the numbers on the right and the curvy line show temperature. You can see at a glance that St Louis is hottest in July, but December is the driest month.

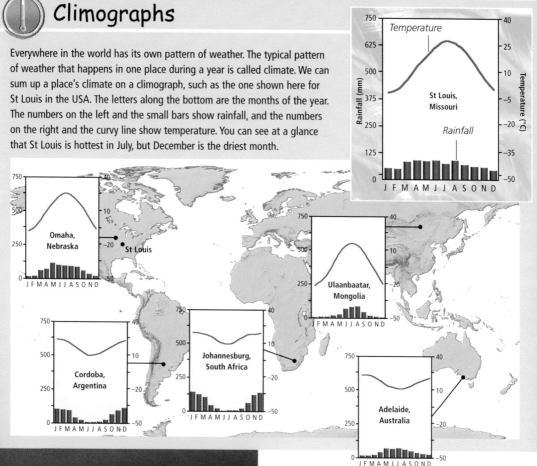

severe blizzards every winter. They tend to occur when a deep low-pressure system whirls in from the west, gathering power and moisture as it travels eastwards.

In North America, these low-pressure systems migrate down the east side of the Rocky Mountains and develop into raging blizzards as they move out across the Great Plains. The problem for weather forecasters is that less than one in ten winter lows go on to turn into blizzards. So there is real difficulty in identifying which will turn bad. Many fatalities from blizzards occur because they can strike suddenly, with great severity.

Grassland plants

Grasslands are some of the most fertile places on Earth. The grasslands burst with enough plant life to feed amazing numbers of animals.

Temperate grasslands go through a constant process of change. In winter they look dull brown or grey because the plants are **dormant** (inactive). When spring returns, the welcome rains and rising temperatures breathe new life into the soil. Fresh shoots emerge all over the place, painting the scenery bright green. Masses of flowers add splashes of intense colour. As summer wears on, the landscape turns straw-coloured. For a brief period in late summer, the grassland is awash with seas of white, yellow and bluish grass blossoms. When the rains finally dry up, the plants die back and the land appears drab and lifeless again.

Natural survivors

To survive such a demanding routine of perpetual change, grassland plants must be exceptionally hardy and adaptable. Grasses fit the bill perfectly; they are natural survivors, the greatest success story of the plant world. They have spread to every corner of the globe and cover 20 per cent of the planet's land surface. There are more than 9000

Kaleidoscope of colours

In spring, carpets of flowers transform grasslands into a riot of colour. In Asian steppes, wild tulips form a mosaic of red and yellow, broken by patches of blue and yellow dwarf irises and scarlet peonies, and a sprinkling of blue sage. In the Texas prairies (below), bluebonnet mixes gloriously with red paintbrush.

Tallgrass prairie was one of North America's wonders, with a profusion of flowers, songbirds and insects. Now there is little left as most has become farmland.

species of grasses, all of which share one very special characteristic – a way of growing that allows them to survive being ravaged by fire, drought or animals.

Back to basics

Most plants grow outwards from the tips of their shoots, twigs or branches, but grasses grow from the bottom up. This is one of the secrets of their success. Each grass plant sends out new shoots from a special base near the soil or underground.

Growing in this way has many advantages. Out in the open, a blade of grass risks being chewed, ripped or burned. Such rough treatment would be fatal for ordinary plants. But it is no problem for grass because the really important bits – the growing buds – are safely out of harm's way. This explains why people can keep mowing lawns frequently without killing off the grass.

Below: In the moist conditions of the eastern prairies, tallgrass prairie species such as Indian grass and big bluestem can grow up to 3 metres (10 ft) high.

Tall and short

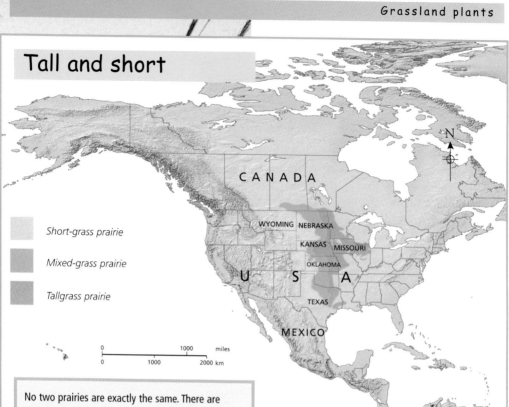

Short-grass prairie

Mixed-grass prairie

Tallgrass prairie

CANADA

WYOMING NEBRASKA

KANSAS MISSOURI

U S A

OKLAHOMA

TEXAS

MEXICO

| 0 | | 1000 | miles |
| 0 | 1000 | 2000 km | |

N

No two prairies are exactly the same. There are short-grass prairies in the driest parts of the USA's Midwest and tallgrass prairies in the wetter areas.

Heavy clouds that move in from the Pacific Ocean dump most of their rain on the western USA and Canada, especially the Rocky Mountains. By the time the clouds have passed the Rockies and reached the Great Plains, they have little water left. This is why the short-grass prairies are in the west in dry states like Montana, Wyoming and Colorado. These dusty prairies provided the location for many old westerns and for popular TV series such as *Bonanza* and *High Chaparral*.

Further east, it starts to rain harder again, which is why there are tallgrass prairies in eastern Midwest states such as Minnesota, Iowa and Missouri. Between these two types of prairies lies a halfway zone called mixed prairie. Some central states, such as North and South Dakota, Nebraska and Kansas, have all three kinds of prairies.

Whenever a grass plant loses one of its blades, it quickly grows back. Nibbling by animals, mowing and burning actually encourage the grass to grow faster and healthier. It's a bit like having a haircut. Left on its own, grass soon gets straggly and out of control, but regular trimming helps keep it in good shape.

Perfectly formed

Grasses are the ideal shape for highly exposed places like plains and hillsides. Instead of broad leaves they have thin, flattened blades clustered around tall stems. This is a winning design for lots of reasons. Blades of grass are flexible and bend in the wind without breaking off. If a heavy animal treads on them, they usually spring back. Just as important, the narrow blades stay cool when the sun is directly overhead in the middle of the day. At midday in high summer, the sun's rays are fierce, and temperate grasslands have few bushes or trees to give shade. However, the powerful rays beat straight down at this time so touch only the tip of each grass blade. If grasses had wide, round leaves, they would soon shrivel up and die.

Root of the matter

We can see only a small part of each grass plant – most of it is hidden beneath the surface. A massive network of roots spreads outwards in every direction and pushes a long way into the soil. The roots of some grasses, such as the bluestems found in America's

tallgrass prairies, reach 3 metres (10 ft) deep. Deep roots can tap into underground water in times of no rain. Shallow roots soak up surface moisture from brief cloudbursts.

An extra function of roots is to store food. Many grassland plants are equipped with fat, fleshy roots for just this purpose. Sometimes they also have bulky **bulbs** and tubers – even bigger emergency food reserves.

Testing times

Really dry or cold periods are big problems for grassland plants. Many grasses stop growing entirely, leaving only dead stems and seed heads above ground. When rain falls again or the temperature rises, they burst back into life from their roots.

When the spring rains come, grasses like this creeping soft grass are astonishingly quick at growing and putting out seeds to establish new plants.

In the high, dry western plains of Wyoming, USA, there are still vast areas of short-grass prairie where buffalo grass and blue grama grass grow 45 mm (18 in) tall.

Wild turf looks totally different from the lawn in a garden or the manicured ground at the local sports field. Gardeners keep their lawns neat, but natural grasslands are very messy by comparison, with many clumps and bumps everywhere.

Turf is a mix of different plants jumbled together. Besides grasses, there are all kinds of sedges, herbs and flowers. Sedges look similar to grasses but prefer wetter places beside streams or in damp hollows. Many grassland plants grow together in bunches, while others are scattered about here and there. Some plants are tiny and cling to the soil; others are much taller. A few grasses have become giants. In parts of Nepal, strands of grass reach 8 metres (26 ft) high.

Sand and mud

Bare patches of dirt appear in the driest grassland areas. For example, sandhills pop up throughout the short-grass prairies in parts of Colorado, Kansas and Nebraska. Dry-country plants grow on these dusty little mounds, including spiky yuccas, sagebrush and prickly

Many of the flowering plants that grow among the grasses rely on a different survival strategy. They die away completely when the going gets tough, but not before scattering enormous quantities of seeds. The seeds are miracles of packaging that can endure parched earth or freezing cold for months – or even years – on end. When conditions improve at last, the seeds sprout immediately, sending out roots, shoots and stems to establish brand new plants.

A living carpet

As grass plants grow, they join up with their neighbours to make a carpet, called turf. Below the surface, turf is a crazy mass of tangled roots. Turf is what holds grasslands together. Without this tightly woven mat of plants, the soil would be too loose. Gales and rain showers would blow and wash it away in no time, leaving a desert.

Windblown wanderers

Tumbleweeds make use of the wind to spread their seeds. In the summer heat, tumbleweeds dry out and die, turning into prickly balls. Strong autumnal winds easily pick them up and send them hurtling across the landscape. As the dead tumbleweeds bounce along, they scatter thousands of seeds. There are many kinds of tumbleweeds on the North American prairies, especially in the west.

Each area of grassland has its own unique range of plants. Here in the dry Western Australian bush, tussocks of spinifex grass mingle with mulga bushes.

pear cacti. Yuccas have tough, waxy leaves to stop them from losing moisture. At the other extreme, heavy rains swamp huge areas of pampas in spring. Marsh-loving plants thrive in the muddy ground. The eastern pampas are the lushest of temperate grasslands.

Lots of layers

Up close, a wild grassland is like a miniature forest. If you go to a meadow, prairie or wasteland and get down on your hands and knees, you'll find the plants form several layers. Tall grasses and flowers hide lots of smaller grasses, herbs, mosses and lichens that are growing underneath. These dwarf plants flourish in a **microclimate** down near the ground, protected from the worst weather by the taller plants. It's a hidden world,

Soil matters

The soil in temperate grasslands is tremendously fertile. Its vital ingredient is an organic material called humus, which forms when plants and animals die and their bodies decompose (rot away). Temperate grasslands have much deeper, richer soil than tropical grasslands or rainforests. The cooler conditions slow the process of decomposition, allowing an extra-thick layer of humus to build up. The interlinked maze of grass roots holds all this goodness in place. You can tell how rich soil is from its colour. The darker the soil, the more fertile it is. In the most fertile grasslands of all, such as the prairies of eastern Nebraska in the USA, the earth is jet black. Elsewhere, the colour of the ground varies from chestnut to pale brown, as in the northern-most prairies. Savannas and other tropical grasslands have thinner, reddish or yellowish soils.

All about grass

In any grassland, no matter how small, you should be able to find several kinds of grasses. Many grasslands have dozens of varieties. Some of them are highly distinctive – prairie needlegrass is sharp enough to pierce clothing. But it is true that the great majority look pretty similar. Usually a few species are far more plentiful than the rest, and this is one of the ways biologists sort grasslands into different categories.

Animals can be very fussy eaters. Sometimes they depend on just one or two types of plants, ignoring all the others. In many of the American Midwest's short-grass prairies, the main species is buffalo grass, which has curly, bluish-green blades. As its name suggests, buffalo grass was the favourite food of the huge herds of buffalo – or bison – that once roamed the Great Plains. Most grasses may look the same to us, but buffalo obviously know the difference.

Nature's medicine store

Native Americans have known for generations that natural remedies prepared from certain prairie plants can treat a variety of illnesses. They used extracts taken from coneflowers, or echinacea, to help fight colds and flu. These plant drugs work by stimulating the human immune system. There are nine species of coneflowers. In late spring and summer they produce a cone-shaped mass of tiny petals, surrounded by a ring of larger purple, pink, yellow or white petals.

swarming with billions of insects and other small animals. Turf is truly the pulsing heart of the temperate grassland biome.

Larger bushes and trees get only a foothold in the most sheltered spots. Wherever rivers or streams carve shallow valleys into the prairies, ribbons of cottonwoods, willows and oaks line the banks. In the southern African veld, thickets of thorny shrubs and flat-topped acacia trees grow in stony valleys and on the sides of small rocky outcrops. These features give protection from the region's wildfires and winter frosts. However, the weather conditions are still too severe for normal forest to develop.

Remarkable trees

Not all grasslands are tree-less. The dry, grass-covered plains of southern Australia are studded with certain kinds of eucalyptus trees (gum trees). These are special because they can thrive in virtual deserts and survive bush fires. Their bark is thick enough to resist flames. The searing heat of a bush fire causes a chemical reaction inside the trees, which triggers new growth. Soon, there are green

Grassland flowers like Texas bluebonnet have to bloom quickly in spring to reproduce before they are swamped by the rapidly growing grass.

Shaped by fire

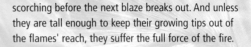

Although grassland fires can be ferocious, they are essential to the health of the biome. Heaps of dead plant material goes up in flames, clearing the way for new growth next year. The blazes also release vital nutrients trapped inside the old debris, pumping up the fertility level of the soil.

Grassland plants have many features that help them cope with even the fiercest fires. Their deep roots and often their low-level buds remain unscathed, and their fireproof seeds can survive being roasted. Once the ashes cool, it is only a week or two before the first shoots begin to reappear. Drawing on the reserves in their fleshy roots, the grasses soon spread to take advantage of the open ground and newly enriched soil. Trees are often not so lucky. They grow more slowly than grasses so barely have time to recover from one

scorching before the next blaze breaks out. And unless they are tall enough to keep their growing tips out of the flames' reach, they suffer the full force of the fire.

shoots sprouting all over the scorched trunks, repairing the damage. The white-hot temperatures also make the eucalyptus seeds split open and fall to the ground, ready to start growing into new trees as soon as there is enough moisture.

Turf wars

Every grassland is a battlefield, although the struggle taking place is invisible to human eyes. Plants never stop competing with one another to get the most sunlight and water. Those that win the fight for resources grow bigger and crowd out the losers, which may wither away. It is a race against time.

Grassland plants can't afford to wait around – they rush to make full use of the spring rains before the summer dry season arrives. On the prairies and steppes, some flowers appear even before the winter snow has finished melting. Many of the world's fastest growing plants are types of grass, including the fastest of all – bamboo.

Modern wheat plants are descended from two wild grasses – einkorn and wild goat grass – that grew in the Middle East thousands of years ago.

Most grassland plants have another trick. By releasing vast amounts of seeds, they make sure they are first to take over patches of bare ground. When ground is cleared, grassland plants are the first to colonize.

Flower power

Grasslands contain far more flowers than most biomes. Surprising though it may seem, grasses and weeds are flowering plants themselves, though their flowers are small and inconspicuous – a far cry from the flamboyant colours of roses or orchids. Most grass flowers are pale, feathery spikes – not always easy to see amid the sea of green blades and stems.

Edible grass

Vast areas of grassland are covered by a cultivated grass – wheat. Wheat is an annual grass plant, with a head containing 50–75 kernels, or seeds, which are ground to make flour, or sown to grow a new crop. The seed begins to grow once there is enough moisture in the soil. In spring, the plant sprouts many green leaves (below) and twenty or so golden flowers or spikes. As it ripens in summer, the whole plant turns golden.

Flowers play a crucial role in a plant's life cycle. They enable the plant to reproduce sexually. Unlike animals, plants can't move around to find mates, so they need other ways to bring their male and female sex cells together. The solution is to make pollen – a dust-like substance that carries male sex cells. Most flowers have both male and female parts. The male parts make pollen; the female parts have a sticky surface to capture pollen. When a grain of pollen lands on the female part of a flower, it sprouts and grows downwards into the flower, delivering the male cell to a female sex cell. The two cells then join, and a seed forms around them.

Grassland plants have lots of ways of transferring their pollen between each other. Plants with colourful flowers use insects such as bees and butterflies. To attract the insects, they produce bright blooms or strong perfumes. When an insect lands on a flower, it gets dusted with pollen, which rubs off on the next flower it visits. It won't do the job for nothing, so as a reward, every flower it goes to offers it an energy-boosting drink of sugary nectar.

On the wind

There's no need for grass flowers to be impressive because they don't have to tempt insects to visit them. Grasses use another technique to spread their pollen to other grass plants – the wind. However, wind is less efficient than insects because it blows most of the pollen away. To compensate, grass flowers produce masses of very fine pollen so at least some will land on other plants.

Grassland winds are strong and reliable, which is perfect for **pollination**. When the wind blows a spike of grass flowers, clouds of microscopic pollen grains fly into the air. Virtually all of them degrade within a day, but just enough pollen reaches waiting grass flowers in the surrounding area.

Grassland animals

Life in a temperate grassland is a real endurance test for animals. But for those that can survive the harsh climate and keep enemies at bay, there are rich pickings to be found.

In a grassland, all the usual hiding places such as bushes, trees, dense undergrowth, fallen timber or rock piles are in short supply. An obvious solution is to create your own hiding place – a burrow. Temperate grasslands are home to far more burrowing animals than any other of the world's biomes.

Half of all the mammals found on steppes live in burrows of one sort or another, compared to just 5 per cent of forest mammals. They include dozens of different small rodents, such as mice, voles, hamsters and gerbils, as well as larger species such as marmots. Their secret world of tunnels and passages adds a whole extra dimension to the featureless landscape above.

Digging the dirt

The simplest shelters are just hollows in the ground, which rabbits, hares and ground-living birds such as quails and partridges scrape out in no time. These give temporary protection until the danger has passed.

Above: With their unusually long legs, burrowing owls
are well-equipped for peering over short-grass prairie
and scurrying after prey.

Left: A mole's bite contains enough venom to paralyze
an earthworm. When the hunting is good, moles make
stashes of worms for eating later – still alive.

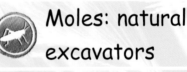 Moles: natural excavators

Moles are extremely common in prairies and steppes,
though seldom seen – they rarely leave their tunnel
networks and move to deeper tunnels in cold or very
dry weather. They constantly repair and extend their
tunnels, shunting the waste soil up to the surface as
molehills. Moles are incredibly efficient digging
machines, with broad, spade-like forefeet attached to
massive shoulder muscles. Their short, supersoft fur
helps them slip through their tunnels without getting
stuck. Moles have poor eyesight but a good sense of
smell. They feel around with their delicate, naked
snouts to locate earthworms and other prey.

But many animals dig down much further to make complex underground homes. Grassland soil is perfect for digging in. Because of the dense mat of tangled roots, it rarely caves in, unlike loose earth or sand.

A life spent digging requires lots of **adaptations**. Burrowing mammals have muscular legs with long, strong claws for excavating. Their bodies are compact for moving down twisting tunnels and squeezing past awkward roots and stones. They need special eyelids that stop flying dirt from getting in, although hearing and smell are far more important than vision in pitch-black tunnels. The pocket gophers of North America even have lips behind their front teeth that stop them from swallowing soil. Most burrowing mammals also have sensitive whiskers on the front of their head. Twitching constantly, the whiskers feel the tunnel walls to pick up faint vibrations made by the movement of other animals. The vibrations tell the burrowers what is going on around them, like messages travelling along telephone wires.

Trading places

Animals that can't dig their own burrows often take over the old ones of other species. Many grassland snakes do this, including several of the ratsnake and rattlesnake species found on the prairies.

The burrowing owl moves into burrows too, because there are no trees to nest in. It lives throughout much of the Americas, from the prairies to the pampas of Argentina. In its North American range, the burrowing owl likes to nest in the old burrows of prairie dogs and badgers. Burrowing owls are unusual among owls not only because they live in grasslands rather than forests and nest underground, but also because they are often active during the day. They can sometimes be seen watching for prey in broad daylight.

Secret cities

Black-tailed prairie dogs (left) are a kind of ground squirrel that live on the Great Plains in colonies, or 'towns', containing many thousands of animals. Each town is a huge burrow up to 5 metres (16 ft) deep that often extends for thousands of square metres. The underground maze includes many entrances, sleeping chambers and breeding dens. Prairie dogs play a key role in the wildlife of the prairies and more than 200 other kinds of creatures make their homes near their colonies. The burrows are so big that many other animals live inside them, from cottontail rabbits (right) to prairie rattlesnakes (below).

Taking cover

Going underground allows animals to escape not only their **predators** but also the worst of the weather. Burrows offer protection from driving winds, sudden storms, grass fires, scorching summers and freezing winters. They are cooler than outside in summer, and warmer than outside in winter. Many grassland animals avoid the midsummer heat by spending the day in their burrows and emerging only at night. Lots of grasslands come alive in the dark after being really quiet during the day.

Large mammals that must spend all their lives out in the open cope with harsh weather in other ways. North American bison (also known as buffalo) have shaggy, windproof fur, and in winter they grow a much heavier coat with a very thick mane. Herds of bison tend to huddle together for warmth in winter, keeping the younger calves snug in the middle, well out of the wind.

Protected against the cold by their shaggy coats, bison find grass to eat in winter by swinging their great heads from side to side to clear the snow.

Saiga antelope face even tougher conditions on the high steppes of central Asia. They, too, grow a thick coat in winter, twice as thick as their summer coat and almost white. Their weird, drooping noses – like small elephant trunks – may also help them stay alive during long droughts and bitterly cold winters. Each time a saiga inhales, its extra-long nostrils moisten and warm the air. Even so, winter takes its toll – especially on males, which go through their rutting battles in winter. Often, barely 3 per cent of male saigas survive severe winters.

On the surface, the prairies may seem almost lifeless in winter, but below ground, millions of creatures, from rodents to rattlesnakes, are biding their time until spring.

Deep sleep

Rodents, tortoises, snakes and lizards survive wintery weather by entering a deep sleep-like state called **hibernation**. In autumn, animals with burrows retreat there, while the rest, such as tortoises, simply bury themselves. The body temperature of hibernating animals plunges, and their breathing and **metabolism** (body chemistry) slow down considerably.

The thirteen-lined ground squirrel is a good example of an animal that hibernates. Safe inside its winter den, the squirrel lowers

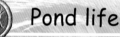

Pond life

Open water in grassland attracts wildlife from far and wide. Like oases in sandy deserts, ponds in grasslands provide a very different habitat from the surrounding land. They teem with frogs and toads for a short period in spring and early summer. Swarms of these amphibians trek overland to mate in the shallows, leaving behind masses of gel-like eggs, or spawn. Ponds in the northern prairies offer a refuge for the vast numbers of ducks, geese and shorebirds that leave northern Alaska and Canada at the end of summer. In the pampas, there are salt lakes covered with flocks of Andean flamingos, black-crowned night herons and other waterbirds, such as black-bellied and white-faced whistling ducks (below).

Sleepy summers

Amphibians become inactive in summer. If they stayed active, the hot, dry weather might dry out their moist skin and kill them. For this reason, many grassland frogs and toads retreat to hiding places and spend the summer in a kind of suspended animation. This summer equivalent of hibernation is called **estivation**.

Frogs and toads enter this special resting state whenever their pools or creeks dry up. They hide in dense tangles of turf or wriggle into the ground. Spadefoot toads use ridges on their back feet as shovels, and once below ground they shed several layers of skin to make a watertight cocoon around themselves. When rain falls, the toads break out. African bullfrogs are much fatter and may wait under the veld for several years if necessary.

The power of flight

Birds can fly long distances in search of food and shelter – a huge advantage in temperate grasslands. Small perching birds such as larks, pipits, buntings, sparrows and finches feed on insects and seeds, which quickly become scarce as winter sets in. As a result, the birds gather in flocks and fly for miles, giving them more chance of finding new food supplies, with many eyes scanning the ground.

In spring, bobolinks arrive in the North American prairie from their wintering grounds far south in Argentina. The males fill the air with their bubbling mating calls.

its body temperature from 35°C (95°F) to around 3°C (37.4°F) – barely above freezing point. It breathes just once every five minutes, and its heartbeat slows to only a few beats per minute.

Grassland animals use far less energy when they hibernate, allowing them to spend long periods without eating or drinking. They stay alive by slowly using fat reserves built up during the spring and summer. Reptiles sleep all winter without a break, while mammals often wake up at regular intervals to feed. Many of them, including hamsters and pocket gophers, store large quantities of food in their burrows to snack on through the winter. The regular wake-ups are thought to be vital for keeping the animal's immune system working well and disease at bay.

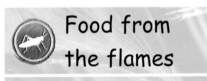

Food from the flames

When a serious grass fire breaks out, most animals flee for their lives. But several kinds of birds take advantage of the confusion and panic. As the advancing flames force masses of insects, small mammals and snakes to abandon their hiding places, flocks of swallows, martins, hawks and storks arrive to grab an easy meal.

Most people think parrots live only in tropical forests, but several brightly-coloured species make their homes in the plains of south-eastern Australia. They include small long-tailed parakeets and cockatiels, and crow-sized cockatoos. During the day, small groups of these grassland parrots spread out to search the open country for seeds. In the evening, the groups assemble noisily into much larger flocks to visit water holes and roost together in eucalyptus trees.

Many grassland birds undertake longer journeys, or **migrations**, to escape winter food shortages. This is especially true of prairie and steppe birds. For example, the bobolink breeds in the northern prairies but spends winter in the Argentinian pampas. To get there it must fly south to the southern US states, cross the Gulf of Mexico, then travel the length of South America. In spring, it flies all the way back to raise a family. Migratory birds that breed in the Asian steppes spend the winter in Africa or India.

Harris's hawk catches prey by watching patiently from a low perch, then swooping silently over the grass to grab its victim in its talons.

Light show

On warm summer nights, tiny lights flicker on and off all over many damp grasslands. They belong to lightning bugs, or fireflies, which are trying to attract a mate. The flashes are a code that indicates the bugs' species, sex and readiness to mate. The light is given off by a chemical reaction inside the abdomen (the rear body section of insects).

Hide-and-seek

In open country, predators can spot their prey from a long way off. This forces grassland animals to keep a low profile – no wonder grasslands often seem like empty places where nothing much happens.

Small animals try to stay out of sight inside the forest of grass stalks. Eventually, the endless comings and goings of mice, voles, rats and other small rodents create hidden pathways through the turf. All kinds of animals use these paths to commute between their burrows and feeding areas. However, they are up against predators with extremely acute senses. Birds of prey have razor-sharp

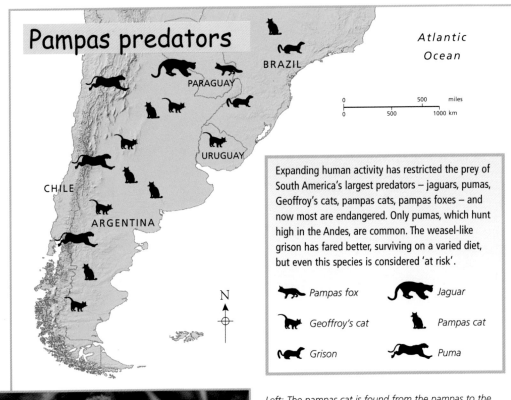

Pampas predators

BRAZIL

Atlantic
Ocean

PARAGUAY

URUGUAY

CHILE

ARGENTINA

0   500   miles
0   500   1000 km

Expanding human activity has restricted the prey of South America's largest predators – jaguars, pumas, Geoffroy's cats, pampas cats, pampas foxes – and now most are endangered. Only pumas, which hunt high in the Andes, are common. The weasel-like grison has fared better, surviving on a varied diet, but even this species is considered 'at risk'.

Pampas fox

Jaguar

Geoffroy's cat

Pampas cat

Grison

Puma

N

Left: The pampas cat is found from the pampas to the savanna regions of Brazil called Cerrado. It hunts mostly at night, catching small mammals, birds and reptiles.

vision for spotting tiny movements in the grass far below. Eagles and hawks soar high in the air to scan for prey, while harriers hunt by gliding silently just above the grass. Snakes are often the most common predators in grasslands. Many are rodent killers. They hunt by using a flick of the tongue to taste the air for a prey's scent. Up close, some snakes can also sense infrared (heat) and 'see' an animal's body heat through the grass. Burrows are not always safe havens from snakes. On the prairies, for example, king snakes and corn snakes often slide quietly into rodent burrows to go hunting.

Most large hunters in temperate grasslands belong to the dog family. Among them are the coyote and swift fox of North America, the jackals of Africa and the Australian dingo. All dogs have excellent senses of smell and hearing. They usually detect their prey before catching sight of it.

A big proportion of the coyote's diet consists of small animals like mice. Its favourite technique for catching them is to advance slowly through the grass, pausing regularly to watch and listen. When the coyote pinpoints its target, it leaps straight up into the air, then drops on top of the victim.

The great escape

Being able to move fast can mean the difference between life or death for many grassland animals. Some species, such as the eastern cottontail rabbit of North America, make a dash for the nearest available cover. Others, including the black-tailed jackrabbit, have the strength to run a long way until predators give up the chase. Really fast species like jackrabbits can live in more open habitats with shorter grass.

Coyotes are among the most adaptable of predators, eating anything from pronghorns to rubbish. In winter they catch mice in the snow with a sudden pounce.

Speed is so important that you see some strange-looking animals in temperate grasslands. The Australian emu and the rhea of South America are giant, long-legged birds that can run faster than a person. They are far too big and heavy to fly. The springhare of the African veld looks like a cross between a kangaroo and a rabbit. It has chunky back legs that allow it to leap forwards up to 2 metres (6.5 ft) with one bound.

A number of other grassland rodents also have enormous back legs for making quick getaways, including the gerbils of central Asia, the rat kangaroos of Australia and the kangaroo rats and mice of North America. All these creatures also use their back legs for excavating burrows and for scrabbling around for seeds. Males drum on the ground with their hefty legs to produce a mating call. Although all these animals look alike and behave in similar ways, they live thousands of miles apart and are not closely related to one another. The Australian rat kangaroos may look rat-like, but in fact they are small kangaroos, not rodents. They have evolved along the same lines because they live in similar habitats, a process scientists call **convergent evolution.**

Record breakers

Pronghorn antelope are easily the fastest mammals on the prairies. Their name is misleading because they are not real antelope but relatives of wild goats. Unlike goats, however, pronghorns are built for speed.

Pronghorn antelope have phenomenal stamina. They can run non-stop for up to 24 km (15 miles) at an average speed of around 56 km (35 miles) per hour. To put this feat in perspective, the world's top athletes can sprint at 32 km (20 miles) per hour for barely ten seconds before having to slow down. Even two-week-old baby pronghorns are able to race along at tremendous speed, which is just as well because they are a favourite prey of predatory coyotes.

Sticking together

Many large grassland animals live in herds. It pays to stick together because predators then find it much harder to catch the animals by surprise – with so many eyes and ears on the lookout, an approaching predator is soon spotted. And when all the members of a herd are running along together, it is difficult for a hunter to select an individual and keep track.

Antelope, deer, horses and bison all live in herds. So does the blesbok, a reddish brown antelope with white 'stockings' that lives on the veld of Africa. Until the 18th century, blesboks gathered in herds of many thousands, but human hunters killed most of them. The same happened to the bison and pronghorn antelope of North America.

Playing defensive

Only a few grassland animals stand their ground when threatened, because it is such a risky thing to do. At night, the crested porcupine leaves its burrow in the veld to feed on roots and fruits. Its black-and-white spines are longer and sharper than those of its distant North American relative. The spines usually frighten off even big carnivores such as leopards and brown hyenas. As a last resort, the porcupine charges backwards at its enemies and tries to stab them with heavy-duty spines called quills.

The African leopard tortoise is equally tough for predators to deal with. It simply retreats inside its hard shell if it is attacked. If a predator picks up a tortoise, it finds the tortoise hard to crush due to the shell's high, domed shape.

Hungry hordes

The reason grasslands are able to support such impressive numbers of animals is simple. There is plenty to eat. Grass is packed with nutrients. It tastes awful to us, and we have not evolved the ability to digest it. However, grazers (animals that eat grass) have very different stomachs from humans. Special micro-organisms that live inside their stomachs and intestines help them convert the grass into sugar.

Grazing mammals such as antelope and bison – and today vast numbers of livestock such as cattle and sheep – are the most obvious grass eaters, but they are not alone. Grassland plants are also attacked by vast armies of invertebrates (animals without backbones), including ants, termites, beetles, grasshoppers and snails. The larvae (grubs) of many flies, butterflies and moths also feed on grassland plants. Together, these tiny animals eat more grassland plants than all the large grazers combined.

Termites have a particularly big impact on grasslands. They use their strong mouthparts to shear off grass stems. Then they carry the small pieces to their nests to feed the grubs. Some termites dig nests underground, but others build mounds on the surface from thousands of mouthfuls of soil stuck together with saliva. They soon harden in the sun to become rock-solid castles.

Wonderful worms

The rich soil of temperate grasslands crawls with countless numbers of earthworms. They are vital to the health of the biome. Every earthworm spends its entire life burrowing through the soil. It sucks soil into its mouth, located right at the front, and digests the

Marvellous manure

Dung can tell us a surprising amount about the animal that left it. Bison produce soft dung that crumbles into a fine powder. This shows that bison have a highly effective digestive system that can squeeze all the goodness out of the grass they eat. Horse dung is harder and lumpy, with bits of grass stalks in it – horses are less efficient at digesting grass than bison.

minute particles of rotting plant matter as the soil passes through its body. Then it squirts the waste soil out of its rear end. Worms move so much earth around that their activities improve the soil. Their hard work allows in more air and churns up all the nutrients, just like the ploughs and spades of farmers and gardeners.

Horses' ancestors were short-legged woodland animals, and they only evolved into fast-running, long-legged animals as climates changed and grasslands spread.

The prairies

The prairies are at the crossroads of North America. They stretch from the Rocky Mountains east across the heart of the continent. These windswept lands now form one of the world's biggest farming regions.

Prairie chickens

Each spring, male prairie chickens get together in large groups, or leks. They rapidly stomp the ground and strut about making loud moans, clucks and hoots. The aim of all this fuss is to attract female prairie chickens from the surrounding area. The females gather around the edge of the circle, and at first they don't look very interested. But in the end, some of them mate with the best dancers.

1. The prairie provinces
Fertile plains in the south of Alberta, Saskatchewan and Manitoba mark the northern limit of the prairies. The northern short-grass prairie is the largest remaining natural grassland in North America.

2. Chimney Rock
Chimney Rock rises 150 metres (500 ft) above the grassy plain just to the south of the North Platte River in western Nebraska. This natural tower is all that's left of an ancient rocky plateau.

3. Potholes
Potholes are small ponds sunk into the northern prairies. Thousands of them are scattered across a wide area, from eastern Montana to western Minnesota. They appear every spring as the snows melt, and provide a summer home for 100 species of birds and many rare frogs.

4. The Badlands
Settlers found this wilderness of cliffs, crags and gullies so hard to cross they named it the Badlands. It features strange rock formations created by years of wind and rain.

5. Hills of sand
A dry zone of barely covered sandy hills and ridges lies in the middle of Nebraska.

6. Big Basin
This is an enormous hole in the plains of west Kansas, created when a series of huge caverns collapsed. It is 1.6 km (1 mile) wide and 33 metres (100 ft) deep. Famed for its flowers, this mixed-grass prairie is home to many birds, including western meadowlarks.

7. Salt plains
In northern Oklahoma there are plains of white salt that stretch for 115 square km (45 sq miles). They are the remains of an ancient salt lake.

8. Wichita Mountains
The Wichita Mountains of western Oklahoma are 300 million years old – much older than the seas of grass that encircle them.

9. Flint Hills
The Flint Hills of eastern Kansas have steep grassy slopes and limestone crags. Along with the nearby Osage Hills, this is the last area of North America's unique tallgrass prairie. These hills were once home to vast herds of bison and elk. Prairie chickens are still common.

10. Ozark Plateau
On the upland plains that cover much of central Missouri, ponderosa pines and spruce stands are mixed with the grass and small shrubs.

Prairie facts

▲ The prairie region is around 4000 km (2500 miles) from north to south and 1000 km (about 600 miles) wide. It covers an area of about 3 million square km (1,125,000 sq miles).

▲ Wild prairie once covered most of North Dakota, South Dakota, Nebraska, Kansas, Oklahoma, Iowa and Illinois, and some Canadian provinces.

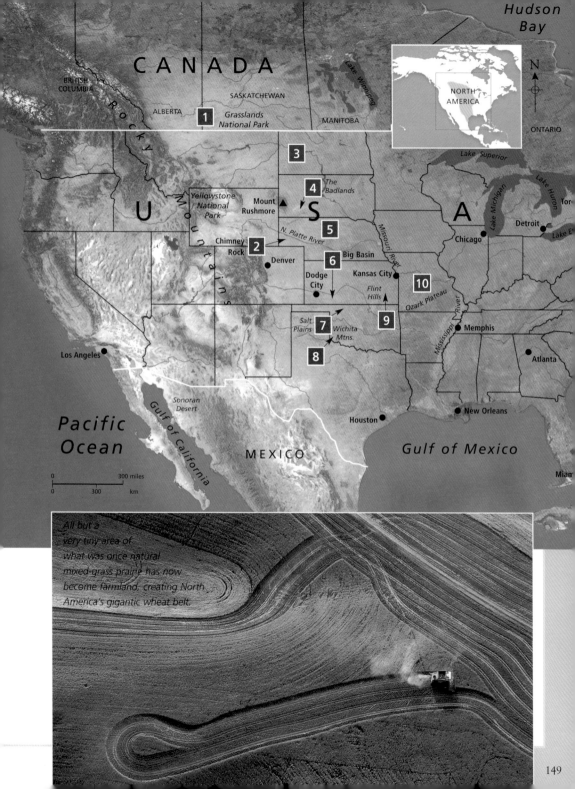

Hudson Bay

CANADA

BRITISH COLUMBIA

ROCKY

ALBERTA   SASKATCHEWAN

MANITOBA

Lake Winnipeg

1 Grasslands National Park

NORTH AMERICA

N

ONTARIO

Lake Superior

3

Yellowstone National Park

Mount Rushmore

4 The Badlands

U

S

A

Lake Michigan

Detroit

Lake Huron

Tor

Lake E

Mountains

5

N. Platte River

Missouri River

Chimney Rock

2

Denver

Dodge City

6 Big Basin

Kansas City

10 Ozark Plateau

Chicago

Flint Hills

9

Mississippi River

Memphis

Salt Plains

7 Wichita Mtns.

8

Los Angeles

Atlanta

Sonoran Desert

Pacific Ocean

Gulf of California

MEXICO

Houston

New Orleans

Gulf of Mexico

Miam

0   300 miles
0   300   km

All but a very tiny area of what was once natural mixed-grass prairie has now become farmland, creating North America's gigantic wheat belt.

149

Steppes

Stretching right across the heart of Asia is a vast belt of desolate, windswept grassland – the steppes. They form one of the last great wilderness areas on the Earth.

 Steppe facts

▲ The steppe region extends from Ukraine and Russia in eastern Europe, through southern Siberia and Kazakhstan, all the way to Mongolia and northern China. The southern-most steppes reach as far south as Turkey, Iran and Iraq.

▲ The steppes stretch almost a third of the way around the world.

▲ Most of the steppes are uninhabited. Despite being a vast country, Mongolia's population is only 2.5 million – smaller than Greater Manchester.

▲ In Mongolia, horse racing is a children's sport. Most champion jockeys retire by the time they reach their teens.

1. Kirghiz Steppe
The Kirghiz Steppe is an immense grassy plain reaching from the Caspian Sea east to the Altai Mountains. This is the world's largest area of dry steppe, home to marmots and pikas, saiga antelopes and corsac foxes, as well as many birds, such as pallid harriers.

2. Zhezkazgan
The Russian space programme has its headquarters here in central Kazakhstan, south of the Kazakh capital of Astana.

3. Astana
The capital of Kazakhstan, once known as Akmola.

4. Lake Balkhash
One of the few large areas of water in the dry Kazakh steppes, Lake Balkhash is home to a unique range of fish, including wild carp and perch.

5. Nayramdal Uur
On the Kazakhstan–Mongolia border, this peak is one of the highest in the Altai range, at 4374 metres (14,350 ft).

In spring, the snow melts and the warm sunshine brings a profusion of wild flowers into bloom on the steppes, including vivid patches of red tulips.

6. Altai Mountains
The Altai Mountains stretch for over 2000 km (over 1200 miles) from Siberia to the edge of the Gobi Desert and have peaks rising to 4250 metres (14,000 ft). Many of the rivers of the eastern steppes flow from these mountains.

7. Hustain Nuruu National Park
Hunting and herding cattle are banned in this reserve to the south of Ulaanbaatar, which has a small population of Przewalski's wild horses, introduced in the 1990s.

8. Gobi Desert
This wasteland of sand and gravel, sandwiched between the grassy steppes of Mongolia and the highlands of Tibet, is home to the Bactrian camel.

9. Lake Baikal
Lake Baikal in Siberia is the world's oldest lake, formed over 25 million years ago as water collected in a deep crack in the Earth's surface. It is also the world's deepest lake – up to 1743 metres (5714 ft) deep – containing a fifth of the world's fresh water. Its long isolation from the rest of the world means a unique range of creatures has evolved there, including the coregone fish and the Baikal seal, the world's only freshwater seal.

10. Mongolian Plateau
Large parts of Mongolia lie above 2000 metres (6500 ft). Further west, the steppes are much lower and flatter.

11. Ulaanbaatar
Mongolia's capital is highly industrialized, and its factories provide one of the region's few sources of employment other than herding cattle.

12. Manchurian steppes
The vast Manchurian steppes are roamed by huge herds of Mongolian gazelles. Spread around the steppes are also extensive marshes and reed beds where gigantic flocks of oriental storks and demoiselle cranes breed.

The original horse

Most so-called 'wild' horses, including the mustang of North America, are descendants of escaped domestic horses. But on the steppes of Mongolia, until quite recently, lived the only truly wild horse – Przewalski's horse, first identified by Russian explorer Nicolai Przewalski in the 1880s. The last one was seen in the wild in 1969, but more than 1000 survived in zoos. In the 1990s, a handful were reintroduced into the wild in the Hustain Nuruu reserve in Mongolia.

Deserts of the world

There are deserts on every continent, from the sun-baked heart of Africa to the chilly plains of northern China. Together, deserts make up one of Earth's largest biomes.

Deserts come in all shapes and sizes. Some are tiny, such as the desert of Almería in south-east Spain, but others are huge. The vast **arid** (dry) area that spreads across North Africa, the Arabian peninsula and western Asia is really one gigantic desert, though we give different names to different parts of it.

The world's major deserts lie in two bands near the tropics of **Cancer** and **Capricorn** (two imaginary circles around the planet, north and south of the **equator**). There are also deserts near the poles – Greenland and Antarctica are part of a biome called polar desert. You can find out more about them in Arctic Tundra and Polar Deserts (pages 6–39).

Like most biomes, deserts do not generally have definite boundaries, except where they meet the sea or a major mountain range. In many places they merge gradually into another land biome, such as **shrubland**.

Petrified (or 'fossil') sand dunes in the Sahara desert, Tunisia, that date from 86,000 years ago.

The land near the edge of the desert, which is not quite desert and not quite shrubland, is known as **semi-desert**.

The word desert conjures up images of rolling sand dunes or plains covered in rubble, but not all deserts are like that. Parts of North America's Great Basin, for

instance, are completely flat and glittering white, thanks to a coating of salt crystals. The Sonoran Desert in Arizona is sometimes carpeted with colourful flowers, though only for a short time. Yet, despite their many differences, all deserts do have one thing in common: water is in very short supply.

Most biomes exist because of a distinctive pattern of weather through the year. We call these weather patterns **climates**. Tropical rainforests have a warm and wet climate, for example, while deserts have a very dry climate. So, to understand the desert biome, we need to look first at the desert climate.

Desert climates

Deserts exist for a very simple reason: lack of rain. But desert climates are surprisingly varied. There are hot deserts, cold deserts, polar deserts, windswept deserts and even deserts covered with fog.

A l Azizia in Libya is probably the hottest place on Earth. On 13 September 1922, the temperature there reached 57.8°C (136°F) – the highest temperature ever recorded. That's really sizzling. The ground there that day would have been hot enough to fry an egg.

Under the burning sun

Al Azizia is in North Africa's Sahara, one of the world's hot deserts. Not all deserts are hot, but the Sahara certainly is. Hot deserts extend all around the world in two belts, to the north and south of the tropical zone around the equator. Further north and south are the cold deserts, and

Even from space, the expanses of sand in the Namib Desert are easily visible. This view is from a satellite looking south.

further still are the ice-covered **polar deserts**.

All deserts are dry, since it is lack of water that makes a desert. They are dry because what little water reaches the desert **evaporates** from the ground and escapes into the **atmosphere**. Intense sunshine and hot, windy weather speed up the evaporation of water from deserts, making them even drier. But how dry is dry? Dictionaries define a desert

Waterless world

The hot deserts, such as the Namib (pictured here), do not lie on the equator but are created by what happens there. The sun shines more directly all year at the equator than it does anywhere else. This heats the surface of the land and ocean, and the warm land and sea heat the air above them. When air warms, it rises, so air over the equator is rising rapidly most of the time. The rising air is also very moist because it contains water vapour (evaporated water) from warm oceans. Once the air gets high in the atmosphere, it cools, and the vapour turns into droplets, forming clouds. So it's often cloudy at the equator, and it rains a lot. At a height of about 16 km (9 miles), most of the water vapour has turned into cloud, and the air is dry. This is as high as air can rise, so it starts to move away from the equator.

High in the atmosphere, the dry air gets very cold, which makes it start to sink. This sinking dry air stops clouds forming, so it causes dry, sunny weather and clear blue skies. Most of the sinking air falls near the tropics of Cancer and Capricorn, which is why hot deserts are in these regions. They are hot because there are no clouds to shield the ground from the tropical sunshine, so the land heats up and warms the layer of air above it.

as a place that receives less than 250 mm (10 in) of rain a year; for comparison, the city of Aberdeen in Scotland receives about 608 mm (24 in).

Some deserts receive almost no rain at all. In the town of Aswan in southern Egypt, for instance, there are many years when the rainfall is zero. On the rare occasions that it does rain in the desert, the downpour can be torrential. Intense thunderstorms quickly wet the soil surface, then further water just runs off the wet surface in sheets, creating flash floods. In the summer of 1997, heavy rain in the Atlas mountains of Morocco caused floods that killed more than 250 people. In the same year, floods after rainstorms in north-eastern Iran drowned eleven people.

Although deserts can get very hot during the day, the nights can be bitterly cold. In January, the temperature in the Sahara is high in the early afternoon, but at night it often drops below freezing. That's because dry sand and bare rock heat up quickly when the sun shines on them, but they cool down again just as fast. And because there are no clouds to trap warmth rising from the ground, the heat soon escapes into space once the sun has gone down.

Dust storms and dust devils

Besides being dry, deserts are windy. The ferocious wind blows sand into rolling seas of dunes – it can even wear away solid rock by blasting it with sand. Sometimes the wind blows strongly enough to lift dust and sand into a vast cloud thousands of feet tall. Then it's a dust storm or sandstorm that arrives as a screaming gale, driving dust and fine sand into every corner. People caught in the open can't see and can barely breathe, because the hot air is full of choking grit.

At other times the wind plays tricks. Around the middle of the afternoon, when the ground has been heating for several hours, some places are much hotter than others. Air rising over the hot spots draws in surrounding air and starts to spiral as it rises. If the swirling, dusty air rises only a few feet, it's called a dust devil. But sometimes the swirling air rises much higher – and then it's a whirlwind.

Whirlwinds can be 1.6 km (1 mile) tall. They leap up suddenly and produce howling gusts that are strong enough to smash a wooden hut. During its brief life, a whirlwind wanders about randomly – you can't tell where it will go next. It survives for only a few minutes, but as one dies down, another can leap up nearby. Long ago, before anyone knew what caused whirlwinds, desert peoples were terrified of them. Some people believed God sent whirlwinds as a punishment for sins.

Cold deserts

When we think of deserts, it's the hot, sandy ones that spring to mind. Not all deserts are like this, though. Most of the Sahara and the deserts of Southwest Asia, for example, are covered by bare rock and gravel; the wind blows away the dust and sand. Neither are all deserts hot. The city of Hohhot in China lies on the edge of the Gobi desert. In January the temperature here averages a bitterly cold –13°C (8.6°F), and in July – the warmest month – it barely rises above room temperature. Straddling the border between Mongolia and China, the Gobi looks fairly small on a map showing the whole of Europe and Asia. In fact, it is about 1600 km (1000 miles) from west to east. To its west is another great desert, the Takla Makan, which is about 970 km (600 miles) across.

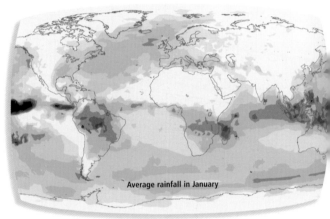

Average rainfall in January

Dark blue in these maps shows areas of rain. Deserts are pale in both January and July, showing that they are dry all year round.

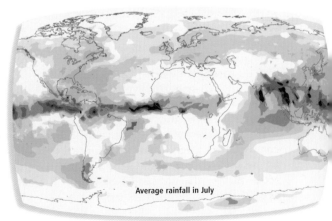

Average rainfall in July

Left: These rocks have been sculpted by the power of windblown sand. In many desert locations, wind, not water, is the most important force shaping the land.

The Gobi is a harsh place – dry, windswept and bitterly cold in winter – but the Takla Makan is much worse. In winter the temperature falls to about –24°C (–11°F), and the wind makes it feel even colder. In summer, though, the Takla Makan is hot, with temperatures around 30°C (86°F). It is a sandy desert, with great expanses of dunes that are constantly shifting between small, bare hills, where the rock has been swept clean of sand. Sandstorms are common and often last for days.

The Gobi and the Takla Makan are continental deserts: they're dry because they are thousands of kilometres from the ocean. Moist air from the sea sheds most of its water as rain on its journey inland, and then it has

Dust storms can be unpleasant and dangerous. Some animals, such as camels, close their nostrils and shield their eyes from the sand with long eyelashes. These oryx are taking cover beneath a tree.

to cross high mountains, where it loses the rest. By the time it reaches the Gobi and the Takla Makan the air is bone dry. The deserts are cold partly because they are high above sea level, but also because they are well to the north of the tropics.

By the sea

Continental deserts are dry because they are so far inland. So you might think that a desert could never exist right next to the coast. But you'd be wrong. There are deserts like that, and they include the driest deserts of all. The Namib Desert, for instance, which runs along the coast of south-west Africa, receives about 50 mm (2 in) of rain on average each year; London gets about the same in a month. And certain parts of the Namib are even drier. The Namib town of Swakopmund, for instance, has an annual rainfall of only 14 mm (0.6 in). The Namib is not baking, though – the daily temperature does not vary much, and is about 22°C (72°F) throughout the year.

The world's driest desert is the Atacama in South America, which stretches for about 965 km (600 miles) along the coast of Chile and southern Peru. There are places in the Atacama where it has rained no more than four times a century. Iquique, a town in north Chile, once went for four years with no rain, then a single shower fell in July of the fifth year. For people in Iquique, July is now the rainy season! At Arica, to the north of Iquique, the average annual rainfall is a minuscule 0.9 mm (0.03 in). It's hard to

Climographs

Each place in the world has its own pattern of weather. The typical pattern of weather that happens in one place during a year is called climate. We can sum up a place's climate on a climograph, such as the one shown here for St Louis in the USA. The letters along the bottom are the months of the year. The numbers on the left and the small bars show rainfall, and the numbers on the right and the curvy line show temperature. You can see at a glance that St Louis is hottest in July, but December is the driest month.

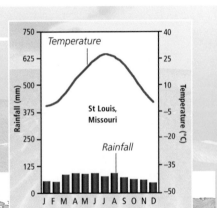

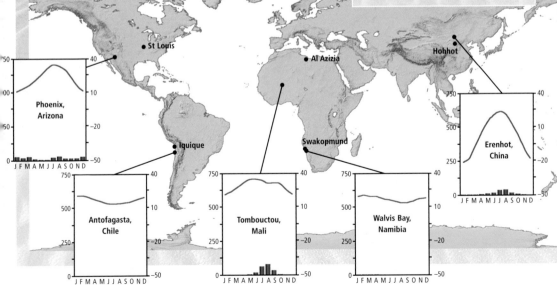

158

Young deserts

Compared to Earth's grand old age of 4.5 billion years, some of our planet's deserts are surprisingly young. The Great Basin in the USA, for instance, has been a desert for only about 12,000 years. About 15,000 years ago, forests covered the Great Basin, and mammoths, sabre-toothed cats and giant sloths roamed among the trees. When the ice age ended and the climate warmed, the desert began to form. The vast salt flats of the Great Basin, such as this one in Death Valley, are the parched remains of lakes that dried out.

Death Valley

California's Death Valley, near the edge of the Mojave Desert, is the hottest place in the USA and almost as hot as Al Azizia in Libya. The temperature in Death Valley can reach 57°C (135°F) in summer. In 1849, during the great California Gold Rush, a party of 30 settlers decided to take a shortcut to the gold fields. Their route took them through the valley, where twelve of them died from heat and thirst. That's how the valley got its name. Today it's a place for tourists.

imagine just how dry that is, but if you plan to visit you certainly won't need to pack an umbrella.

Fog but no rain

There's something very odd about the Namib and Atacama deserts. Despite the incredibly dry climate, the air in these deserts is very moist. Fog is common, and iron objects rust quickly. So how can these deserts exist when there is so much moisture in the air?

The cause of the peculiar climates is cold ocean currents near the coasts. The cold Benguela Current flows north along the coast of the Namib Desert, and the cold Peru (or Humboldt) Current flows north along the coast of the Atacama. The chilly water cools air travelling towards the land. Because the air gets cold, it stays low and doesn't rise

Flat-topped mountains like this are called mesas.

high enough to form clouds. That's why rain is so rare. It's also why these coastal deserts are relatively cool. At Lima, Peru, the average temperature is only 19°C (66°F) and doesn't change much through the year.

Air that has crossed the ocean is very moist because it picks up a lot of **water vapour**. When the moist air crosses a cold ocean current and cools down, its moisture condenses into tiny droplets, forming fog. It's a bit like exhaling on a cold day – the moisture in your breath condenses into mist as it hits the cold air. The cold ocean currents near the Atacama and Namib both produce sea fogs that roll into the desert regularly. Some plants and animals get nearly all their water by collecting the fog droplets.

Cold ocean currents tend to occur on the west coast of continents, so the Atacama and Namib are sometimes called west-coast deserts. Parts of the Sonoran Desert in Baja California and the part of the Sahara on the north-west coast of Africa are also west-coast deserts, with similar cold currents nearby.

Below: In this part of Patagonia, an ancient lava flow has been broken down by river action in an earlier, wetter time. Later, when Patagonia became a desert, the hills were eroded by wind.

Rain shadow

Patagonia is a cold desert region that covers most of Argentina. It is a different kind of desert from most others. It is neither in the subtropics, nor in the centre of a big continent thousands of miles from the sea, nor on a west coast. Why, then, is it so dry?

Patagonia lies in the 'rain shadow' of the Andes mountains. The wind in Patagonia comes mainly from the west, but before it reaches the desert it has to cross the high Andes. As the air rises over the mountains, it cools, causing moisture to condense and fall as rain, hail or snow. When the air reaches the far side of the mountains, it is very dry.

The wind occasionally blows from the east, across the nearby Atlantic Ocean. There, though, is yet another cold current, named the Falkland Current, for the air to cross. So air approaching from the east is chilled before it reaches the coast, like the air that reaches the Atacama and Namib deserts.

Patagonia is not the only desert in a rain shadow. North America's Great Basin owes its dry climate to the Sierra Nevada mountains, which cast a rain shadow over the region. However, only the valley bottoms in the Great Basin are true desert. The tops of many of the Great Basin's mountains catch just enough snow to support forests of conifer trees.

Desert plants

How can anything survive in a dry, scorching desert? Amazingly, there are many plants that can, from tiny 'living stones' the size of pebbles to giant cacti three times taller than a giraffe.

P lants need to be tough to survive in the desert. They have to deal with daytime temperatures that soar above 30°C (86°F) and night-time temperatures that plunge to freezing or below. Then they have to find water – and hang on to it. Finally, they have to protect themselves from hungry animals. To cope with these challenges, desert plants use all kinds of clever tricks.

Keeping cool

Plants elsewhere gather as much of the sun's energy as they possibly can, but desert plants are bathed in more sunlight than they can use. Lots of people wear light-coloured clothes in summer. That's because light colours reflect the sun's rays and so help keep you cool. Desert plants use the same method. Many of them are pale green or silvery grey, while the quiver tree of the Namib and Kalahari deserts of southern Africa grows branches that are covered in a chalky white powder.

The quiver tree of southern Africa stores water in the soft, spongy wood inside its trunk and branches. Local hunters find the branches easy to hollow out, and use them as quivers for their arrows.

Old-timers

Strangely enough, deserts are home to some of the longest-living plants in the world.

▲ Some bristlecone pines growing on the dry slopes of California's White Mountains are around 5000 years old. This means that they were already 500 years old when the ancient Egyptians built the great pyramids. The tallest of these trees are only 15 metres (50 ft) high – but it might have taken them 3000 years to reach this height.

▲ The creosote bush, which also grows in the deserts of California, sends out roots in all directions. From these roots grow a circle of clones (identical copies) of the original plant. Scientists calculate from the size of one circle that the original plant was alive nearly 12,000 years ago, when prehistoric people first started to grow crops.

▲ *Welwitschia* plants like the one below in the Namib Desert of southern Africa can live for up to 2000 years. Some started growing when the Roman Empire was at the peak of its power.

Getting a drink

Plants get most of the water they need through their roots. Because there is little water to be found in deserts, the plants that grow there need to send their roots very deep

The saguaro cactus, like many other cacti, has a ribbed surface. This allows it to expand like a concertina to absorb water.

to get as much water as possible. While deserts may be quite dry at the surface for most of the time, there is often water deep underground. To get at this water, some desert plants have a long, thick central root, called a taproot. The taproot of the mesquite tree, which grows in the American South-west, can pierce down 15 metres (50 ft) – the height of a five-storey building. The root of the camelthorn **acacia** tree of Africa can reach down twice as far.

Another way that a plant can collect scarce water is to spread its roots over a broad area, and this is exactly what many cacti do. They send out a wide net of hair-like roots in all directions, just below the surface. When it rains, the network of roots collects the water before it seeps deeper into the ground. The same roots can even absorb the dew that sometimes forms in deserts overnight.

Water from thin air

Other desert plants take in water through their leaves. One such plant is the bizarre *Welwitschia* of the Namib Desert in south-western Africa. The *Welwitschia* is a low-growing plant with long, tattered, strap-like leaves. These leaves can take in tiny droplets of water from the sea fogs that roll in from the Atlantic Ocean in the early morning – about the only regular source of water in the Namib.

The *Welwitschia* might look like a ragged mess, but it's a survivor. Many have lived for five to six hundred years in the Namib, which is one of the world's driest deserts, and some have lived much longer.

Storing water

Getting hold of water is only half the battle – desert plants also have to store it somewhere, because there might not be any more water around for a very long time.

Some kinds of plants are particularly good at storing water inside themselves. These plants are called **succulents**, which means juicy. The succulents include the cacti and agaves of the Americas and the euphorbias of Africa and Asia. Agaves have thick, fleshy, sword-shaped leaves spiking outwards from the centre of the plant. Euphorbias come in all shapes and sizes, from little herbs called spurges to spine-covered trees.

When it rains, cacti suck in huge amounts of water and swell up like balloons. The organ-pipe cactus, which grows three times taller than a man, can hold more than 380 litres (100 gallons) in its stem – enough to fill six bathtubs. This reservoir can see the cactus through four months of drought.

Plants don't have to be big to be good at surviving dry periods. For example, the wild tulips of the deserts of Central Asia live through most of the year as small underground bulbs. When the spring rains come, the bulbs quickly send up leaves and flowers. These die back at the start of the long summer, but the bulbs store enough food and water to last until

Like the saguaro cactus, the organ-pipe cactus is typical of the Sonoran Desert of Arizona and Mexico.

Homes in the desert

Although there are hardly any trees in the deserts of the American Southwest, the giant saguaro cacti are the next best thing as far as birds are concerned. The cacti have places for birds like the red-tailed hawk (left) to nest, and gila woodpeckers and elf owls nest in holes in the great stem. The camelthorn acacia tree of southern Africa also makes a home for many animals, including acacia rats and bushbabies (galagos).

Left: Many species of euphorbias live in African deserts. They are not cacti, but look just like cacti because they have thick, juicy stems that store water, and because they protect themselves with spines.

more water from the ground, bringing up other useful chemicals with it. However, in the fiercely hot conditions of the desert, water evaporates from leaves too easily, and there's very little water in the ground to replace it. Most plants would quickly shrivel up and die, but desert plants have ways to stop this from happening.

Looking at a spiny cactus, you might think, 'That's a strange plant. It doesn't have any leaves'. Only spines emerge from its thick, fleshy stem. Cacti have lost their leaves and replaced them with small spikes that do not lose water. Instead of making food in leaves, they make food in the green stem, where there are far fewer pores.

In the Kara-Kum desert of Central Asia, the black saxaul tree uses an alternative method. For most of the year it has no leaves

the next spring. The tulips that people grow in their gardens are all descended from these tough little desert survivors.

Preventing water loss

Once a plant has built up a good store of water, it needs to hang on to it. But no plant can avoid losing some water – it's part of the way they keep themselves alive.

All plants give off water vapour into the air. Most of the water vapour escapes through tiny pores (holes) in the leaves, which plants have to keep open to survive. The pores serve to take in **carbon dioxide**, a vital gas that they use to make food. So, to get carbon dioxide, plants have to lose a bit of water. Losing water can sometimes help them, though, because it makes their roots suck up

Right: Tulips, like this one growing in eastern Turkey, were taken to Belgium and Holland in the 16ᵗʰ century, starting the tulip-growing industry. They were so popular that some people made a fortune selling them.

Beckoning branches

Mormons named this desert plant the Joshua tree because they imagined its branches were the arms of the Hebrew leader Joshua beckoning them to the promised land. The Joshua tree is the largest type of yucca plant, and it lives in the Mojave Desert, where it has to cope with thin, rocky soil and extremely hot, dry weather. These conditions might seem inhospitable to us, but Joshua trees seem to like them – they live nowhere else.

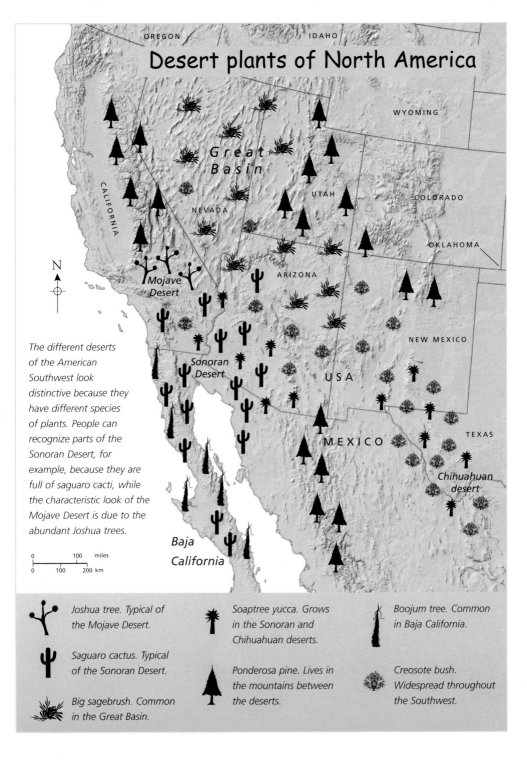

Desert plants of North America

The different deserts of the American Southwest look distinctive because they have different species of plants. People can recognize parts of the Sonoran Desert, for example, because they are full of saguaro cacti, while the characteristic look of the Mojave Desert is due to the abundant Joshua trees.

Joshua tree. Typical of the Mojave Desert.

Saguaro cactus. Typical of the Sonoran Desert.

Big sagebrush. Common in the Great Basin.

Soaptree yucca. Grows in the Sonoran and Chihuahuan deserts.

Ponderosa pine. Lives in the mountains between the deserts.

Boojum tree. Common in Baja California.

Creosote bush. Widespread throughout the Southwest.

and makes food instead in its whitish-green twigs and branches. Once the tree has flowered, borne fruit and spread its seeds, it often sheds some of its branches to cut down evaporation even more.

Cacti, like the other succulent plants, only open their pores to take in carbon dioxide at night, when it's a lot cooler. At these low temperatures, very little water can evaporate.

Tubby plants

Many cacti have a shape that helps reduce water loss. You might think that all cacti are the tall, thin giants you see in cowboy movies, but most of them are small and squat and round. Spherical (round) shapes have a small surface area compared to their size. Since it's from the surface of plants that water evaporates, spherical cacti have the smallest possible surface area from which they can lose water. At the same time, they contain the greatest space for water storage.

Desert grasses also tend to have shapes that help them cut down on water loss. For example, esparto grass, which grows on the northern edge of the Sahara, has rolled-up leaves. Most of its pores are on the inside surface of the rolled leaf, so rolling shades its pores from the sun. In the semi-desert areas of south-west Asia, the spear grasses lay their leaves out flat when it rains, but roll them up when it gets hot and dry again.

Desert plants sometimes use chemicals as well as shape to stop them from losing water. Euphorbias have stems filled with a white, sticky, poisonous liquid that does not evaporate easily. Many desert plants ooze poisonous chemicals into the ground around them. This stops other plants from growing nearby and tapping into their water supplies. Other desert plants send out a dense mat of roots that stops other young plants from growing nearby. This is why plants in deserts are often spaced very regularly.

Desert feasts

In the deserts of the USA and Mexico, people eat some types of agaves. The leaves of agaves are tough, sword-shaped and spiky, but the stem and flowers of some types are delicious roasted, boiled or scrambled with eggs. In southern Africa, the local people have found all sorts of plant food in the Kalahari Desert. They get starch (a source of sugar) from some corms and tubers (swollen roots), and protein from foods such as mongongo nuts and tsin beans. The fruits of the marula tree (related to the mango) and the bottle-shaped baobab tree are both full of vitamin C. The Kalahari is also home to the wild watermelon (below), which quenches the thirst of both people and animals.

Self-defence

In the deserts of the American Southwest, the chemicals in the sagebrush not only poison the ground around it but also give the plant a revolting taste. Being poisonous is one sure way that a plant can protect itself from being eaten.

Another well-known example of chemical defence is the creosote bush. Its leaves contain a poisonous oil that smells

The stumpy, rounded shape of these living stones makes them look like small pebbles – useful for camouflage, but also good for preventing water loss.

One desert plant makes itself even more difficult to eat by hiding underground. This is the window plant of the Namib Desert, which buries its plump, upright leaves under the surface. Only the tips of the leaves appear above the surface. These tips – the 'windows' – are made of a see-through material that lets sunlight reach the rest of the leaves below ground. Burying its leaves underground also helps the window plant cut down on water loss.

The next best thing to staying completely out of sight is to use a disguise. The living stones of the Namib Desert look just like pebbles. Only when you peer at them very closely can you see that the round stone is made up of two mottled, fleshy lumps that are in fact leaves. From a distance, people can recognize a living stone as a plant only when it flowers – but the flowers, although wonderfully bright and colourful to attract insects, last only for a couple of days.

Cactus facts

▲ There are more than 1600 species of cactus. They live on the American continents, all the way from Canada to Argentina.

▲ The smallest cactus is about 1 cm (0.5 inches) across. The largest is the saguaro cactus, which can grow as tall as 18 metres (60 ft).

▲ Large cacti can take in 800 litres (210 gallons) of water at one time when it rains.

▲ A saguaro cactus 6 metres (20 ft) tall can hold more than a tonne of water in its stem.

▲ Many wild cacti are protected by law. People who steal a saguaro cactus in parts of the USA can be given a heavy fine or even a jail sentence.

like creosote, the foul-smelling chemical that people use to preserve timber. Only the creosote bush grasshopper can stand the disgusting taste.

Desert plants also have more visible defences. Cacti, agaves and desert euphorbias are all armed with sharp spines. Some cacti, such as the cholla of American deserts, also have barbed bristles, while a large variety of desert trees and shrubs, such as acacias, are covered in vicious thorns. The milkweed plant of south-west Asia has long ribs between its leaves. When the ribs die they become hard and sharp, forming a kind of spiky cage around the flowers. Milkweed also grows very close to the ground, which makes it more difficult for animals to eat.

Heavy rainstorms often soak the North American deserts in spring. Cacti and other plants burst into flower after the rain, and insects emerge to feed on the nectar.

The blooming desert

We don't normally think of deserts as colourful places, but in the Sonoran Desert in Arizona and Mexico, millions of flowers sometimes appear together in spring, after winter rainstorms. They are 'ephemerals' – plants whose life cycle lasts a matter of days. For most of the time only their seeds are present, lying dormant (inactive) in the soil. After heavy rain, they sprout, burst into flower and quickly produce more seeds before the ground dries out. Then they shrivel up and die. Desert ephemerals include poppies, daisies and members of the pea family. The seeds can survive years waiting for rain, but they take as little as two hours to produce leaves once they get soaked.

Desert animals

We often think of deserts as empty places, where no animals live. In fact, a great variety of animals are at home in deserts, from tiny insects to large mammals like antelopes and camels. There are even elephants living in deserts.

All land animals depend on plants for food. Either they eat plants themselves, or they eat other animals that feed on plants.

In the driest deserts there are hardly any plants, so plant-eating animals can survive only by eating seeds or other bits of plants blown into the desert by the wind. Such food is enough only for very small animals, like insects. Spiders, snakes and lizards eat the insects, and they, in turn, are eaten by larger animals, such as birds of prey.

Wetter deserts have a wider range of plants, including grasses, cacti, shrubs or even scattered trees. Deserts that are rich in plant life provide enough food for larger animals, such as rabbits, antelopes, camels and – in Australia – kangaroos. In Africa, herds of antelope travel huge distances to find enough plants to keep them alive, and **predators** such as lions and leopards often follow them into the desert in the hope of an easy meal. Other desert hunters include

There is hardly anything to eat on the dunes of the Namib Desert in southern Africa. Oryx, a kind of antelope, survive there by drinking at the water holes and eating the sparse plants on the plains.

coyotes and foxes in the deserts of North America, and pumas in the cold Patagonian desert of South America.

Most desert animals can't afford to be too fussy about what they eat, but some have very particular requirements. The yucca moth, for example, depends entirely on yucca plants for its survival – and yucca plants depend just as much on the moth.

Yuccas are plants with a rosette of long, sharp-tipped leaves surrounding a flower stalk in the middle. The female yucca moth lays her eggs in the middle of a yucca flower, and the caterpillars that hatch feed on a few of the developing seeds inside the flower. To make sure the flower will make seeds, the moth first collects a ball of pollen from a different yucca flower, and then rubs this on her chosen flower after laying the eggs. No other insect can pollinate the yucca flower, and no other flower provides a suitable home for the caterpillars – so yuccas and yucca moths depend on each other to survive.

Another specialist feeder is the gerenuk, a long-necked gazelle that lives in the deserts of Somalia in east Africa (*gerenuk* means 'giraffe-necked' in the Somali language). The gerenuk feeds on the leaves of thorny bushes. By standing on its hind legs and stretching its long neck, it can reach much higher leaves than other animals can.

The remarkable spadefoot toad

You wouldn't think deserts were a good place for toads to live. Most toads, like other amphibians, must keep themselves moist. But certain amphibians manage to survive in very dry conditions. Some spadefoot toads live in the deserts of western North America. They lay their eggs in the small pools that appear after rainfall. The tadpoles that hatch from these eggs can turn into toads in as little as two weeks – much quicker than most other tadpoles. This is because tadpoles can't live out of water, so they need to develop quickly before the pool dries up.

Spadefoots get their name from the spade-like growth on their hind feet. This helps them burrow down into the soil where they escape the dry heat of the desert. They only ever come out of the soil at night, during a short time in spring and early summer when they frantically breed. They spend the rest of their time buried alive. They might not emerge for eleven months of each year.

Many types of scorpions, such as this bark scorpion of California, have made deserts their own. In some places there is a greater total weight of scorpions than any other animals except ants and termites.

Other desert animals can go without drinking for a long time. Camels can survive for a week without drinking when they are working, and for several months when they're not. When they do drink, they can take in over 100 litres (26 gallons) – more than a bathtub-full – in one session. People often think that camels store water in their humps, but the humps are full of fatty tissue. Camels use this as a sort of emergency food supply, and it can be broken down inside the camel's body to release water.

Finding water is not easy in the desert. Large desert animals like antelopes travel long distances to get to water holes, where they can drink. Some antelopes, as well as wild horses and asses, are good at breaking up the dry ground with their hooves to get at

Finding water

Like a number of other desert animals, the gerenuk never has to drink – it gets all the water it needs from the leaves it eats. In fact, all animals can make water inside their bodies by a chemical reaction. This water comes from the chemical process that releases energy from food. Some desert rodents get nearly all their water this way.

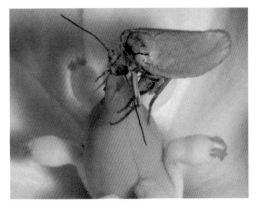

The yucca moth has a very close partnership with yucca plants. The moth helps the plant reproduce, while the plant provides a meal for the moth's caterpillars.

 Desert makers

Animals can help make deserts. During the time of the ancient Romans, parts of North Africa were much greener than today, and the Romans even grew wheat in the region. After the fall of the Roman Empire, the complicated irrigation systems that watered the crops fell into ruin. Rather than growing wheat, people took to raising sheep and goats. If there are too many sheep and goats in an area, the animals strip the vegetation – grass, shrubs, trees, everything. They also eat any new shoots that appear, so there is no chance for plants to recover. This process, called overgrazing, can turn fertile land into a desert. In North Africa today you can still see the ruins of magnificent Roman towns, surrounded by desert.

small amounts of water under the surface. The thorny devil, a spiky lizard from Australia, has scales on its body that can soak up water from damp sand.

It's important for desert animals not to lose water. Animals lose water when they urinate, but they have to urinate to get rid of waste products in the body. This process is called **excretion**. To reduce water loss, camels and other desert animals have very concentrated urine; in other words, their urine contains only a small amount of water, which makes it particularly dark and smelly. Some desert reptiles excrete solid crystals instead of liquid urine. Other reptiles get rid of certain waste products, such as salts, through glands on the sides of their snouts.

Wasting nothing

Animals also lose water in their droppings, so most desert animals have very dry droppings. Camel dung is incredibly dry and solid – for thousands of years desert people have used it as a fuel instead of firewood, which is hard to find in the desert. North American kangaroo rats make sure they don't waste any water in their droppings by eating them.

Another way animals lose water is by sweating. Sweating is a way of keeping cool, but camels can stand being warmer than most other mammals before they need to start sweating. They have fewer sweat glands than other animals, and their thick coat keeps the scorching sunlight off their skin, which stops them from getting too hot.

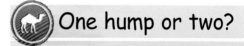

One hump or two?

There are two kinds of camels. The Arabian camel (also called a dromedary, below) has one hump. It lives in North Africa and south-west Asia. It is now a domestic animal, although some of the camels introduced to Australia in the 19th century have become wild. The other kind of camel is the two-humped Bactrian camel, which lives in Central Asia. Most Bactrian camels are also domesticated (bred), but there are still a few wild herds in remote parts of Mongolia and western China. Camels are sometimes called ships of the desert because they are so good at carrying goods and people across seas of sand. They can keep going for a long time without food or water, and have many other ways of dealing with life in the desert. For example, camels have a web of skin joining the two toes on each foot. This web spreads out as they walk, keeping the foot from sinking into soft sand. It's a bit like wearing snowshoes. When the wind blows sand in their faces, camels can close their nostrils. They also have long, thick eyelashes that protect their eyes from sand.

Above: Sand in desert dunes is so loose that animals can swim through it. Some small geckos even have webbed feet, like a frog's feet, to help them swim.

Surviving heat and cold

Many deserts are very hot during the day, but at night the temperature can plummet to freezing. To avoid the heat of the day, small desert animals often shelter under rocks or dig burrows. Some animals only come out at night, when it's cooler. Night-time hunters include the fennec (a fox of North Africa) and the western diamondback rattlesnake of the American Southwest. The western diamondback has little pits beneath its eyes that can detect infrared radiation (heat). This helps it 'see' its prey – usually warm-blooded rodents – in the dark.

Sometimes it gets too cold to go out at night. Animals like the kangaroo rat of North America and the mouse-like jerboa of Asia and North Africa come out of their shelters mainly at dawn and dusk, when the temperature is most comfortable.

Ears that radiate

Jerboas, which are also called desert rats, have very long hind legs that enable them to hop along quickly. They also have big ears. Other desert mammals, like the fennec and the similar kit fox of the American South-west, have big ears, too. A big, flat ear is like a radiator. There is very little volume and a lot of surface area to give off (radiate) heat. So big ears help lose heat from the animal's body and keep the animal cool.

Most birds have a higher body temperature than mammals. Nevertheless, the intense desert sun would cause them to overheat unless they had some method of cooling off.

This round-tailed ground squirrel lives in the American deserts. It gets all the water it needs from its food, but it needs food rich in water, such as this cactus flower.

Not all oryx make it in the harsh
environment of the Namib Desert.
The remains of this one might
have been scavenged by jackals
and hyenas, which range widely
across the dunes.

Desert animals of Asia

The deserts of central Asia are barren. The sparse rains support few plants, so the food supply for animals is meagre. Plant-eating mammals such as the wild ass, Bactrian camel and Mongolian gazelle travel widely to find enough grazing. Even outside the migrating season, gazelles cover more than 20 km (12 miles) per day in their endless search for food.

Meat eaters in the desert must make the most of each rare opportunity to feed. So while the corsac fox and the steppe eagle hunt desert rodents, they also survive by scavenging carcasses whenever they can.

The houbara bustard is also a flexible feeder and has a wide taste in food. It collects seeds and shoots but also preys on locusts, beetles and lizards when it finds them.

- Asiatic wild ass
- Bactrian camel
- Steppe eagle
- Mongolian gazelle
- Houbara bustard
- Corsac fox

Many desert birds have a way of fanning themselves to keep cool: they flutter a patch of skin on their throats.

Sunbathing reptiles

Birds and mammals are sometimes called **warm-blooded** because their bodies are always at the same warm temperature. They use a lot of energy in keeping their bodies at the right temperature, and all this energy comes from their food. In fact, they use about 90 per cent of the food they eat to keep their body temperature steady.

Cold-blooded animals, such as snakes and lizards, don't need to keep their bodies at a steady temperature. They can spend most of their time cold and inactive, using very little energy. Because of this, reptiles can get by on a tenth of the food that mammals and birds need. This gives snakes and lizards an advantage in deserts, where food is scarce.

Cold-blooded isn't a very good description, because a reptile's body temperature changes with that of its surroundings. Its body is colder than a mammal's at night, but at midday in the desert it might be warmer.

A viper can detect its prey with heat-sensitive pits on its snout. These pits are so sophisticated that they work like a second pair of eyes, forming a picture of the victim's body heat.

When a desert lizard wakes up in the morning, its body is cool. Its body processes, including the movement of its muscles, work slowly. The lizard can only move sluggishly, but once it has crawled from its shelter and into the sun, it begins to warm up. Moving slowly is one disadvantage of being cold-blooded, especially if a warm-blooded predator is on the prowl. When the lizard is warm, its muscles work quickly enough for it to scuttle about looking for food, or escape from birds of prey. As the air gets hotter, desert lizards often climb to the higher branches of a bush, where there is more breeze to cool them. By midday, when the sun is at its hottest, the lizard might look for shade under a rock.

Being cold-blooded has other advantages in the desert. Animals lose water as they breathe, but cold-blooded animals only need

The Arabian jerboa is one of the many desert rodents that scrape out a living scurrying beneath the thin desert soil by day, coming out to steal seeds at night.

to breathe very, very slowly when they are resting. As a result, reptiles lose much less water than birds or mammals. And while mammals have to sweat to cool themselves in hot weather, cold-blooded animals simply let their bodies heat up. This allows reptiles to survive on much less water than mammals or birds, making them expert desert dwellers.

Staying out of the heat

Some desert animals, like spiders and scorpions, avoid the problems of heat and lack of water by becoming **dormant**. When an animal is dormant, it stays completely inactive – sometimes for weeks or months on end. It neither eats nor moves, and appears so lifeless that it seems to be dead. Dormant animals wake up only when there is a chance of eating something, or of mating. In the Sahara, desert snails can remain dormant for years until brought back to life by rain. In Australia, various kinds of tiny shrimps lie dormant in the desert. The wind blows their eggs until they settle in a crevice or a hollow in rock, and the eggs stay there until it rains. When the hollow fills up with water, the eggs hatch. Such shrimps have even been found in hollows high up on the sun-baked sides of Uluru (Ayers Rock), the famous giant rock in the middle of the Australian desert.

Some birds search for food in the desert, but they build their nests in more comfortable places beyond the

The Australian desert pool where these shield shrimps live is drying up. But when it forms again with the next rains, the shrimps' eggs are ready to hatch and grow, before any other pond creatures arrive in the pool.

edge of the desert, such as forests, mountains or grasslands. This is no problem for birds like eagles and vultures, which can fly great distances with little effort. These birds also have incredibly sharp vision and can spot an animal on the ground from a long way off. By roaming vast areas, such birds can find just enough food for themselves and their distant chicks back at the nest.

The strange duckbill of the shovelnosed lizard helps it burrow in the loose sand of the Namib Desert. It can quickly plunge in to extract prey such as this fly.

Life on the dunes

Sand dunes are a unique and challenging habitat for both plants and animals. The sand is always blowing about in the wind, making it difficult for any plants to grow. Nevertheless, a great variety of small animals live there. For example, the huntsman spider makes its home in a tunnel in the sand. It lines the tunnel with silk and makes a trapdoor at the entrance to keep out windblown sand. Beetles and small lizards can dive into the sand to escape from other animals hunting them.

Lying in wait for larger prey is the sidewinding adder (below). This small snake shuffles completely into the fine sand of the Namib Desert. It leaves only its eyes exposed, and the tip of its tail, which it waves to attract lizards near enough to catch.

On the sandy surface, sidewinding adders get about by slithering sideways, curving their bodies so that only a small part of the body presses against the sand at a time. Lines of parallel J-shaped marks on the sand show they have passed. Sidewinders, or horned rattlesnakes, of the American Southwest use the same method, but they are not closely related.

Sahara

The Sahara stretches across North Africa, from the Atlantic Ocean to the Red Sea. It is the largest desert and covers one-twelfth of Earth's land surface.

Desert mammals

Mammals in the Sahara avoid the scorching heat by staying underground during the day. The fennec, a kind of fox, hides out in its burrows in large family groups. Nevertheless, to survive in the Sahara, it must have the ability to go without a drink for long periods. At night the fennec comes out to hunt small rodents, lizards and insects such as locusts. Its densely furred feet allow it to run fast on loose sand, and it can keep cool by losing body heat through its huge ears.

Sahara facts

▲ The Sahara covers parts of eleven countries: Morocco, Algeria, Tunisia, Libya, Egypt, Western Sahara, Mauritania, Mali, Niger, Chad and Sudan.

▲ The desert ends gradually in the south as it blends with the belt of semi-desert called the Sahel.

▲ Few people live in the Sahara. On average there is less than one person per square kilometre (0.4 square miles) – the same as Alaska.

Together with the seasonal streams that fill valleys called wadis, oases such as this one are important life-supporting features of the Sahara.

1. Disputed territory
Both Morocco and Mauritania have made claims for the region called Western Sahara. The area used to be administered by Spain.

2. Tombouctou (Timbuktu)
For centuries this city has been both a trading post for merchants crossing the Sahara and a centre of Islamic culture and learning.

3. Atlas Mountains
Stretching across northern Algeria and Morocco, these mountains mark the northwestern border of the Sahara.

4. The Great Ergs, or Sand Seas
The Sahara has varied terrain, but seas of sand dunes such as the Great Ergs cover a quarter of its area.

5. Oil fields
The Sahara's richest oil fields occur in southern Algeria and eastern Libya. Half of Africa's known oil reserves are in Libya.

6. Chott al Jerid
A vast, flat salt lake. The lake sometimes holds water in winter, but it dries out in summer.

7. Chad Basin
A huge wetland that is only a fraction of its former size. Due to climate change, arid lands and salt pans now cover much of the area once covered by the waters of Lake Chad.

8. Tibesti Mountains
At 3415 metres (11,204 ft), Mount Koussi in the Tibesti Mountains is the highest point of land in the Sahara.

9. Al Khufra Oasis
This group of five oases covers an area the size of Israel.

10. Lake Nasser
An artificial reservoir created in 1971 by the completion of the Aswan High Dam. Its waters irrigate land to the north.

A Cape fox checks out its surroundings in the Kalahari
desert, southern Africa. The Cape fox is a type of wild
dog that lives in semideserts as well as grasslands.

Gobi and Takla Makan

The cold deserts of Mongolia and China experience extreme temperatures and bitter winters as well as scant rainfall. Despite this, herders and travelling traders have crossed these deserts for thousands of years.

Basin

3

Tian Shan

EUROPE   ASIA

AFRICA

Tian Shan (mountains)

Tarim River

Takla Makan

1 Tarim Basin

Hotan ● **2**

Kunlun Shan (mountains)

▲ K2   ▲ Muztag

PAKISTAN   DISPUTED TERRITORY

Tibetan

INDIA   ▲ Nganglong Kangri

Beasts of burden

In the Gobi and Takla Makan lives the two-humped Bactrian camel. It has the long eyelashes, large, splaying feet and closable nostrils of other camels, but it also has a long, shaggy coat to protect it from the winter cold. Most Bactrian camels are kept by people, but some herds run truly wild in remote areas of Mongolia and China. A camel's ability to lose a quarter of its body weight in water has been useful to people wanting to cross deserts. For centuries traders and their camels crossed the Gobi and Takla Makan in groups called caravans. They carried silk and spices from China to Europe. Today, camels are still useful to desert people. The camel on the right is waiting outside its owner's dwelling, a canvas and felt tent called a yurt, or ger.

The Gobi is dominated by vast, treeless wastes. Its grey-brown surface is sparsely covered with hardy grass and bushes. Here, sand dunes dwarf a pair of yurts.

1. Tarim Basin
This region lies in the rain shadow of towering mountains on three sides, and very little rain reaches it. Around the rim, some rivers flow. They are fed by groundwater welling up and by snow melting on the mountains.

2. Hotan
In ancient times, merchants stayed here while travelling on the Silk Road, the major trade route from China to Europe.

3. Dzungarian Basin
Where Przewalski's horses, the last truly wild horses, roamed until the 1960s.

4. Lop Nur salt marsh
The Konqi River evaporates away in the desert sun, creating this salty marshland.

5. Turpan Depression
The lowest-lying and hottest place in China, with a record temperature of 47°C (117°F).

6. Altai Shan
A mountain refuge of the endangered snow leopard.

7. Karakorum
Warlord Genghis Khan's capital, from which he controlled a huge empire in the 13th century.

8. Yelyn Valley
A national park whose craggy cliffs are home to vultures.

9. Yellow River (Huang He)
This great river skirts the edge of the Gobi and irrigates a large area of farmland. Inside its wide meander is a further, smaller desert, the Mu Us, or Ordos.

Gobi facts

▲ There are hardly any roads in the Gobi, but the bare rock and gravel terrain is often so flat and even that you can drive a car for long distances in any direction.

▲ Some large mammals scrape a living in the Gobi, including the two-humped Bactrian camel, the Asiatic wild ass and the Mongolian gazelle.

▲ The Takla Makan desert is mainly covered in windblown sand. In the eastern foothills of the Tian Shan mountains, the sand dunes reach heights of 200–300 metres (650–1000 ft) – as tall as the Eiffel Tower in Paris.

Shrublands of the world

Tougher than trees and often much better armed, shrubs form the main plant cover in some widely scattered parts of the world.

Brown heather covers the top of a Welsh hill. Heathland is a type of European shrubland where low-growing shrubs such as heather grow.

Shrubs occupy an in-between slot in the world of plant life. Like trees they have woody stems, but unlike trees they rarely grow more than a few feet tall. **Shrubland** plants grow in places where the climate is too dry for trees but still moist enough to prevent desert from taking hold.

Shrub, scrub or bush?
Compared to some biomes, shrubland has a confusing variety of names. Many experts call it **scrub** or **scrubland**, while in Australia it is often known simply as the bush.

In North America, the shrubland on the California coast contains a rich variety of plants. This kind of shrubland is known as **chaparral**, while in South America a similar kind of shrubland is called **chaco** or **matorral**. If you travel eastwards, beyond the California chaparral, the landscape becomes drier still. Chaparral gives way to the semi-desert of the Great Basin, where **sagebrush** scrub stretches

for mile after mile to the Rocky Mountains, creating scenery that is familiar the world over as the backdrop to westerns.

On the other side of the Atlantic Ocean, around the shores of the Mediterranean, shrubland hugs the coast and the hillsides. In one type of shrubland, called **maquis**, the

shrubs grow to more than head height, making them a good refuge for animals. In drier parts of the Mediterranean, maquis is replaced by a kind of shrubland called **garigue**. Its shrubs are small, stunted and scattered, with tiny leaves that are good at coping with the burning summer sun.

Shrubland grows in Australia and Africa, too. In tropical Africa, dry shrubland merges into savanna (grassland). In the far south, however, in the Cape region, it forms a dense green carpet. Called **fynbos**, this form of shrubland is made up of the most concentrated variety of plants on Earth.

Shrubland climates

Most of the world's shrublands have one thing in common: they normally grow where water is scarce for several months each year.

If you imagine being burned by strong sunshine and battered by dust-laden winds, you will have an idea what the shrubland climate is often like. However, unlike deserts, shrublands are not always dry. Although some shrublands receive less than 200 mm (8 in) of rain a year, it is unevenly spread, and a lot of rain might arrive within a short time. Meanwhile, the rest of the year might be endlessly dry. The unevenness of the rainfall makes it hard for trees to survive.

Mediterranean climate

Most of the world's shrublands are on the west coast of continents, sandwiched between regions where it is always hot and regions where winters are cold. In shrubland regions, much of the year's rain falls in winter, and although it can get cold, hard frosts are rare. When spring arrives, the temperature quickly climbs, and by the time summer sets in, weeks can go by with hardly a cloud in the sky. At the height of summer, temperatures sometimes reach more than 38°C (100°F), leaving dead plant matter tinder dry.

This mixture of moist winters and dry summers is known

Fire!

In shrublands, fires are a natural fact of life. Triggered by lightning, they are often fanned by summer winds, and they can move faster than a person can run. During these fires, shrubs are left charred and blackened, but when the fire has passed, the shrubs can re-sprout from the ground. The trees of shrubland regions are often killed by the heat, so occasional fires help stop shrubland from turning into forest. These days, fires are also started by campfires and cigarettes. The more frequent blazes make it even harder for trees to survive.

as a Mediterranean climate, but the Mediterranean region is not the only place where it occurs. Across the world, from California and Chile to South Africa and Western Australia, similar conditions encourage similar shrubland plants. The climate is ideal for grapevines, which is why so many of the world's wines come from these parts of the world.

Wind and fire

Warmth and rainwater are not the only things that shape life in places with Mediterranean climates. Another important factor is the wind. In summer, a daytime breeze often blows onto the land from the sea, helping to take the edge off the heat. But sometimes the wind swings around and blows from inland, and when this happens, conditions can quickly change.

This is exactly what occurs in southern California, when the Santa Ana wind blows. It brings hot dusty air from the desert, and it sends temperatures shooting up. Because the Santa Ana wind is hot and bone dry, it can turn sparks into major scrub and forest fires. Shrubland plants have their own ways of coping with this threat, and once the fire is over, most of them recover. But for people, these fires are much more of a problem – particularly when their homes stand in the path of the flames.

In the Mediterranean region a similar wind, called the sirocco, sometimes blows northwards out of Africa. It brings the same kind of stifling heat and often carries sand from the Sahara, dropping it hundreds of miles away. Mediterranean wildlife also has to deal with cold winter winds, such as the mistral, which blows down from the north.

Nature's thermometer

The olive tree thrives in the Mediterranean climate. The distribution of olive trees reliably shows us which parts of the world have a climate similar to the Mediterranean. Olive trees like lots of hot sunshine in the summer, but they will not grow in places where the average winter temperature drops below 3°C (37.5°F). Even a few hours of frost can kill them. The olive tree originally came from the eastern Mediterranean, but its fruit and oil are so useful that farmers now grow it in places as far apart as the western USA and Australia.

Climographs

Each place in the world has its own pattern of weather. The typical pattern of weather over a year in one place is called the place's climate. We can sum up a place's climate on a climograph, such as the one shown here for St Louis in the USA. The letters along the bottom are the months of the year. The numbers on the left and the small bars show rainfall, and the numbers on the right and the curvy line show temperature. You can see at a glance that St Louis is hottest in July, but December is the driest month.

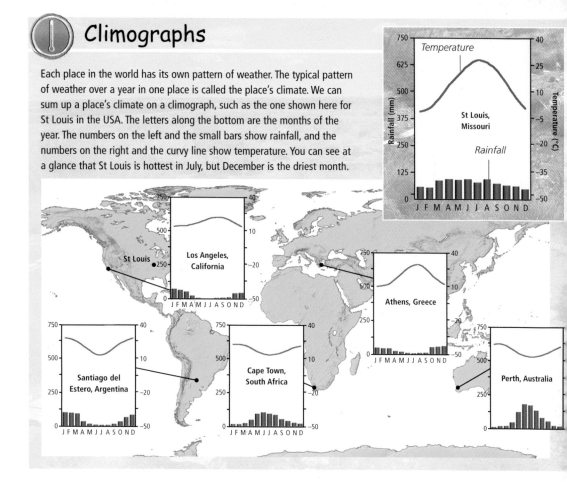

When the mistral is blowing, the temperature can fall to near freezing, spelling danger to animals and plants that cannot cope with frost. The olive tree is one of these vulnerable species: every few years, the cold wipes out large numbers of them.

Storms and salt

On the fringes of deserts, the climate is drier than the typical Mediterranean climate, and shrubs fight a constant battle to stay alive. A tiny amount of extra moisture can make all the difference. Many desert-edge shrubs survive in dry riverbeds, where flash floods occur after sudden storms. Between these floods, there is no sign of water on the surface, but water collects underground, beneath the dry riverbed. The shrubs survive by soaking up this leftover moisture.

When rain does fall in dry shrublands, it can create problems. It can run off the dry ground instead of soaking in, forming sudden floods. These floods often dissolve salt from the soil and carry it downhill. Once a storm has passed and the sun comes out, pools and puddles left by the flood quickly dry up, leaving their salt behind. The leftover salt makes the ground sparkle and feel crunchy underfoot, and it spells deadly danger to many plants. Salt makes it hard for plants to soak up water, and it eventually kills their roots. But some shrubs survive in salty soil.

193

Saltbushes on Australia's Nullarbor Plain appear grey-green because of the salt crystals on their leaves. The crystals reflect sunlight and keep the saltbushes cool.

Saltbushes, for instance, live in areas that receive their rainfall in less than a dozen sudden bursts each year.

Australia's vast Nullarbor Plain is one place where saltbushes have the ground largely to themselves. *Nullarbor* means 'no tree', and as plains go, this one could hardly be plainer. It is wide open, pancake flat and twice as big as England. Small trees do grow here, but saltbushes are the most common plants. They stretch from horizon to horizon, creating a lonely landscape crossed by a railway that does not need to bend for 500 km (300 miles). It is the longest straight stretch of railway in the world.

Like saltbushes in other dry shrublands, the Nullarbor's saltbushes have a way of getting rid of surplus salt. They make crystals of the salt on their leaves, which gives the leaves a grey-green colour and a rough texture.

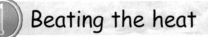 ## Beating the heat

On the Greek island of Rhodes, summer can get too hot even for insects. Here, millions of tiger moths spend the hottest time of the year in a handful of shady valleys, where they cluster in rock crevices and over shrubs and small trees. Their black-and-white forewings camouflage them well when they are at rest, but as soon as they take off, their brilliant orange hind wings seem to flash through the air. Because the moths fly by day, they are often mistaken for butterflies.

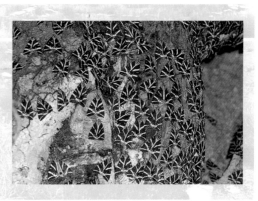

Shrublands in the tropics

In the tropics, the climate is usually wet enough for forest or grassland to flourish, so shrubs find themselves crowded out. But in some places, such as north-east Brazil and parts of Africa, there is a long dry season each year. In this climate, trees and even grasses may struggle to survive, so shrubs can get the upper hand. In these places, most of the rain falls at the hottest time of year – the exact opposite of the Mediterranean climate. In southern Africa, for example, July is the coolest month, because it is the middle of the southern hemisphere's winter. It is also the driest month, often with no rain at all. In January, though, the air is sticky and humid (moist), and towering thunderclouds release torrential downpours almost every afternoon.

This switch between wet and dry times has some far-reaching effects. During the wet season, shrubs are covered with leaves, so even large animals are well hidden. But during the dry

In the stressful, dry climate of east Africa's shrublands, plants can't put up with too many browsing animals. The shrubs defend themselves with thorns, but the black rhino is tough enough to eat them.

In Baja California, the climate is drier than the Mediterranean climate of California. There are more succulent (fleshy) plants like the prickly pear cactus.

when water holes become very busy, as animals arrive from far and wide to take a much-needed drink.

Africa has more large plant-eaters than anywhere else on Earth, so it's not surprising that many shrubs and small trees have spines and thorns for self-defence. During the dry season, their bare branches are like strands of barbed wire, and anything that tangles with them can take a long time to work itself free.

Coastal shrubland

Even in places with plenty of rain, climate can sometimes give shrubs the edge over trees. This often happens on cold, windswept coasts, where trees would be uprooted and blown away. This kind of environment is common around the shores of northern Germany and Denmark, and on the western shores of the United Kingdom. Storm-force winds can lash these coasts with salt-laden spray at speeds of more than 103 km/h (65 mph). Winds this fast can knock people off their feet, but shrubs like gorse and buckthorn are small and tough enough to stay in place.

season, many of the shrubs lose their foliage, and the grass between them dies down. This is the best time to watch wildlife, because there is much less cover and far fewer places for animals to hide. It is also the time of year

The Welsh coast doesn't have a Mediterranean climate. Shrubland develops here because trees can't grow in the wind and salty spray. Tough gorse and heather grow in their place.

These coastal shrubs are like natural windbreaks. They create a sheltered **microclimate** near the ground. Tucked away inside them, animals can sit out the storm, waiting until it is safe to venture outside.

These seaside stowaways include small birds, small mammals and even delicate animals like butterflies, which flit over shrubs and coastal grass when calm weather returns. Because the sea breeze almost always blows from the same direction, these shrubs are often lopsided, with their twigs and branches pointing inland.

Guilty goats

Climate is not the only thing that can create or destroy shrublands: humans can also play a part. Sometimes the changes people make are easy to see. For example, shrublands are ploughed up and turned into fields. But in some parts of the world, the changes occurred so long ago that it is not easy to work out what happened. To unravel this hidden history, scientists examine today's plant cover and climate. They then compare it with what they would expect to see if the land had been left truly wild. This research shows that some shrubland regions are not nearly as natural as they seem.

One of the biggest shrubland areas, around the Mediterranean Sea, probably formed when people began to farm the land and cut down many of the trees. Some 10,000 years ago, the Mediterranean area was thickly forested, and forest stretched down to the shore. But as farming expanded, more and more spaces were opened up, so that crops could be grown and animals fed. Once the forest had been felled, goats nibbled away at young saplings and stopped the forest from growing back.

The story of the Mediterranean shows that people, as well as climate, have helped create the shrublands that we see today.

This ancient Roman plate shows that people and their goats have been living in the shrubland biome of the Mediterranean region for thousands of years.

From forest to chaparral

At Rancho La Brea in the USA, the remains of thousands of prehistoric animals have been found in natural pools of oily tar. The animals include mammoths, giant ground sloths and sabre-toothed tigers, all of which fell into the tar by accident, mistaking it for solid ground. These giant mammals lived during the last ice age, when the area was covered by forest. They died out during the time when humans spread into North America, between 20,000 and 12,000 years ago. This was also a time when the climate warmed at the end of the Ice Age, and the biomes of North America moved and changed. The widespread forest biome in the southern USA turned to chaparral.

Shrubland plants

Shrubs are tough customers. Besides hot sunshine and long droughts, they have to survive hungry animals and the threat of catching fire.

In the Stirling Range of south-west Australia, fresh green shoots burst out of the blackened trunks of grass trees and mallee shrubs after a bush fire.

Shrubs put up with damage that would kill many other plants. If they are eaten, chopped down or even set on fire, most of them simply grow back.

Rebirth from the ashes

One of the best places to see how shrubs bounce back is in the interior of southern Australia, where **mallee** shrubland covers thousands of square kilometres. Mallees are eucalyptuses or gum trees, but instead of growing tall and lean, like most eucalyptuses, they are usually small, with gnarled and twisted stems. They don't win any prizes for beauty, but they are experts at staying alive.

As a mallee shrub grows, it drops dead leaves and old branches on the ground. Mixed with dry grass, and baked by the sun, they make the perfect recipe for a fire. A flash of lightning or a discarded cigarette is all it takes to set this fuel on fire, and within hours, thousands of hectares can be ablaze.

The plant life in South Africa's fynbos shrubland is as spectacular as it is diverse. The king protea is crowned by gigantic blooms that are pollinated (fertilized) by Cape sugarbirds.

For small animals, such as crickets and lizards, these blazes are a deadly danger. Even birds can be threatened when the mallees burst into flames. But once the fire has passed, the shrubland stages an incredible recovery. Within a few weeks, the charred trunks start to sprout new stems and leaves. The cleared ground between the shrubs begins to turn green with plants springing from previously dormant (inactive) seeds. Because all the dead wood and leaves have been burned away, years pass before a serious fire can strike again.

Mallees can stage a miraculous comeback because each one has a stockpile of water and food. It is hidden in a swollen root called a **lignotuber**, which is safely buried underground. Lignotubers can be as big as wheelbarrows, and they contain all that mallees need to get going after a disaster.

Scents in the air

Mallees are 100 per cent Australian, and you won't find them anywhere else. In the same way, many other shrubland plants live in just one part of the world. For example, papery-petalled shrubs called cistus grow only around the Mediterranean, while **greasewood** lives only in California's chaparral in the USA. But despite looking different, and living far apart, shrubs like these share some features that let them live in the same conditions.

Grass trees

In Western Australia, plants called grass trees flower only after a fire. They look like small palm trees topped by a tuft of grass-like leaves. When a fire strikes, the leaves soon burn away, and in bad fires, the trunks themselves can burn almost to the ground. But within a few weeks, new leaves sprout, followed by flowers. Grass trees can grow up to 10 metres (30 ft) tall, and their trunks are usually black and covered with soot. Their young leaves are sweet and succulent, and for Australia's aboriginal people, they were once a useful source of food.

One of these features can't be seen. You can smell it, though, if you brush past a shrub or rub some of its leaves. If you are in a place with a Mediterranean-type climate, the chances are that an **aromatic** smell fills the air. This smell comes from oils in the leaves, which **evaporate** (turn to vapour) when the leaves are touched or bruised.

To human noses, some of these oily smells are not nice. Others, for example those of lavender and sage, are much more pleasant, which is why these plants are used for making perfumes or for flavouring food. But these plant oils have not evolved for our benefit – shrubs use them for protection. Oils prevent leaves from losing too much water when they are heated by sunshine. This is an essential feature for life where summers are hot and long. To back up this water-saving system, oily leaves often have a leathery surface or a covering of microscopic hairs. A leathery surface keeps water in, while hairs work like sunshades, helping to keep the leaf cool. Another way shrubs beat the heat is to keep their leaves small. Greasewood has leaves like small pine needles, making it very good at surviving on hot windswept ground.

Oils also discourage hungry plant eaters, because oily leaves are difficult to digest. This smelly defence explains why few animals can stomach the leaves of Australia's mallees or of many other shrubs that grow where it is dry. In fact, oily plants often benefit when farm animals arrive on the scene: cattle or goats eat all the tastier plants, leaving more room for the oily plants to spread.

The summer sleepers

After several months of drought, shrubs often look parched and dusty, and the ground between them seems bare. But beneath the surface, a host of plants lie hidden, waiting for the right moment to grow. These are the shrubland's summer sleepers – plants that

After a hot summer in Africa's dry shrubland, the only sign of life from shrubs such as the impala lily is a display of flowers. It will grow its leaves again in spring.

disappear during the hottest time of the year. In summer, the plants live on their private stores of food and water, which they keep underground, usually inside swollen roots.

Sea squill of southern Europe is one of the biggest of these sleeping plants. Its swollen root is a bulb almost as big as a football, and it is packed with poison that helps keep hungry animals at bay. During winter, the plant has a cluster of succulent (fleshy), shiny leaves, but when spring arrives, they slowly die away. At the height of summer, the leaves

Some wasps help the fig plant by pollinating its tiny flowers when they crawl into a fig to lay their eggs. This wasp cheats: it uses a long tube on its abdomen, called an ovipositor, to insert eggs directly into the fig.

have completely disappeared, and the plant is deep in its summer rest. But when summer nears its end, the bulb comes back to life, and the plant bursts into flower.

Autumn flowering is a common feature of dry shrubland, but an even more spectacular flowering takes place in spring. This is the time when thousands of small plants rush to reproduce, before the hot weather bakes their leaves. They include tulips, lilies, irises and crocuses, all of which have fleshy roots, bulbs or tubers that store food. Some orchids that grow from tubers also join the spring bloom. If conditions get really difficult, some can survive without sprouting for several years. In Western Australia, one species of shrubland orchid spends almost its entire life underground. A sharp-eyed farmer discovered

it in 1928, while he was ploughing. Only the flowers of this fascinating plant, the western underground orchid, appear at ground level, to be pollinated by termites.

Chemical warfare

Shrubland plants can be as ruthless as animals in defending their own patch of ground. One way they do this is by producing poisonous chemicals, which seep through the soil and prevent other plants from growing nearby.

In the western USA, sagebrush (below) is an expert at this kind of chemical warfare. Rings of bare soil often surround mature sagebrush plants. These rings are the equivalent of no man's land, and they give sagebrush extra room to grow.

Visitors on the wing

When plants are growing, they need to keep animals away from their leaves. But once they start flowering, they often need animal help to spread their **pollen** and seeds. For shrubland plants, attracting the right kind of visitors at the right time is essential.

Few shrubs are as particular as the edible fig tree, which grows wild around the Mediterranean. The figs – the fleshy parts that people sell in fruit markets – are not really fruit, but hollow swellings packed with tiny flowers. Each fig has a concealed entrance at its tip, which is the way in for the female fig wasp – a flying insect not much larger than a flea. The wasp pollinates the fig's flowers, and in return, the fig acts as a nursery for the wasp's young.

The female wasp has to crawl along a narrow passage leading inside the fig. During this journey, she often loses her feelers or wings. As she clambers about, choosing the

These colours reflect the richness (number of different species) of plant life. Intense pinks and reds show the places with the most plant species. They include mountain ranges, where several biomes are squashed together. They also include patches of rich tropical rainforest in the Congo and Borneo.

The other hot spots of plant richness are shrublands, such as south-west Australia and the fynbos. So why are shrublands filled with some of the most diverse mixtures of plants?

Shrubland often has a canopy of tall shrubs, with a layer of undergrowth, so there is room for more types of plants than in grassland. A shrubland canopy, however, is broken and patchy, and it lets plenty of light through for different plants to crowd in below. This makes shrubland different from temperate (cool) forests, where a few dominant species of tree form a dense canopy and stop many other types of plant from growing. Even in the Mediterranean, the blue area on the map shows there are more plant species than in the green temperate forest regions nearby.

Shrubland hot spots

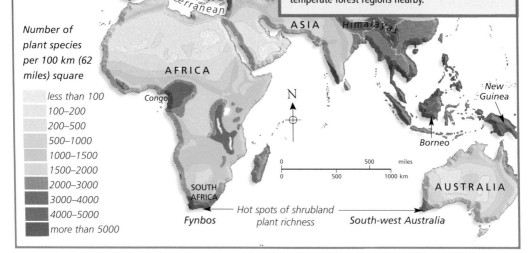

Number of plant species per 100 km (62 miles) square

- less than 100
- 100–200
- 200–500
- 500–1000
- 1000–1500
- 1500–2000
- 2000–3000
- 3000–4000
- 4000–5000
- more than 5000

EUROPE

Mediterranean

ASIA   Himalayas

AFRICA

Congo

N

New Guinea

Borneo

SOUTH AFRICA

AUSTRALIA

Fynbos

Hot spots of shrubland plant richness

South-west Australia

0   500   miles
0   500   1000 km

Heathers

From Scandinavia, through the Mediterranean (right) to South Africa, heathers are important shrubland plants. There are more than 700 different kinds, but most live in the fynbos. They all have woody stems and small leaves so they can withstand heat as well as cold. Some heathers are almost tree-sized, while others creep along close to the ground. Heather flowers provide nectar for bees, while grouse and other ground-feeding birds eat the leaves. In Europe and Africa, heather was once an important building material, used for making thatched roofs.

right spot to lay her eggs, she dusts the flowers with pollen that she is carrying. The female's work is hard and when it is over, she soon dies. A short while later, her young start to hatch, and they feed on some of the flowers. The male wasps spend their lives in the fig, but the females crawl out and fly off to find figs of their own. Once they have laid their eggs and pollinated their figs, the strange cycle is complete.

The cultivated figs that we eat have flowers too long for fig wasps to lay their eggs in. The wasps pollinate them all the same, because they mistake them for wild figs.

Bee flowers
Fig trees depend entirely on fig wasps, but many other shrubland plants are not as fussy about which insects they attract. Bees or wasps pollinate some, while other plants attract butterflies and moths. Bee-pollinated shrubs include hundreds of species in the pea family. Peas are easy to recognize, because many of them have yellow flowers with a built-in landing platform for bees, known as a keel. Flowers like these are the right shape for a bee to push open, but they will also open if you give them a slight squeeze.

For butterflies and moths, pea-flower **nectar** is often beyond reach. Butterflies cannot risk pushing and shoving their delicate bodies into flowers. Instead, they are attracted by tube-shaped flowers, which they probe with their long, slender tongues.

Butterfly-pollinated shrubs grow all over the world, but some of the most handsome kinds, called butterfly bushes or buddleias, come from South America and China. Butterfly bush nectar is packed with sugars, and it is so strong-smelling that it can lure butterflies from nearly 1 km (up to half a mile) downwind. It's small wonder that gardeners love these shrubs, which is why you can see them growing thousands of kilometres from their original homes.

Attracting birds and mammals
In shrublands north of the equator, most plants rely on insects to pollinate their flowers. But in the southern hemisphere, many shrubs attract birds instead. Because birds are much heavier than insects, their flowers have to be tougher, and they double up as a feeding station and a sturdy perch.

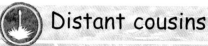

Distant cousins

Proteas and banksias have a lot in common, and they belong to the same family of plants. But proteas live only in Africa, while banksias (below) are Australian. So why do these similar-looking relatives live such an enormous distance apart? Scientists now think that the ancestors of the bushes were trees of tropical rainforests that covered a giant continent called Gondwana. Around 100 million years ago, Gondwana broke into Africa, Australia and South America, and stretches of ocean separated the common ancestors of proteas and banksias. The plants continued to evolve (change), but they did so separately on different continents. Over millions of years, both developed thick, leathery leaves and shrubby growth. Because they evolved in similar conditions in Africa and Australia, they ended up looking alike.

The king protea of South Africa is one of the most impressive of these bird-pollinated plants. It is an evergreen bush up to 1.8 metres (6 ft) tall, studded with flower heads shaped like giant ice-cream cones surrounded by spiky flaps. Each flower head is made up of several hundred mini-flowers, or florets. When the king protea is in full bloom, it's a spectacular sight, which is why it is South Africa's national flower.

The king protea flowers throughout the year, and once each flower head has opened, it lasts for several weeks. The pollen and nectar soon attract beetles, but during the day more useful visitors arrive to feed. They include sunbirds – Africa's closest equivalent to hummingbirds – and also the Cape sugarbird, which lives only where proteas bloom. As these birds probe the flower heads with their slender beaks, their foreheads become covered with pollen, and they transfer this to the next flower head they visit. During the Cape sugarbird's breeding season, it can visit up to 250 flower heads a day. The bird not only gets its food from the protea flower, it also uses parts of the flower to build its nest. The protea's fluffy seeds, in particular, make a cosy nest lining.

There are more than a hundred kinds of proteas, and at least half of them use birds to spread their pollen. Thousands of kilometres to the east, in Australia, shrubs called banksias have similar flower heads, and live in much the same way. Birds pollinate most banksias, but in western Australia a tiny marsupial called the honey possum pollinates some types. The honey possum feeds at night, and hides in old birds' nests during the day.

Spreading seeds

In shrubland on a sunny day, listen for a distinctive sound. It's a sudden snap, followed by a brief pattering on the ground. This is the noise of exploding pods – just one of the ways that shrubs scatter their seeds.

Like most plants, shrubs scatter their seeds to give them the best chance of finding the space to grow. Exploding pods are grown by many pea-family shrubs. The pods work by building up tension, like someone winding up a spring. As sunshine dries the pod, the two sides try to twist. When the pod eventually splits open, the sides suddenly curl, flicking the seeds into the air.

A big pod can catapult seeds several metres away, safely out of the shade of the parent plant. But many shrubs scatter their seeds much further. For real long-distance travel, they rely on one of two different methods: animals and the wind.

In return for a meal, birds do the seed-scattering work for figs and for other shrubs with juicy fruit. They eat the fruit and digest its succulent flesh but scatter the seeds unharmed in their droppings. If you ever wondered why shrubs often grow near

abandoned buildings and rocky outcrops, it's because this is where birds like to perch after they have eaten. Other shrubs take a more direct approach – they use hooks to fasten their seeds to animals' fur or feathers. Some of their hooks are too small to see, but a few – such as the African devil's claw – are as big as fingers, with sharply pointed tips. These hooks latch onto large mammals, allowing the seeds to hitch a lift for many kilometres.

Many shrubs have feathery seeds that are easily blown by the breeze, but a few have their own unusual ways of using the wind. One of these plants is bladder senna, which grows pods that look like miniature balloons. When the pods are ripe, the wind breaks them off, and they bounce like small pieces of litter across the ground.

Primed by fire

Seeds are usually scattered as soon as they are ripe, but some shrubs seem reluctant to let them go. Proteas and banksias shut theirs up inside old flower heads or tough pods. They can hold onto their seeds for more than twenty years. It seems like a strange thing to do, so why do they wait so long?

For these plants, fire is the key. They protect their seeds until there is a blaze, which clears away most of the plant matter on the ground. Once the flower heads or pods have been scorched, they open, dropping their seeds on a fertile bed of ash.

In California, greasewood has its own way of making sure that its seeds sprout at the right time. It drops its seeds soon after it flowers, but most of them then lie waiting in the soil. To sprout, they need to be heated to 650°C (1200°F) – something that only happens when a blaze passes overhead. However, it hedges its bets, because greasewood also produces seeds that don't need fire at all. These are triggered to sprout in the usual way – by getting wet.

Nature's planters

Some plants have their seeds spread by ants carrying them away. This happens to the seeds of a type of protea called a common pagoda or *rooistompie* (left). The *rooistompie* lives in the fynbos of South Africa's Western Cape. Its seeds are coated with a substance attractive to ants, but the inner part of each seed is hard and difficult for ants to break open. When ants find these seeds, they quickly carry them underground. Once the ants have chewed off the tasty part, they leave the rest of the seed to germinate and grow into a new *rooistompie* plant.

Shrubland animals

Shrublands can be tough going for people, but for many animals they are perfect places to live and find food.

The Mediterranean shrubland in summer is buzzing with insects. Crickets, such as this Provence cricket, make chirping sounds with their wings to attract a mate.

If shrublands were restaurants, the menu would run to dozens of pages. The animals that feed here include lots of meat-eaters, but the ones with the greatest impact on plants are vegetarians. They are vital to shrubland life, because they become the food that **predators** and scavengers eat.

The Cape sugarbird visits the pincushion protea blooms of the South African fynbos to drink their nectar. In doing so, the bird pollinates the flowers.

Chewing it over

In shrublands, plant food is often easy to find, but it's difficult to digest. Most of the plants are so tough, or so full of oils, that a person couldn't digest them at all. But shrubland plant-eaters manage to thrive because they have special equipment to tackle this sort of food.

The largest shrubland plant eaters are hoofed mammals, such as antelope and deer. They are **ruminants**, which means they have complicated digestive systems that can deal with leaves. Instead of one stomach, they have four. The biggest – called the rumen – is packed with millions of micro-organisms bathed in saliva (spit). The micro-organisms are at home in these surroundings, and they earn their keep by releasing chemicals that break down chewed-up leaves. In return for doing this work, they get a small share of the food, and their host gets the rest.

Ruminants need tough teeth to tear off and chew up their food, particularly if they feed on shrubs. To make sure that their micro-organisms can do a thorough job, they bring up the food they have swallowed, and chew it a second time. This is called ruminating, or chewing the cud. Cattle are ruminants, and they often chew the cud lying down. But antelope and deer live in a more dangerous environment. They chew the cud while standing up, so that they can be ready to make a quick escape.

Antelope and deer

If you imagine a herd of antelope, the chances are that you will think of them on Africa's grassy plains. But not all antelope live in grassland, and not all of them come from Africa. Many species spend some of their time in shrubland, and some of them never stray onto grassland at all. In shrubland, there is more cover from prying eyes. There are also more places where females can conceal their newborn calves.

Grassland antelope live in large herds for safety. In shrubland, where it is easier to hide from predators, antelope often live in family groups rather than big herds. Many antelope are small, since shrubland can be difficult to move through. One of the smallest is Kirk's dik dik, a miniature antelope from eastern Africa. It can weigh as little as 3 kg (6 lbs), and its slender shape allows it to dash through the densest thickets. When it runs off, it makes a sharp 'dik dik' cry, warning its relatives that danger is nearby.

Most shrubland antelope live in the tropics. Deer, on the other hand, generally live in cooler parts of the world. They can look very similar to antelope, but they are easy to tell apart: male deer grow antlers, while antelope of both sexes have horns.

The gerenuk is an antelope that browses thorny shrubs in Ethiopia, Somalia and northern Kenya. Standing on its hind legs for long periods, it takes only the most nutritious morsels it can find.

Bee-eaters are colourful and conspicuous birds of the Mediterranean shrubland. During courtship, a male bee-eater offers a gift of food to his intended mate.

Antelope's horns are made of keratin, the same material that forms hair and fingernails. Deer's antlers, however, are made of bone, and they fall off and re-grow each year. For deer, growing antlers is a demanding business – there is often more bone in a single antler than in a whole human arm.

More than a dozen kinds of deer live in shrublands, and the North American mule deer is one of the biggest. Its antlers have lots of prongs and can measure 1.2 metres (4 ft) from tip to tip. Despite its size, the mule deer moves quietly and seldom gives itself away. It needs to be secretive because its chief predator – the mountain lion – is efficient and deadly. An adult mountain lion can eat a fully grown mule deer every two weeks, but during the breeding season, a female with cubs might kill a deer every three days.

Despite this danger, mule deer are very successful animals, thanks partly to their flexible diet. They eat hundreds of different

 ## Famous flies

In Australia's bush, summer brings an unwelcome insect – the bushfly. This small fly doesn't bite, but it does have a strong liking for the moisture and salt on human skin. To satisfy its craving, it settles on people's faces and even crawls into their nostrils and their ears. Bushflies start life as maggots in animal droppings before transforming into adult flies in the soil. When the fly season is at its height, clouds of them fill the air. The only way to keep them off is to wear a hat with a net, or a hat with corks on strings.

Mallee animals

The mallee shrublands in Australia have a unique mixture of animals. Many of them rely on the shrublands and can't live in the surrounding desert. Bandicoots, for example, are small marsupials that use the dense cover of mallee shrubland to hide from predators, while ant-eating marsupials called numbats forage in dead wood for ants and termites. Certain legless lizards and snakes also rely on the dead wood and leaf litter that build up in mallee shrublands. They use the dead plant material as both hiding place and hunting ground.

Unfortunately for shrubland animals, the climate is ideal for farming, and much of the land has been cleared. The western swamp tortoise has suffered more than most. Not only has it lost habitat, but it is hunted by cats and foxes, and killed by frequent bushfires triggered by people. Only 300 tortoises survive. They live in a patch of habitat near Perth.

plants, and they feed on twigs and bark when leaves are hard to find. It's the ultimate in high-fibre food, but with their on-board micro-organisms, deer can break it down.

The night watch

Compared to deer, the small plant-eaters in shrublands can be very picky eaters. For example, the caterpillars of the two-tailed pasha butterfly feed only on the leaves of the strawberry tree, which grows around the Mediterranean Sea. Despite its tasty-sounding name, this small tree has flavourless fruit, and its leaves taste even worse. Most animals avoid them, but pasha caterpillars eat nothing else. By concentrating on this undesirable food, they almost have it to themselves. For birds, though, the warty red fruit are a valuable source of food in winter.

Nuyts' southern brown bandicoot

Striped legless lizard

Mallee black-backed snake

Numbat

Rosenberg's heath monitor lizard

Western swamp tortoise

N

Tanami Desert

AUSTRALIA

Gibson Desert

Simpson Desert

Great Victoria Desert

Nullarbor Plain (shrubland)

Stuart Desert

Perth

Areas of mallee shrubland

0   500   miles
0   500   1000 km

In North America, several kinds of grasshoppers feed entirely on the creosote bush, an ultra-tough desert shrub. The caterpillars benefit in the same way: hardly anything else is interested in the bush's oily leaves, so the caterpillars don't compete with any other animals for food.

Grasshoppers are good at jumping away from danger, so they can risk feeding during the day. But in shrublands, most plant-eating insects avoid the daylight and feed under the cover of darkness. As dusk falls and grasshoppers stop chirping, crickets and katydids begin their noisy chorus, signalling the start of the night shift.

These animals are relatives of grasshoppers, and they have a similar shape, with a long body, tough jaws and strong legs. They also call in a similar way, by scraping parts of their bodies together. Many are amazingly well **camouflaged** – even with a bright flashlight they are difficult to find. But if you do track one down, don't be surprised if you find it munching a fellow insect, instead of leaves or flowers. Crickets and katydids are not strict

vegetarians, and many have a soft spot for animal food. If an insect lands nearby, it risks being grabbed and eaten.

Insect eaters

With so many insects on the move, shrublands are ideal hunting grounds for insect eaters. These hunters include birds, lizards, spiders and centipedes, as well as insects themselves. Crickets and katydids are only part-time hunters, but many other insects – such as assassin bugs and praying mantises – never touch plant food.

These useful but alarming animals have different ways of dealing with their prey. An assassin bug stabs its prey, then sucks up the victim's juices through a syringe-like mouth.

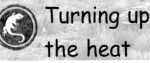

Turning up the heat

Mallee fowls of Australia have a bizarre way of keeping their eggs warm. Instead of sitting on them, these shrubland birds build giant compost heaps from fallen leaves and lay their eggs inside. When the leaves start to rot they give off heat, and this makes the eggs develop. The heap has to be at just the right temperature, and the parents check it by using their beaks like thermometers. If it is too hot, they scrape away some of the leaves, but if it is too cool, they pile more on. Once the eggs hatch, the chicks struggle to the surface. Their parents do not feed them, so they wander off to start life on their own.

The ocellated lizard is one of the largest and most handsome of the Mediterranean's many lizards. A true Mediterranean species, it lives as far north as the most northerly olive trees but no further.

Once an assassin has drained the victim dry, it usually drops the remains of its meal. A young assassin bug, however, sometimes stacks the dried-out bodies on its back – camouflage of a gruesome and unusual kind that disguises it from its prey. Praying mantises are much more thorough: they eat the whole corpse. A mantis usually starts with the head, then slowly works towards the tail, cutting up the crunchy outer skeleton with its efficient jaws.

Lizards hunt insects in most of the world's shrublands, usually on the ground. But in Africa and southern Asia, some lizards stalk their prey in shrubs and trees. These are chameleons – peculiar animals that are famous for being able to change colour.

Spiked by a shrike

Shrublands are the favourite habitat of shrikes – starling-sized songbirds that behave like miniature birds of prey. They hunt grasshoppers, mice and even other birds, and they have a grisly habit of spiking their dead victims by pushing them onto thorns. Shrikes do not have the powerful talons of large birds of prey, so they need to spike their prey to make it easier to tear apart. Each shrike (right) has a food store in a favourite tree or shrub, where it keeps a collection of impaled corpses. These stores are useful for times when food is scarce.

Instead of running like most lizards do, chameleons creep stealthily along branches, gripping them with their toes and their tails. Their eyes can swivel independently, so they can see in two different directions at once. When a chameleon spots an insect, it slows down until it is moving no faster than a snail. As soon as the insect is in range, the chameleon shoots out its tongue and instantly hauls in its catch. A chameleon's tongue can be as long as the rest of its body, and the tongue has a sticky tip that makes sure there is no escape for the insect.

Chameleons are well camouflaged, but in shrublands some of the best disguises belong to birds. In Europe, the common nightjar spends the daytime resting on the ground, where its mottled brown feathers make it look exactly like a piece of a fallen

Below: Praying mantises stalk the shrublands of South Africa, hunting by stealth and ambush. They catch prey by rapidly extending their long, folded front legs and stabbing their victim with spines on the inner surface.

Left: Most of chameleons' colour changes are not for camouflage. Instead, they usually change colour to communicate with other chameleons.

Shrubland rodents

Compared to leaves, seeds are packed with energy. They are also easier to digest, and much easier to store. This explains why there are lots of seed eaters in shrublands, even though seeds can sometimes be tricky to find.

Rodents are the real experts at this lifestyle because they are well equipped for carrying their food back home. Their secret is a pair of built-in cheek pouches, which can fill up like stretching shopping bags. The pouches can be closed off from the rest of the mouth, so a rodent can eat or drink even when its pouches are full. For their size, hamsters and

Right: A tawny frogmouth's huge mouth funnels flying insects into its stomach during night-time hunting. During the day, it can put on a frightening display.

branch. But when the sun sets, the branch miraculously comes to life and takes off. The nightjar has a short beak but a very wide mouth, fringed with feathery bristles: It is a living funnel that catches moths and other insects on the wing after dark.

In the Australian bush, another of these nocturnal birds, the tawny frogmouth, pounces on its prey from a perch. During the day, it sits bolt upright with its eyes almost closed, making itself look like a piece of dead wood. But if anything comes too close, it suddenly opens its cavernous mouth, revealing bright pink skin inside. With luck, this display frightens the intruder away, otherwise the frogmouth would have to escape or end up as a meal itself.

American pocket mice have some of the largest pouches of all. Theirs reach back as far as their shoulders, so they can carry hundreds of small seeds at a time.

Shrubland rodents range from the dormice and spiny mice of the Mediterranean to the giant tuco-tuco and the lesser mara (which looks like a small deer) in the Gran Chaco of South America. Many are good climbers, but most prefer to collect seeds that have fallen to the ground. Their main harvest is usually in the summer, but with some careful searching, they can turn up seeds at other times. In the chaparral of California, in the USA, pocket mice do this by sifting the soil with their front paws. These have long front claws, which help sort seeds from the soil. Once a pocket mouse has collected a pawful, it transfers the seeds to its cheek pouches, ready for the journey back to base.

Seed-eating birds

For safety, rodents do their seed collecting at night, when there is less chance of being attacked. Seed-eating birds cannot see well after dark, so they collect their food by day. To avoid getting eaten, both rodents and birds have to stay on the lookout and be ready to run or fly away.

Tinamous, which live in South American scrub, take off only as a last resort. If danger threatens, these chicken-sized birds run for cover, before suddenly freezing, which makes them hard to see. But if something is hot on their trail, they take emergency action and burst into the air on stubby wings. Being exposed in the air is risky, and they don't fly far. Once they have dropped back into the scrub, they seem to disappear instantly.

 Worm lizards

Underneath the dry scrub of north-west Mexico, one of the world's strangest animals hunts its prey. It's the ajolote – a pink, worm-like reptile with just one pair of legs. Its legs are small and stubby and are positioned just behind its head. The ajolote thrusts its head forwards through the soil to create its burrow, and feeds on the termites and worms it finds as it moves along. It belongs to a group of reptiles called amphisbaenians, or worm lizards. Worm lizards live on most continents, but people rarely see them and we don't know much about their lives.

Throughout the world's shrublands, many seed-eating birds behave in a similar way. By sticking to the ground until the last possible minute, they make themselves harder to find. But the biggest seed eaters cannot fly at all, because their wings are far too small. These flightless giants include the rhea of South America and the emu of Australia. Emus can form roving flocks hundreds strong. The ostrich of Africa also wanders into shrubland, although it is more at home on grassy plains.

For a land bird, not being able to fly might sound disastrous, but all of these seed-eating species manage. The chief reason for this is that they have extremely good eyesight and marathon-runners' legs. With their long necks, they can peer above the vegetation around them, and within seconds they can be speeding away. They can run for 20 or 30 minutes at a time, which is enough to give most of their enemies the slip.

Seed-eating birds don't only swallow seeds; many also gulp down insects and the occasional stone. Stones lodge in a muscular chamber called the crop, which is in front of a bird's stomach. Here the stones help in grinding up food so it is easier to digest. Birds are not very good at telling stones from other hard objects that they find lying around. This explains why ostriches swallow coins and bottle caps, or even car keys if they get the chance.

Snake alert

If you're planning a walk in shrubland, it's worth remembering that it's an ideal habitat for snakes. Shrubs themselves can hide plenty of prey, while the spaces between

Rheas' diets are varied in the South American Chaco, and when they get the chance, rheas eat almost any crop grown by people. So they are hunted, and many end up as leather products or even dog food.

them are tailor-made for basking in the sun. Most snakes are harmless to people, but even so, wear thick, ankle-high boots and watch where you put your feet – and your hands.

Most shrubland snakes slither away the moment they sense approaching human feet. They can hear you approach by detecting vibrations travelling through the soil. But in tropical shrubland, some snakes have trouble doing this because they spend their lives off the ground. One of the most remarkable of these climbers is the brown vine snake, which is distributed all the way from the south-western USA to Brazil. It grows up to 1.5 metres (5 ft) long, and its slender body and pointed snout make it look just like the stem of a climbing plant. The disguise tricks lizards, which are the vine snake's favourite

Listening for lunch

Africa's shrubland and grassland is home to the bat-eared fox – a dainty mammal that uses giant ears to listen for its food. It feeds after dark on beetles and termites, and it tracks them down almost entirely by sound. Its teeth are much smaller than those of other foxes, and it has eight extra ones at the back of its jaws to help it squash and chew its food.

Like the vine snakes of the North and South American shrublands, Africa's twig snakes hide by pretending to be twigs or stems.

prey, and it often fools people as well. To make its camouflage even more effective, the snake spends most of the time keeping absolutely still. If someone comes too close, it tries the same trick as the tawny frogmouth, and opens its mouth wide in the hope of frightening the intruder away.

Although the brown vine snake is poisonous, its bite does people little harm. The same isn't true of the most feared of North American snakes – the rattlesnakes. The red diamond rattlesnake is a chaparral specialist and, like all vipers, has long hinged fangs that inject **venom** into prey. It is a species in decline, though, and does not need persecuting by people.

The snakes in Australia's shrublands have particularly potent venom, but as far as people are concerned, the most

dangerous of all shrubland snakes is probably the black mamba. This African species is an amazingly rapid climber, and even quicker on the ground. It grows to 3 metres (15 ft) long and can move at 20 km/h (12 mph), so it can outrun a child. Small mammals and birds make up most of its prey, but its venom can easily kill people, too.

Top predators

Most animals have some natural enemies, but a few are so large and powerful that they have none once they are fully grown. These are the biome's top predators – hunters that have nothing to fear apart from people and the changes that people cause. The mountain lion, or puma, is a top predator in California's chaparral, while the leopard is top predator in most of the shrublands of Africa. Big cats are now very rare around the Mediterranean, so the top predators there

are eagles and other large birds of prey. In Australia and a few islands in Indonesia, the top shrubland predators are not big cats, birds or even snakes but giant lizards.

These lizards belong to a family called the monitors, which contains about 45 species. In Australia, the largest shrubland variety is the lace monitor, which grows up to 2 metres (6 ft) long. Its powerful legs make it a good climber, and it has sharp claws that it uses to rip apart prey. But even this animal is dwarfed by the largest monitor of all: the Komodo dragon, which lives in forest and scrub in Indonesia. The heaviest specimens can weigh twice as much as an adult person, and measure 3 metres (10 ft) head to tail.

Komodo dragons feed on almost anything they can find, from live deer and snakes to dead remains. They have a keen sense of smell and can track down carcasses from up to 5 km (3 miles) away. Once fully grown, they can expect to live for up to forty years, but not all of them get a chance. Adult Komodo dragons often behave as **cannibals**, and young ones can end up as a meal.

A Komodo dragon can kill with just one bite. Bacteria in the lizard's saliva infect the victim's wound, crippling it. Sooner or later, the lizard tracks down its hobbling quarry by smell.

California chaparral

The backdrop to dozens of Hollywood films, chaparral is typical of southern California in the USA. Large areas have been cleared, but on the mountains lots of chaparral remains almost untouched.

Scrub oaks

If you are used to thinking of oaks as trees, the oaks of California's chaparral could come as a surprise. These oaks often have prickly leaves, and are often less than 1.8 metres (6 ft) tall even when fully grown. They may not look like the tall oaks of Europe, but their acorns make it easy to see through their disguise. The California scrub oak is one of the most prevalent of the chaparral's shrubby trees. Spanish colonists called it *chaparro*, which is how the chaparral got its name.

1. Sierra Nevada
California's highest mountains prevent moisture from reaching the Great Basin, creating the climate for dry sagebrush scrub.

2. San Francisco
This city marks the northern limit of the chaparral.

3. Central Valley
Formerly an area of grassland and shrubland; now a major fruit-growing region.

4. Coast ranges
The rare California condor soars over the montane chaparral that grows on these mountains.

5. Angeles National Forest
Chaparral-covered foothills lead to pine-clad summits.

6. Santa Monica Mountains
A national recreation area where visitors can hike, bike and enjoy the wild flowers.

7. Los Angeles
This major city lies in the heart of California's shrublands.

8. Channel Islands
Rugged islands that have unique animals such as the island night lizard and the Santa Catalina shrew.

9. Santa Catalina Island
On this island, conservationists are restoring chaparral by removing introduced animals.

10. Torrey Pines State Reserve
The rare torrey pine grows in only one place on the mainland: a patch within this reserve 5 sq km (2 sq miles) in area. The pine also lives on Santa Rosa Island.

11. Baja California
The chaparral extends into the north of this peninsula. Prickly pears and yuccas become more common in the drier south.

Lupins burst into flower on the California coast in spring.

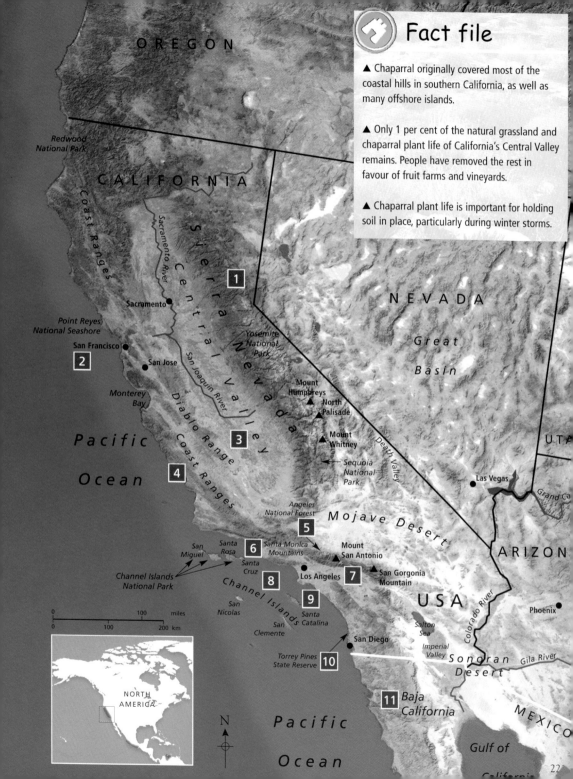

OREGON

Redwood
National Park

CALIFORNIA

Coast Ranges

Sacramento River

Central Valley

Sierra Nevada

[1]

Sacramento

Point Reyes
National Seashore

San Francisco

[2]

San Jose

Monterey
Bay

Diablo
Range

San Joaquin River

Coast Ranges

[3]

Pacific

Ocean

[4]

Yosemite
National
Park

Mount
Humphreys

▲ North
Palisade

Mount
Whitney ▲

Sequoia
National
Park

NEVADA

Great

Basin

Death Valley

Las Vegas

UTA

Grand Ca

Angeles
National Forest

[5]

San
Miguel

Santa
Rosa

[6] Santa Monica
Mountains

Santa
Cruz

Channel Islands
National Park

[8]

Mount
San Antonio ▲

[7] ▲ San Gorgonia
Mountain

Los Angeles

Mojave Desert

ARIZON

USA

San
Nicolas

[9]

Channel Islands

San
Clemente

Santa
Catalina

Salton
Sea

Imperial
Valley

Colorado River

Phoenix

Torrey Pines
State Reserve [10]

San Diego

Sonoran
Desert

Gila River

[11] Baja
California

MEXICO

100   miles

100   200 km

NORTH
AMERICA

N

Pacific

Ocean

Gulf of
California

Fact file

▲ Chaparral originally covered most of the coastal hills in southern California, as well as many offshore islands.

▲ Only 1 per cent of the natural grassland and chaparral plant life of California's Central Valley remains. People have removed the rest in favour of fruit farms and vineyards.

▲ Chaparral plant life is important for holding soil in place, particularly during winter storms.

22

The fynbos

South Africa's Cape region is small, but its shrubland – the fynbos – contains almost as many types of flowering plants as the whole of Europe.

Proteas, with their distinctive, leathery leaves, and ericas, with their clusters of small flowers, are both common in the fynbos shrublands.

Fact file

▲ The Cape region covers less than a thousandth of the world's land surface but is home to more than 8000 species of plants.

▲ 70 per cent of fynbos plants live nowhere else.

▲ More than eight hundred species of heathers live in southern Africa, mainly in the fynbos.

▲ Because of the richness and distinctiveness of the fynbos plants, scientists classify the Cape region, despite its small size, as one of the world's six floral kingdoms.

Kalahari Desert

Namib Desert

NAMIBIA

Orange River

Ve l d

Namaqualand

4 K a r o o

SOUTH

AFRICA

AFRICA

9

Atlantic

Ocean

Vanrhynsdorp

Skilpad
Wildflower
Reserve

3

G r e a t   E s c a r p m e n t

5

7 Mountain Zebra
National Park

N

G r e a t   K a r o o

Little Karoo

Wilderness
National Park

8 Addo Eleph
National Pa

Cape Town

Table
Mountain **1**

Cape Peninsula
National Park **2**

Cape of
Good Hope

George

Tsitsikamma
National Park

6

Port Elizabeth

Humansdorp

0   200   miles
0   200   400 km

1. Table Mountain
This famous flat-topped mountain dominates Cape Town, which lies below.

2. Cape Peninsula National Park
Rugged coastline and richly varied fynbos plant life attract visitors to this park.

3. Skilpad Wildflower Reserve
A reserve named for the Afrikaans word for the tortoises that come to drink here. Visitors come to see the spring display of flowers such as Namaqualand daisies.

4. Karoo
The Karoo region is drier than the fynbos, and the plant life is succulent (fleshy).

5. Great Escarpment
A ridge that separates the high plateaus of the interior from the coastal plains.

6. Tsitsikamma National Park
This strip of rocky coastline has deep river gorges, fynbos plants and forests of giant yellowwood. Visitors can see deer, antelope, baboons and vervet monkeys.

7. Mountain Zebra National Park
This park protects the shrubland habitat of a critically endangered subspecies (local type) of zebra, the Cape mountain zebra.

8. Addo Elephant National Park
Spiny and succulent shrubs form dense thickets here. Tourists can watch wildlife at night beside a floodlit water hole.

9. Veld
A type of grassland that covers much of South Africa's interior.

Fynbos zebras

Fynbos plants are tough and unappetizing, and few large mammals live off them. One exception is the Cape mountain zebra. At one time, thousands of these zebras roamed the fynbos but were easy to hunt, and by the 1930s fewer than fifty were left. Since then, a conservation program has helped the zebra survive. More than two hundred live at the Mountain Zebra National Park, and several hundred are at large in other parts of the fynbos. The Cape mountain zebra has been luckier than its close relative, the quagga. This animal, a kind of zebra whose stripes faded to brown toward its rear, lived in open, dry country but was hunted to extinction by 1883.

Earth's tropical grasslands

About 40 per cent of the land in Earth's tropical zone is covered by grass or a mix of grass and other plants. Such areas form the tropical grassland biome.

Earth's tropical zone is the area between the **tropics of Cancer** and **Capricorn** – two imaginary circles drawn around the planet 2600 km (1600 miles) north and south of the **equator**. In parts of the tropics that are too dry for forest but too wet for desert or **shrubland**, grasslands thrive.

Tropical grasslands often have a scattering of trees, forming a landscape called **savanna**. Most areas of tropical grassland are like this, so the terms savanna and tropical grassland are often used interchangeably. Where the trees get close enough to form a closed **canopy**, the grass disappears and the savanna merges into the **tropical forest** biome.

The biggest area of tropical grassland is in Africa, where flat-topped trees called **acacias** dot the plains. Africa's savannas are home to gigantic plant-eaters such as elephants and giraffes, vast herds of grass-eating antelope and some of the world's most dangerous carnivores, including lions and hyenas.

A mother cheetah and young at rest. Cheetahs use fast bursts of speed to hunt deer and antelope on the tropical grasslands of East Africa.

South America has two large areas of tropical grassland: the llanos and the Cerrado. Both are mainly savanna, but instead of acacias there are palms or short, gnarled trees. Surprisingly, there are few large animals that live only in the grasslands of South America – most also live in the neighbouring tropical forests or shrublands.

In the savannas of northern Australia, **eucalyptus** trees take the place of acacias, and kangaroos replace antelope. Australia's savanna forms a transition zone between the forests of the north and the central desert. As you travel south across it, the forest thins out and gives way to grassland, which in turn peters out into desert.

The map above shows the biggest areas of tropical grassland, but there are also small patches of tropical grassland mixed in with other biomes. There are even patches of savanna in the heart of the Amazon rainforest. Some people also consider most of India to be a kind of artificial savanna, formed long ago by **deforestation**.

Grassland climate

Tropical grasslands mostly occur in warm countries with marked wet and dry seasons. However, there are many factors besides climate that influence where tropical grasslands grow.

Right: The sun sets over the savanna of East Africa. Day turns to night surprisingly quickly near the equator, the sun sinking straight down at about 6 p.m. every day.

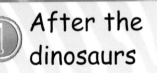

After the dinosaurs

Tropical grassland is one of the youngest biomes. During the age of the dinosaurs, there was no such thing as grassland because grass plants hadn't evolved. Plant-eating dinosaurs probably ate ferns, conifer trees and palm-like plants called cycads.

Scientists know from fossil evidence that grass plants had appeared by about 50 million years ago, but it was another 30 million or so years before savannas formed, starting in South America. In the last 20 million years, Earth's climate has become cooler and drier. As a result, the lush forests that once covered the tropics have shrunk, and tropical grasslands have expanded in their place.

In the rainforest of central Africa, the weather is hot and humid all year round. Winter doesn't exist, and the sun rises and sets at about the same time every day of the year. Travel north to the Sahara Desert, though, and things are different. Instead of cloudy skies and frequent downpours, the sky is a flawless blue, and it almost never rains. In summer it is unbearably hot – even in the middle of the night – but in winter the nights can be bitterly cold.

The African rainforest and the Sahara Desert both have their own distinctive pattern of weather through the year, which we call their **climate**. The rainforest has a constantly wet climate, the desert a constantly dry one. The climate of tropical grasslands is typically a mixture of the two: soaking wet for half the year and bone-dry for the rest.

The tropical zone

Climates are caused by the uneven way that sunlight warms our planet as we hurtle through space. The Earth spins like a top as it orbits the Sun, staying roughly upright. The equator faces the Sun directly, so it basks in strong sunshine every day of the year. The poles, on the other hand, get very little warmth. What sunlight they receive is spread over a wide area because of the Earth's curved shape, making the Sun's rays feeble. It's a bit like shining a torch on a wall: if you hold the torch at an angle, the beam spreads out and casts a weaker light.

Tropical grasslands are in the warm region near the equator, where the Sun's rays are most intense. They are part of the Earth's tropical zone – the region between the tropics of Capricorn and Cancer, two imaginary circles on either side of the equator. Outside the tropics is the Earth's **temperate** zone, where the weather is cooler.

Land in the tropics receives about five times more heat and energy per square mile than in the far north and south, so it isn't surprising the climate is much warmer. The average daytime temperature in tropical grasslands is usually more than 24°C (75°F), and it doesn't vary a great deal through the year. The steady, warm temperature gives plants and animals a great advantage over the wildlife of temperate grasslands, since they never have to deal with freezing winter weather. And the endless, intense sunshine makes plants grow quickly.

Rain belt

The Sun's energy doesn't just create warm weather in the tropics – it also produces rain. Sunlight warms the surface of the tropical oceans, filling the air with water vapour and making the weather humid and clammy. Because the air is warm, it rises into the sky, carrying the water vapour with it. As the water vapour rises, it cools, which makes it turn back into liquid and fall as rain. As a result, the Earth's equator is surrounded by a belt of warm and rainy weather – the climate that creates tropical rainforests.

The warm air that rises over the equator can't continue rising forever. When it cools high in the **atmosphere**, it stops rising and gets pushed

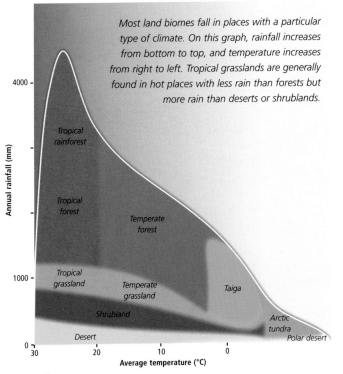

Most land biomes fall in places with a particular type of climate. On this graph, rainfall increases from bottom to top, and temperature increases from right to left. Tropical grasslands are generally found in hot places with less rain than forests but more rain than deserts or shrublands.

Annual rainfall (mm)

4000

Tropical rainforest

Tropical forest

Temperate forest

1000

Tropical grassland

Temperate grassland

Taiga

Shrubland

Arctic tundra

Desert

Polar desert

0

30   20   10   0

Average temperature (°C)

⏱ Grassland microclimates

Maps of the world's biomes give the impression that each biome covers a vast area without change, but the truth isn't so simple. Savanna is really a mosaic of forest and grassland, with the number of trees varying from place to place. Trees are most common in rainiest parts of the savanna, and sparse in drier areas. There are even patches of tropical forest right in the middle of the savanna. These grow in areas with an unusual microclimate – weather or conditions different from the surroundings. For instance, wet riversides in the llanos of Venezuela (left) are often covered with trees, forming a habitat termed gallery forest. These strips of forest occur in most tropical grasslands and often contain the same types of trees that grow in tropical rainforests. Likewise, mountain tops are sometimes covered with cloud forests, which thrive on the fog that forms in cold, high air. In East Africa, an enormous volcanic crater called Ngorongoro has cloud forest around the rim but grassland in the centre.

away from the equator by the air rising behind it. Now cold and dry, the air begins to fall back down, sinking thousands of miles north and south of the equator. Because it no longer carries water vapour, it causes dry weather where it sinks. The world's major hot deserts, such as the Sahara in northern Africa, exist because of this sinking dry air.

Wet and dry seasons

If the Earth stayed completely upright as it orbited the Sun, the belts of equatorial rain and sinking dry air would always be in the same place. But the Earth is tipped over slightly, making it spin at an angle, and this is why there are seasons. During summer in the northern **hemisphere**, the North Pole tilts towards the Sun, causing warm, sunny weather and long days. In winter, it tilts away from the Sun, resulting in cold weather and long nights.

Earth's tilt also affects the climate in the tropics, but it produces wet and dry seasons instead of warm and cold ones. When the North Pole tilts towards the Sun, northern parts of the tropics become warmer than southern parts, so the belt of warm, rising air around the equator shifts north slightly, taking the rainy weather with it. For northern parts of the tropics, therefore, July is usually the middle of the rainy season. At the same time, southern parts of the tropics move into the zone of sinking, dry air, resulting in a dry season. In January the opposite happens: southern parts of the tropics are deluged with rain, while northern areas have a dry season.

Areas close to the equator stay under the belt of rainy weather nearly all year round, creating ideal conditions for tropical forests,

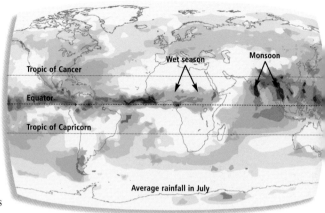

A belt of rainy weather (blue) surrounds the equator. It moves north in summer (above) and south in winter (below), creating wet and dry seasons.

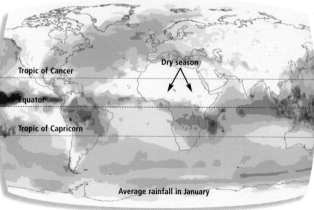

but the zones to the north and south of the forests have marked wet and dry seasons. As a result, grasslands are most common in the northern or southern parts of the tropics.

On average, tropical grasslands receive 1000–1500 mm (40–60 in) of rain a year. By comparison, deserts receive less than 250 mm (10 in), and rainforests may receive more than 2500 mm (100 in). However, there are also tropical grasslands in areas with much less or much more rain than the average. A more important factor than total rainfall is the length of the dry season, which usually lasts five to seven months. If the dry season is any longer, the land is more likely to be shrubland or semi-desert; any shorter and forest takes over.

The severity of the dry season also matters. Tropical grasslands usually occur where the dry season brings weather as harsh as a desert's. Although some rain may fall, it quickly **evaporates** in the heat, leaving the ground parched and dusty. This harsh weather is stressful for plants, especially trees. In grasslands with a less severe dry season, trees can survive by shedding their leaves or becoming **dormant** (inactive). But in the driest tropical grasslands, only grasses survive.

Parts of Venezuela's llanos grasslands are flooded in the wet season. The temporary marshes provide perfect cover for giant anacondas – the world's biggest snakes.

Monsoons

Some parts of the world have an especially severe wet season called a monsoon. One of the most extreme monsoons occurs in India, which is drenched with rain every year from June to September.

The cause of a monsoon's intensity is the uneven warming of land and sea. Land warms up more quickly under strong sunlight than does the sea, making air rise faster above it. During the northern summer, the vast landmass of Asia heats up. The air over land absorbs this heat and rises, sucking in more air from the Indian Ocean like a giant vacuum cleaner. The air travelling from the ocean (called the monsoon wind) picks up moisture from the sea and dumps it on India as rain.

India's monsoon is so powerful that it draws moisture-bearing wind away from East Africa, creating a dry season in the savannas of East Africa – even though these grasslands lie on the equator, where tropical rainforests would normally prevail.

Even within one area of tropical grassland, the length of the dry season varies from place to place. The wettest places, in which trees are most common, are where the grassland borders tropical forest. As you travel across the grassland toward the desert biome, the dry season gets longer and the trees become sparse. In dry parts of the grassland, the rainy season is not only shorter but also less reliable. In some years, it fails to rain at all.

Breaking the rules

Although tropical grasslands generally occur in places with a marked dry season, they often break this rule. There are many patches of tropical grassland mixed in with other biomes, especially tropical forest. There are even patches of tropical grassland in the heart of the Amazon rainforest, where it rains nearly all year round.

The explanation for these rule-breaking patches of biome is that other factors besides climate determine where grasslands grow. One such factor, for instance, is soil

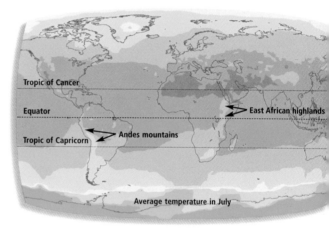

Most parts of the tropics stay warm all year round, shown by warm colours on these maps. Mountains are slightly cooler than lowlands.

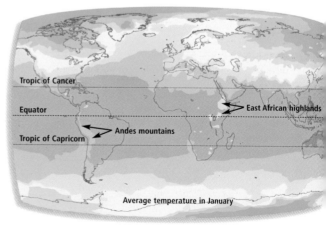

⚠ Unreliable rains

In many parts of the world, people take the seasons for granted. In North America, for instance, winter never fails to arrive, bringing cold weather and long nights. But in the tropics, the seasons are less reliable. The people and animals of tropical grasslands depend on the annual rainy season to bring back the rich grass, but sometimes the rains do not arrive. The result is a drought: the land turns to desert, animals die, crops wither and people may starve.

Some people blame droughts on global warming, but they are a natural part of the tropical grassland climate. The risk of drought has had an interesting effect on how the wildlife has evolved. Unlike the animals and plants of tropical forests, those of tropical grasslands tend to have short lives, but they mature quickly and produce more offspring. This means they can quickly recolonize the land after a severe drought has killed off most of the wildlife.

Climographs

Each place in the world has its own pattern of weather, or climate. We can sum up a place's climate on a climograph, such as the one shown here for St Louis in the USA (right). The letters along the bottom are the months of the year. The numbers on the left and the small bars show rainfall, and the numbers on the right and the curvy line show temperature. Unlike St Louis, most tropical grasslands (below) are hot all year round and have pronounced wet and dry seasons. Nairobi in Kenya has two wet seasons each year.

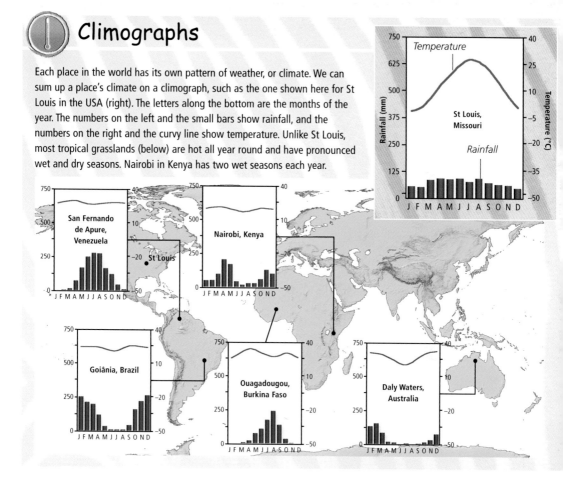

type. If the soil is too stony for trees, or if water drains through it too easily, grasses will flourish where there would otherwise be forest. The well-drained volcanic soil of the Serengeti in Africa is virtually tree-less in places for this reason. Likewise, grass takes over in areas that are so boggy that the soil becomes acidic and low in **nutrients** – many of the patches of grassland in the Amazon rainforest formed this way.

The soil in tropical countries is often red because of an insoluble chemical called iron oxide (rust), which tends to build up over time as the rain washes other chemicals away. Soils that are very rich in iron oxide are called laterites. They tend to bake solid

under the tropical sun, forming a hardpan below the surface that blocks roots and so stops trees from growing. In the wet season, the hardpan traps water, making the ground too waterlogged for trees. Though some types of palm trees can survive in laterites, the plants that usually dominate are grasses.

Grassland fires

Another important factor is fire. Dry grass makes perfect kindling for wildfires in the dry season. Unless animals have nibbled the grass down to the ground, the continuous cover of grass spreads the fire over vast areas. The fire kills tree seedlings, but grass plants survive thanks to underground roots and shoots.

Mist often hangs over Africa's savannas in the cool early mornings. Lions and other big predators do most of their hunting during the night and around dawn, avoiding the stifling heat of the day.

Regular fires, therefore, can create grassland where there would otherwise be forest.

Fires start naturally during thunderstorms, which are common towards the end of the dry season. All it takes is a single dry lightning strike to set the land on fire. However, most tropical grassland fires are probably started by people, often deliberately. In the Sahel region of Africa, for instance, people have been burning grassland for more than 2500 years in order to clear trees and shrubs and thus create better grazing land for livestock. Today, an estimated 75 per cent of Africa's tropical grassland is burnt each year.

Animals, too, can turn forest into grassland. When grazing animals nibble tree seedlings, they kill the plants by biting off the buds. Grass plants, in contrast, have buds

Below: These termite mounds in northern Australia are called compass mounds because they always face east and west. This probably helps control the microclimate inside the mounds. During cool early mornings and late evenings, the mounds catch the warmth of the rising and setting sun, but at midday their thin shape catches much less sunlight, helping to prevent overheating.

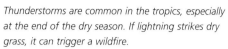

Thunderstorms are common in the tropics, especially at the end of the dry season. If lightning strikes dry grass, it can trigger a wildfire.

nibble the grass very close to the ground, fires cannot spread; without fires to kill off bigger plants, trees and shrubs begin to take over.

Livestock and people have had such a big influence on tropical grasslands, and for so long, that it is often difficult to say which grasslands are natural or artificial. The truth is that most tropical grasslands are probably semi-natural, which means that human activity has been an important part of the biome's ecology for many thousands of years.

at the base of the plant or underground, so they quickly recover from grazing. However, excessive grazing can have the opposite effect, turning grassland into forest. If animals

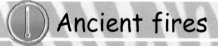

Ancient fires

The Aboriginal people of Australia have probably been setting fire to the savanna since their ancestors arrived on the continent at least 50,000 years ago. While people in other parts of the world use fire to clear land for crops, Aborigines didn't begin farming until very recently. Instead, they used fire to flush animals out of the bush, or to clear scrub to make hunting and travelling easier. Before the arrival of Aborigines, the savanna region of Australia might have been covered with tropical forest. There are still patches of tropical forest in parts of the savanna that fire doesn't reach, such as volcanic crater floors and rocky gullies.

Grassland plants

Grassland plants are among the toughest plants on Earth. They can spring back to life after being starved of rain for months, chewed to stumps by animals and burnt to a crisp.

If you were to visit Africa's Serengeti grasslands twice in one year, you might get a surprise. In May, towards the end of the main rainy season, lush green grass carpets the ground as far as you can see. But in September, in the dry season, things could hardly be more different. What little grass remains has turned to straw, and the dusty ground looks like a desert.

The same thing happens in tropical grasslands in many other places. Every year, a blistering dry season drains the land of colour, and the grass shrivels under the relentless tropical sun. Yet when the rains return, the same desiccated plants somehow spring back to life and turn the landscape green again.

The plants of tropical grasslands spend around half the year living through desert conditions, but that's not the only challenge they face. In the dry season, they have to contend with raging wildfires, fuelled by the tinder-dry straw. And in the wet season, herds of grazing animals trample across them and eat them. To most plants, such constant hardship would be lethal. However, grass plants not only survive being maimed, burned and starved – they thrive on it.

A world of grass

The grass family is the success story of the plant world. Since grass plants first evolved a mere 50 million years ago, grasses have spread across the world and taken over vast swathes of land. One reason for their success was a gradual cooling and drying of the Earth's climate, which favoured drought-tolerant plants. Another reason was the recent appearance of a **species** that has a very special relationship with grasses: humans.

Grasses are expert colonizers, able to establish themselves quickly on disturbed land. As humans spread around the world, felling forests and changing the landscape,

Photosynthesis

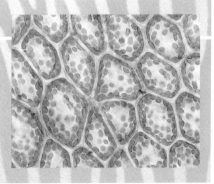

Like animals, plants cannot survive without food. Unlike animals, however, they don't have to eat – they can make food. Plants need only a few simple ingredients to make food: water, air and sunlight. Inside the cells that make up a plant's leaf (right) are tiny food-making factories called chloroplasts. These contain the green substance chlorophyll, which gives plants their colour. Chlorophyll captures energy from sunlight and uses it to combine water and carbon dioxide from air into food molecules.

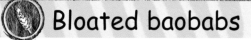

Bloated baobabs

The baobab trees of Africa, Madagascar and northern Australia are expert water storers. During the wet season, they soak up massive amounts of water and store it within soft, spongy wood inside the trunk and lower branches, which swell up like balloons. When the dry season begins, baobabs shed their leaves (which reduces water loss) and slowly draw on their hidden reserves; as the water gets used up, the trunk appears to shrink. Baobabs can cope with very long dry seasons and grow in semi-deserts as well as savanna. They grow slowly but reach enormous sizes. One hollow tree in Zimbabwe is large enough for up to forty people to shelter inside its trunk. Other baobabs have been used as a shop, a prison, a house and a bus shelter.

Tall grass makes a good hiding place for small animals, such as this klipspringer, a type of antelope from Africa.

Topsy-turvy plants

Have you ever mowed a lawn and wondered why the grass plants don't die when you cut them? In most plants, the growing parts (called meristems) are at the top, or inside buds next to branches. If you cut the stalk, you remove all the growing parts and the plant dies. Grasses are different: their growing parts are at the bottom instead of the top. When you mow a lawn, all you do is cut through the blades of grass, leaving behind the growing parts. New blades soon spring up.

The unusual position of the meristems helps grass survive constant munching by animals. In fact, grazing animals can help grass plants. Although they damage the grass blades, the grazers do more damage to other plants growing nearby. In the process,

Despite lacking front teeth, white rhinos nibble grass right to the ground with their lips. Yet grasses can survive even this drastic pruning.

grasses followed them. Grasses are the botanical equivalent of rats – wherever people live, you're sure to find grasses thriving in patches of wasteland and in nooks and crannies among buildings. But grasses are not just weeds – for thousands of years, humans have deliberately bred and grown grasses for their edible seeds. Cereal crops such as wheat, rice and corn, which together form the staple foods for most of the world's people, are the descendants of wild grasses. The seed heads of these plants have become grotesquely enlarged by years of careful breeding, so much so that they hardly look like grasses anymore.

The properties that make grasses successful weeds also equip them for life in tropical grasslands. The harsh dry season, regular fires and hordes of grass-eating animals continually disturb the land, just as human settlements disturb natural habitats. Grasses have evolved all sorts of features that overcome the constant trauma.

Jeepers creepers

Africa's tropical grasses are aggressive plants – so much so that they are taking over other parts of the world. Scientists have found that some parts of tropical America, where forests had been removed for agriculture, are now covered with such African grasses as paragrass, pangola grass and jaragua. In southern parts of the USA, one of the most common grasses in lawns and golf courses is Bermuda grass (right), an African savanna species that spreads by growing creepers (horizontal stems). Oddly enough, American grasses introduced into Africa have not had anything like the same success.

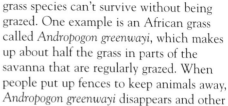

they clear the ground of competition, allowing the grasses to dominate. Mowing a lawn has the same effect: it kills most weeds and so creates a turf of pure grass.

Some savanna grasses respond to grazing by growing faster – the more that animals nibble the grass, the quicker it grows back. In fact, certain grass species can't survive without being grazed. One example is an African grass called *Andropogon greenwayi*, which makes up about half the grass in parts of the savanna that are regularly grazed. When people put up fences to keep animals away, *Andropogon greenwayi* disappears and other plants take its place.

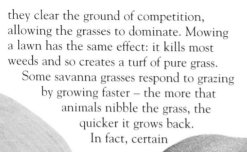

Having a continuous haircut is no problem for grass plants, so they have little need for thorns or poisons to ward off animals. As a result, tropical grasslands are a living banquet – vast herds of plant-eating animals can gorge themselves on the fast-growing grasses, which soon grow back. In contrast, plants in tropical rainforests defend themselves against **herbivores** with an armoury of chemical weapons, such as tannin (which makes leaves indigestible) and strychnine (a lethal neurotoxin). Rainforest animals have to be much more choosy about what they eat.

Going underground

During the dry season, most tropical grasses allow their blades and flowers to wither, dry out and die. But the grass plants themselves do not die – they store their food reserves underground in swollen roots or stems, which

Flame lilies get through Africa's dry season by storing food in an underground swelling called a tuber. They bloom in the wet season, using long, twining leaves to crawl up through the grass and reach the light.

Above: The tussock grasses (bunch grasses) of northern Australia grow in large clumps called tussocks, giving the ground a lumpy appearance.

stay inactive until the next wet season. These underground parts have tiny buds, ready to sprout into action when the rains return. Other tropical grassland plants, such as orchids and lilies, use the same trick. Like hibernating animals, all these plants survive the harsh weather by conserving their energy, doing very little and hiding. In West African savannas, the total weight of plant matter underground may be up to four times as much as that above the surface. All this hidden material provides food for armies of burrowing animals, especially termites, worms and rodents.

Not all grasses stop growing in the dry season, though. Some species continue growing, but much more slowly. These grasses are common in places that have occasional

Pointless pollen

Like other flowering plants, grasses produce flowers, which allow them to reproduce sexually. The male parts of flowers make a windblown dust called pollen, while the female parts produce sticky receptors to catch pollen. When pollen lands on the female part of a flower, the male and female sex cells join and a seed forms. Or at least that's what usually happens – but some grasses have abandoned the sexual process. They still go to the trouble of producing flowers and pollen, but instead of reproducing sexually they clone themselves at the last minute, making seeds that grow into carbon copies of the single parent.

Scientists think the grasses that reproduce this way do so because it preserves a very successful combination of genes. When organisms reproduce sexually, genes from the parents mix together. This results in varied offspring, each with a unique set of genes and unique strengths. However, it also scrambles the parental genes like decks of cards being shuffled, breaking up useful combinations.

Below: Madagascar is home to the bizarre elephant's-foot plant, so named because its bloated stem looks like a severed elephant's foot that has sprouted flowers.

bursts of rain in the middle of the dry season. By keeping a few tiny shoots alive above ground, they are ready to spring to life before other plants when conditions improve.

Hiding underground is not just a good way of surviving dry weather – it's also an excellent defence against the wildfires that sweep across tropical grasslands every dry season. Like grazing, fire can help grass plants. For one thing, it kills tree seedlings, stopping them from growing big enough to shade out the grass. It also clears the ground of debris, allowing new shoots to emerge into full sunlight as soon as they break the surface.

Year after year

In temperate countries, such as North America, many plants are **annuals**. Annual plants don't try to survive the harsh winters. Instead, they simply die after scattering their seeds and leave the seeds to grow into new plants the next year.

In tropical grasslands, there are very few annual plants. Most are **perennials** – plants that carry on growing year after year. Perennials have one big advantage over annuals: by storing food reserves, they can spring to life more quickly in the growing season. In contrast, plants that grow from seeds start off small and take weeks to grow large. When the wet season begins, there is a race to grow as quickly as possible to colonize the bare ground. Perennials are quickest. Helped by the warmth and the intense sunshine, they cover the ground in days. Late starters risk being left in the shade, without enough sunlight to grow properly.

Another strategy that helps grass plants take over quickly is the way they reproduce. Although tropical grasses can reproduce by seed, they rely much more on cloning themselves. Instead of growing upwards, some

Acacia trees develop a flat canopy because giraffes and other animals nibble them from below.

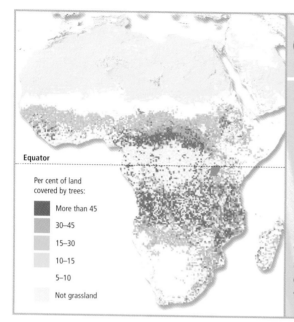

Woodland or grassland?

Books about Africa's savannas sometimes call them woodland, dry forest, bush or scrub instead of grassland. The reason for all the confusion is that savanna is really a mixture of trees and grass, with the number and height of trees varying from place to place.

This map shows how the density of trees varies across all of Africa's grasslands (including grassy areas of desert and shrubland). Towards the centre of Africa, where the climate is wetter, trees get increasingly dense until they merge into rainforests. Further from the equator, where the climate is drier, the trees thin out until there is little but grass.

Equator

Per cent of land covered by trees:

More than 45

30–45

15–30

10–15

5–10

Not grassland

grass stems creep along the ground or grow horizontally under the surface. At a certain distance, these stems take root and produce a new tuft of shoots. The resulting clumps of grass, called tussocks, are a common sight in most tropical grasslands. This way of reproducing is much faster than making seeds and allows a single plant to colonize a large area quickly with clones of itself.

Flat tops and twisted trunks

Most tropical grasslands have at least a scattering of trees and shrubs as well as grasses. The trees are most abundant in the rainiest areas or where the soil is damp, and they gradually thin out as the grassland merges into desert or shrubland. There are also occasional thickets, especially along river banks or near water holes.

In Africa and Madagascar, most of the trees in savannas are acacias – members of the same family of plants as peas and beans. Like their relatives, acacias produce nutritious

seed pods that are full of **protein**, and much sought after by giraffes, elephants and antelope. But the seeds themselves are not always fully digested. When they pass out of the animal, they land on the ground in a heap of dung, which provides the perfect fertilizer. So, in a way, the trees pay the animals to spread their seeds and plant them.

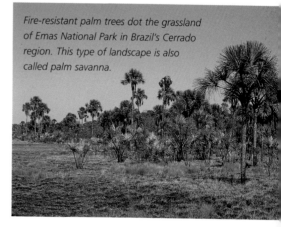

Fire-resistant palm trees dot the grassland of Emas National Park in Brazil's Cerrado region. This type of landscape is also called palm savanna.

243

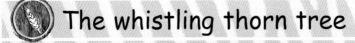

The whistling thorn tree

If you stand next to an acacia tree in the savannas of East Africa, you might hear it whistling. The noise comes from the wind blowing through holes in swellings at the base of thorns (right), which act like tiny flutes. Thanks to the tree's musical ability, people call it the whistling thorn tree. The swollen thorns provide homes for particularly aggressive types of ants, the acacia ants. In addition to housing the ants, the tree produces sugary secretions that feed them. In return, the ants protect the tree from animals. When a giraffe tries to grab a mouthful of leaves with its tongue, the ants swarm out of their thorns and attack with vicious stings.

As young acacias grow, their sides tend to get nibbled by animals, but the centre of the plant, where the leaves and pods are out of reach, grows tall. Once this part of the tree has become too tall for even giraffes to reach, it spreads out, giving the tree its famous flat-topped appearance.

Savanna trees have to contend with the same problems as grasses – the long dry season, unpredictable rain, wildfires and hungry animals – but they overcome these problems in different ways. The baobab tree gets through the dry season by absorbing as much water as it can in the wet season and swelling in size. It also sheds its leaves and stays bare for up to nine months a year.

With deeper roots than grasses, trees can reach further underground for water. One Brazilian savanna tree has roots that grow up to 18 metres (60 feet) deep. Being able to reach deep water allows savanna trees to keep growing in the dry season, and even to flower. To conserve water, such trees often have small, leathery leaves, with fewer pores than other trees. The eucalyptus trees of Australia look like this. They are called evergreen trees because they always have leaves. However, many savanna trees shed their leaves when the dry season begins and wait for the rains to return – they are called deciduous trees.

Most savanna trees are shorter than their forest cousins, with a more twisted shape. This is especially true of Brazil's Cerrado,

The punishing climate makes the trees of Brazil's Cerrado grow into grotesque shapes. The fruits of this monkey-nut tree look and taste like those of its close relative the cashew-nut tree.

One of the most common trees in the savannas of Zimbabwe and Botswana is the mopane tree. In the wet season its distinctive, butterfly-shaped leaves are devoured by caterpillars called mopane worms, which local people harvest for their nutty flavour.

which is dotted with what look like gnarled and stunted little apple trees. The trees grow this way because new twigs and branches develop each wet season, sprouting from buds hidden under the bark. In the driest parts of the Cerrado, the same plant species are so gnarled and stunted that they form shrubs rather than trees.

Fire is less of a problem for tall trees than for grasses because their buds and leaves are out of the flames' reach. Nevertheless, savanna trees generally have thick, corky bark that protects the living tissue below from being scorched. If an intense fire burns through the bark, many trees can produce new sprouts from their roots or stumps. Of all savanna trees, the masters at surviving fire

are the eucalyptus trees of Australia, which can sprout up from the ground year after year despite being completely burned down.

Tropical grasslands are full of life, but they are tough places to survive in. As a result, the plants do not live as long as in tropical forests. Except for baobabs, which can live for thousands of years, very few shrubs or trees last more than a few decades. The same is true of grassland animals. They lead short and stressful lives, and must contend not only with fires and droughts, but also with some of the world's deadliest **predators**.

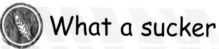 ## What a sucker

The eucalyptus's apparently miraculous ability to survive being burnt is due to its unusual roots. Many eucalyptus trees have large root swellings called lignotubers, as well as a network of underground branches called suckers. After a fire, the tree draws on the food stored in its lignotubers and quickly produces new shoots from the suckers, which emerge from the ash-covered ground as if by magic.

Grassland animals

For animals, grasslands are one of the richest biomes on Earth, with food covering the ground for miles on end. Yet life here is anything but easy – the animals must struggle constantly not only to find their next meal but to avoid becoming someone else's.

African elephants use their vast ears as radiators to help them lose heat. They also flap their ears wide open as a sign of anger.

Trunks have more uses than Swiss army knives. Elephants use them for smelling and touching objects, tearing up grass, stripping bark and leaves off trees, squirting water, throwing dust and scratching itchy skin. They also serve as trumpets for making sound and as snorkels for breathing underwater.

Weaver birds

Grass has other uses besides being food. Mice use it to line their nests, and lions use it for cover while stalking prey, for instance. But perhaps the most imaginative use of grass is that shown by weaver birds. Members of this bird family weave strips of leaves and grass into elaborate nests high in savanna trees. Hanging upside down by their feet, they use their tiny beaks to knot the strips together with incredible dexterity. Some species even add a trumpet-shaped entrance tube. In southern Africa, sociable weavers transform trees into huge colonies, with hundreds of nests joined together. Only the males build nests. The females select their partners by the quality of their craftsmanship.

Tropical grasslands are home to the biggest and most spectacular land animals on Earth. In a brief drive across Kenya's Masai Mara National Reserve, it takes a matter of minutes to spot elephants, giraffes, lions, hippos and cheetahs, not to mention vast herds of zebras and wildebeest, and a handful of different gazelle species. Most of these animals belong to a group that scientists call **ungulates** – the hoofed **mammals**.

On the hoof

An ungulate is an animal that has hooves and eats plants. Ungulates dominate many of the world's grasslands, both temperate and tropical, because they are experts at digesting grass. For many animals, ourselves included, grass is a poor quality food. Its cells have a tough outer coating made of a substance called cellulose, which is tricky to digest. Many grasses also contain crystals of silica (sand), which scratch an animal's teeth and wear them down. Ungulates have several ways of getting around these problems.

The teeth and jaws of ungulates work like grinders, crushing grass so powerfully that the cells split open, releasing the nutrients inside. Powerful cheek muscles move the lower jaw sideways, scraping the flat-topped teeth across each other to mash up the grass caught in between. Silica is no problem because ungulate teeth have huge crowns that continually grow as they wear away.

The digestive system of most ungulates contains billions of cellulose-digesting bacteria. In some ungulates, including wildebeest and gazelles, these bacteria live in a stomach chamber called a rumen; such animals are called **ruminants**. Swallowed food sits in the rumen for up to four days while the bacteria get to work on it. Then the animal brings the rotting grass back up to its mouth to chew it a second time. Ruminants have a very efficient digestive system, but it works

Strange diets

Although ungulates are basically plant eaters, a few sometimes eat animals to supplement their diet. Small antelope, such as duikers, eat birds when they can catch them. Warthogs – ugly relatives of farmyard pigs – eat insects, birds, mice, frogs, worms, beetles, rotten meat and elephant dung, as well as plant food. Giraffes often eat bones (above) left by scavengers, though doing so occasionally gives them fatal food poisoning.

slowly and they can't take in huge amounts of food. As a result, such animals are fussy about what plants they eat, choosing only the youngest, most nutritious shoots.

Other ungulates have cellulose-digesting bacteria in the rear part of their digestive system. Zebras, elephants and rhinoceroses all digest food this way. It's quicker but less efficient than rumination, so they have to take in more food to compensate. These animals can survive on the tougher or older bits of grass, but they have to eat huge amounts of it. Elephants can even eat bark.

Living together
One of the reasons that many different ungulate species can coexist in a savanna is that they feed on different types of plant matter. In Africa, zebras and wildebeest often

Left: Impalas are ruminants, preferring the most tender grasses and herbs. The elegant, lyre-shaped horns of this animal identify him as a male.

live in mixed herds. While the zebras feed on the rough tops of grass plants, the wildebeest eat the small shoots that the zebras have exposed. It doesn't always work out so fairly, however. Wildebeest are often followed by small, nimble gazelles that use their narrow muzzles to steal the shoots uncovered where the ground is trampled. Rather than shooing these intruders away, the wildebeest simply move on to where the grazing is better.

Herbivores can be just as violent as carnivores, especially when fighting over mates. Male plains zebras kick and bite each other viciously in their battles over females.

Some ungulates are **browsers** rather than grazers: instead of eating grass, they nibble leaves or berries from the savanna trees. As with grazers, different browsers prefer different bits of the same tree. Giraffes browse among the highest branches, using their incredibly long and flexible tongue to reach between thorns and pluck off leaves. Long-necked antelope called gerenuks stand on their back legs to reach medium-height leaves, while small antelope such as dik-diks browse near ground level. Because trees have much deeper roots than grass, they can reach deeper water and continue growing in the dry season. This is an advantage for browsers. While grazers have to move away in the dry season to search for fresh pasture, browsers can stay put. They even survive in drier places such as shrublands and deserts.

Moving on

One of the biggest challenges that grassland animals face is the dry season. Browsers can get by on shrubs and trees, but grazers are not so lucky – their main source of food shrivels up and disappears. In South America, white-tailed deer and pampas deer stay near water holes or rivers, surviving on a mixture of grazing and browsing. They live in small herds, which makes the food last longer. In northern Australia, wallabies and kangaroos also survive on a mixed diet. Rather than forming herds, they spread out and live singly, again reducing competition for food. In Africa, however, there are vast herds of animals that eat only grass. They have no option but to migrate.

A life of danger

Grassland herbivores live a life of constant danger – especially in East Africa, where they share the savannas with many of the world's deadliest carnivores. To survive, the herbivores need ways of giving the predators a run for their money.

One defensive strategy is speed. Most ungulates are quick on their feet, especially antelope, gazelles and zebras, which can reach speeds of 64–80 km/h (40–50 mph). Even a newborn antelope can get to its feet and run within about 15 minutes of birth. The fastest savanna ungulates can outrun most predators, though they cannot match the speed of their temperate-grassland cousins the saiga and pronghorn, among the fastest land animals on Earth. Some antelope also try to confuse their pursuers by dodging randomly or making sudden, stiff-legged leaps into the air while running. The springbok earned its name from its spectacular defensive leaps, which can reach 3.5 metres (11.5 ft) high. Australia's largest native herbivores – kangaroos – also use speed to escape predators. Large kangaroos can sustain hopping speeds of more than 56 km/h (35 mph), using their heavy tails to stay balanced and aid sudden manoeuvres.

Big is best

Another strategy is size. Elephants, buffalo and rhinos are too big for most predators to overpower, though their young are much less safe. Large animals are likely to stand their ground rather than flee when threatened, and many can charge at attackers with alarming speed and ferocity. Giraffes also gain some protection from size, but lions can bring them down by driving them into broken ground where they are likely to trip. Despite their ungainly stature, giraffes can run at 56 km/h (35 mph), though their graceful strides give the appearance of moving in slow motion.

The migration

One of the world's most spectacular natural events is the migration of wildebeest in East Africa – biologists simply call it 'the migration'. Every year, herds of up to 1.5 million wildebeest leave the south-east of the Serengeti National Park in Tanzania as the dry season begins. Accompanied by zebras and gazelles, they travel north-west towards Lake Victoria, then north into Kenya's Masai Mara National Reserve, where there is permanent water and lush grass. They face many dangers on this perilous journey, such as river crossings where hundreds fall prey to crocodiles. When the rains return, the wildebeest head south again, braving the rivers once more to return to their starting point. Savanna animals also migrate in other parts of Africa, though on a smaller scale. In the west of Africa's Sahel grasslands, for instance, elephant herds travel in a giant circle that takes in wetlands and lakes when the dry season is at its worst.

There is something puzzling about the great migrations in Africa. In the Masai Mara, there is good grazing all year round, so why don't the animals simply stay put? Scientists have not yet solved this mystery, but there seem to be several factors involved. One is the large number of big cats and hyenas in the Masai Mara. These big predators tend to stay in one territory

rather than migrate, because their babies cannot walk easily (unlike baby wildebeest and elephants, which can walk within hours of birth). So although the Masai Mara has good grazing, the danger of being killed by a predator there is much higher. Another factor is food

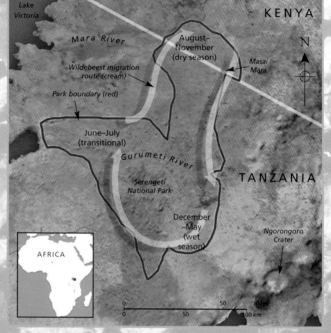

quality. The grass in the Masai Mara contains very little of the mineral phosphorus, which is vital for healthy bones. During the dry season, the wildebeest develop a phosphorus deficiency, but this disappears when they return to the mineral-rich grasslands in the south-east of the Serengeti.

Swarming locusts

Just like wildebeest, some plant-eating insects make mass migrations to find fresh grazing. Certain types of locusts form swarms so vast that they can look like dust storms. A single swarm may contain as many as 10,000 million locusts – enough to strip farmland bare in a matter of minutes, causing a famine.

Locusts are normally solitary insects, coloured green or yellow for camouflage. But if they become crowded together and their food runs out, something strange happens. They lay eggs as normal, but the hatchlings grow into large-winged, black-and-yellow locusts that cluster together before flying off in a swarm. Most swarms form on the dry fringes of the savanna, where the rains are unreliable and the food supply erratic. Although the swarms try to reach greener parts of the savanna, they sometimes get blown off course by the wind and drown at sea. In 1869 a swarm of African locusts was blown all the way to England.

Safety in numbers

Animals that live in herds, flocks or family groups benefit from safety in numbers. With so many eyes and ears on the alert for danger, predators find it much harder to sneak up and take them by surprise. Gazelles warn one another of danger by flashing their white tails and leaping. Like many herbivores, but unlike most predators, they have eyes positioned on the sides of the head. This arrangement gives a very wide field of view, the better to spot an approaching predator. Meerkats take turns keeping a lookout, perched on a bush or rock, while the rest of the group forage about on the ground for food. If danger threatens, the lookout barks a noisy warning, sending the whole group scurrying for cover.

Seeking sanctuary

Burrows provide a relatively safe haven for all sorts of small grassland animals, especially rodents, such as mice and rats. Their underground homes not only provide a hiding place from predators but also protect them from the sweltering midday heat of the dry season or the torrential rain of the wet season. In the llanos of Venezuela, cane mice emerge from their burrows at night to feast on grass seeds. In good years, they explode in number and wear down conspicuous runways through the grass. In Africa, naked mole rats spend their entire lives underground, feeding on roots, **bulbs** and other plant parts. Their social groups are unique among mammals – each colony has a queen that bears all the young, while the other mole rats are workers.

The baboons and patas monkeys of Africa (among the few **primates** that live in grassland rather than forest) spend the night sleeping in trees or on rocky cliffs, where most predators

Small herbivores rely on speed to outrun cheetahs, but youngsters such as this Thomson's gazelle are often too slow or clumsy to escape.

Hopping might look ungainly, but grey kangaroos can reach speeds of 55 km/h (35 mph) – nearly twice as fast as a person can sprint.

cannot reach them. At sunrise they come down to forage for food on the ground. Like most monkeys, they have excellent colour vision for finding food in daylight, but very poor night vision. In contrast, big herbivores such as zebras, which have no choice but to spend their nights on the open plains, have good night vision. They stay awake most of the night, watching nervously for lions and hyenas, which are most active in the hours of darkness. Like horses, zebras sleep in short bursts while standing up, their leg muscles locked in place to prevent their falling over.

A taste for flesh

Where herbivores are common, carnivores are never far away. The savannas of East Africa are famous for the wide range of flesh eaters they harbour, from big cats and hyenas to vultures and birds of prey. Less spectacular, but equally important, are the insect eaters that thrive on the countless ants, termites, caterpillars and grasshoppers. In South

Meerkats give warning calls to their group when they spot predators. They use a special call for birds of prey, telling the group to sprint headlong to the nearest hole.

Long-nosed armadillos snuffle through grass and dead leaves for insects and other small animals. Oddly, their litters always consist of genetically identical offspring.

Pangolins specialize in eating ants and termites. Like armadillos, they can curl up into an armoured ball to defend themselves against predators.

America these include armadillos and giant anteaters, while pangolins and aardvarks play similar ecological roles in Africa.

Animal flesh is a very nutritious type of food – much more so than grass – but predators have to work hard to get it. Grassland herbivores are nervous and quick-witted animals, liable to bolt at the first sign

Only by working together can lions overpower animals as large as adult buffalo. A powerful bite to the throat quickly kills the animal.

of danger, and tough enough to put up a serious fight. To catch them, predators need cunning, strength, speed and perseverance.

Working together

Some hunters use teamwork to trap or overpower their prey. Prides of lions spread out during the hunt, using any cover available to creep within striking distance before making an attack. When their prey tries to escape, a few lions often stay hidden, ready to ambush animals that blunder past.

Wildebeest and zebras are among their favourite prey when lions hunt in packs, while solitary lions often kill warthogs. But, like many carnivores, lions are opportunists, willing to tackle all sorts of prey (including people) in many different situations, as well as scavenge the kills of other predators.

Hyenas are best known as scavengers, but the largest species – the spotted hyena – is also a pack hunter, able to bring down zebras and even buffalo. Spotted hyenas are also called laughing hyenas because of the eerie cackles and 'wooooo-up' calls they make to one another. They are attracted by the sound of commotion and use their sharp sense of smell to sniff out carcasses. Packs of hyenas often muscle in on leopards or cheetahs after a hunt, using strength of numbers to steal the kill. Leopards drag kills into trees to avoid this fate, while cheetahs hunt mainly during the day, when hyenas are usually resting.

Above: Spotted hyenas have immensely powerful teeth and jaws. They can crush and eat all but the largest bones and chew their way though thick hides.

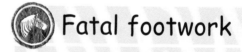 # Fatal footwork

Despite its elegant appearance and sedate manner, the secretary bird is a vicious killer. Its main weapons are heavy, club-like feet, which it uses to stamp the life out of mice, insects, birds and lizards. It can even dispatch poisonous snakes, using a single, well-aimed blow to shatter the spine just behind the snake's head. All but the largest items of prey are swallowed whole.

Clean-up squad

Contrary to popular belief, African vultures do not rely on leftovers from predator kills. They feed mainly on the carcasses of animals that die of sickness or old age. Typically, white-headed vultures find a carcass before any other vultures do. But soon hoards of griffon vultures such as the white-backed vulture (above) arrive, squabbling noisily. Their bald heads let them plunge deep into a carcass and come out clean. Eventually, huge lappet-faced vultures arrive to muscle their way in. It takes only a day or so for a carcass to disappear from Africa's savanna, thanks to the work of nature's clean-up squad.

Unlike the big cats, which generally bring down prey after a sudden dash, African hunting dogs chase their victims over long distances, gradually wearing them out. Small animals are torn apart and devoured in a frenzy as soon as they are caught; larger animals are often disembowelled during the chase by repeated bites to the flank and rear. Once common in Africa's savannas, hunting dogs are now very rare, possibly because of diseases spread by domestic dogs.

Lone hunters

Leopards and cheetahs usually hunt alone, using different strategies to catch their prey. Leopards hunt by stealth, hiding in trees or thickets to sneak close enough to ambush antelope and other prey. Cheetahs use speed to run down small gazelles and antelope in daylight, favouring young animals, which are slower and less nimble than adults. After

With its kill safely wedged in a tree, this leopard can feed without being challenged by lions or hyenas.

Dingoes are the top predators in Australia's grasslands. Though wild today, they are descendants of tame dogs brought to Australia by people thousands of years ago.

tripping the prey with a flick of the paw, the cheetah kills it with a suffocating bite to the neck – a technique common to all cats. Cheetahs are the fastest animals on land, capable of about 100 km/h (60 mph) on level ground, but they can sprint for only 10–30 seconds before they risk overheating.

Around the world

To most people, the word *savanna* conjures up images of vast herds of hoofed mammals roaming over grassy plains, ever watchful for lions, hyenas and other big predators. In East Africa, that's a fairly accurate image, but not all tropical grasslands are like that. Compared to the savannas of Africa, South America's tropical grasslands seem almost devoid of large animals. Africa has around 91 different ungulate species, but South America has just 21, and only 3 of those live primarily in tropical grasslands. Australia has no native ungulates. Instead, wallabies and kangaroos are the main plant-eaters in the savanna.

The reasons for these differences are complicated. According to evidence from fossils, South America's grasslands may once have been as rich in animal life as Africa's, but about 10,000 years ago many of the animals disappeared. No one knows exactly why. Perhaps people hunted them to extinction, or perhaps the climate changed and the animals couldn't adapt. Whatever the reason, the animals that were left behind were much less diverse. Today, most of the mammals that live in the llanos and Cerrado are the same species that live in South America's tropical forests. There are exceptions – such as the maned wolf, a kind of dog that looks like a fox on stilts, and the pampas deer – but they are few.

 # Tasmanian tiger

Until about 4000 years ago, Australia had its own native version of a big cat: the thylacine, or Tasmanian tiger. This strange marsupial looked like a mixture of other animals: it had the head and front legs of a wolf, hind legs more like a kangaroo's and a back covered in the stripes of a tiger. Thylacines probably died out in Australia because of competition with dingoes, but they survived on the island of Tasmania until the 20th century. Sadly, they were hunted to extinction by sheep farmers; the last captive animal died in 1930.

Ostriches (left), rheas (centre) and emus (right) live in different parts of the world but have similar grassland lifestyles. These males are all guarding nests.

Australia's story is different. The mammals of Africa, Asia and the Americas are similar because these continents were joined until recently, allowing species to spread. South America once had elephants, for instance, and its jaguar is a close cousin of Africa's big cats. Australia, however, has been separate from the rest of the world for millions of years, cut adrift like Noah's ark with a unique collection of **marsupials** (mammals with pouches). Another difference is that Australia has no large predators, apart from the ones that people have introduced. The nearest thing to a lion in Australia is the dingo – a wild dog descended from tame dogs brought to Australia by Aborigines.

Despite the differences, there are some striking similarities in the animal life of the world's major tropical grasslands. One similarity is the presence of large flightless birds: ostriches in Africa, emus in Australia and rheas in South America. All three have lost the power of flight and have long, powerful legs for sprinting across the open terrain; ostriches can reach 60 km/h (37 mph) when just a month old.

Ostriches, rheas and emus share some surprisingly similar patterns of behaviour.

In all three species, the male mates with several females, incubates their eggs in a communal nest and looks after the young when they hatch. All three species live in flocks for protection from predators, and their diets are similar, consisting mainly of plants and seeds and supplemented by insects such as grasshoppers. Ostriches – the world's largest birds – also eat lizards and turtles.

Just why these birds are so similar is a matter of hot debate. Some scientists think they evolved along similar lines because they live in similar environments – a process called convergent evolution. However, other scientists think the birds inherited these traits from a common ancestor that lived millions of years ago, when the Earth's continents were joined in one landmass.

Grassland insects

Another similarity among the world's tropical grasslands is their insect life. The biggest grass-eaters in savannas are mammals, but the animals that eat the most grass are much smaller. Hordes of grasshoppers and ants scurry and hop through the turf, while caterpillars munch the leaves and armies of termites collect dead plant litter.

Termite mounds provide handy lookout towers for baboons and other animals. Deep inside, the grotesquely enlarged queen (inset) is busy laying eggs.

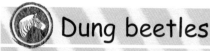

Dung beetles

Dung beetles clear up fresh manure from tropical grasslands almost as fast as it appears. Working quickly while the dung is still soft and pliable, they form it into balls and roll these away to their burrows. Once safely underground, the beetles lay eggs in the dung balls, and the grubs develop inside them. Some dung beetles don't go to the trouble of making dung balls and rolling them away; instead they dig a burrow right under the main dung heap. One Australian species does not even dig burrows – it has evolved into a parasite that lives in the large intestines of wallabies.

Termites play the role of recyclers. They consume a quarter to a third of the dead plant matter in tropical grasslands, though they don't always eat this directly. The fungus-growing termites carry litter deep into their complex nests and use it to grow fungi, which members of the colony then eat. Like ants, termites are social insects. A colony may contain many thousands of individuals, but all the eggs are laid by a single queen. A queen termite can lay thousands of eggs a day and grow as large as a person's finger – so large that she is unable to move. In many savannas, the termites build spectacular, towering mounds that dot the landscape, forming so-called termite savannas. Within the mound, the temperature and humidity are remarkably constant, providing the perfect environment for the fungus garden and developing termite larvae.

A pair of zebra prepare to groom each other. Tropical grasslands in East Africa are the few places left on Earth where large herds of zebra still live.

Llanos

Stretching across northern South America is a huge lowland plain filled with a mixture of wetlands and grasslands – the llanos.

The skills of the llanos's cowboys, or llaneros, are useful when hunting capybaras, the giant rodents of the area. Capybara meat is salted, dried and eaten during Easter.

Giant anteater

The llanos are home to more than their fair share of giants, including giant snakes (anacondas) and giant rodents (capybaras). But perhaps the most spectacular is the giant anteater, which looks all the larger for its enormous bushy tail and disproportionately long snout. Giant anteaters are fussy eaters, feeding exclusively on ants and termites. After using their sharp front claws to dig a hole into an ant or termite nest, they poke their long, toothless snout inside and gather prey with a sticky tongue.

The tongue can extend up to 60 cm (24 in) and flicks in and out up to three times a second, gathering grubs and pupae as well as adults. Giant anteaters walk on their knuckles, keeping their front claws curved inwards so they don't dig into the ground. They are solitary animals, though youngsters ride on their mothers' backs for up to a year after birth.

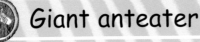

The map shows Venezuela, Colombia, and surrounding regions with labeled locations.

Map labels:

- Caribbean Sea
- GRENADA
- Atlantic Ocean
- Golfo de Venezuela
- Barranquilla
- Cristóbal Colón Peak
- Port of Spain
- Caracas
- TRINIDAD AND TOBAGO
- Maracaibo Lake
- VENEZUELA
- [2]
- [6] Orinoco Delta
- Cordillera de Merida
- Bolívar Peak
- [1]
- Apure River
- [4] Aguaro-Guariquito National Park
- Llanos de Apure
- [3]
- Orinoco River
- [5]
- Georgeto
- Cinaruco-Capanaparo National Park
- Embalse de Guri [7]
- Caroní River
- GUYAN
- Pacaraima Mountains
- Andes
- Cordillera Occidental
- Cordillera Oriental
- Llanos
- El Tuparro National Park
- Roraima
- Angel Falls
- [9]
- [10]
- Rupununi savanna
- N
- Bogota
- Meta River
- COLOMBIA
- Cali
- La Macarena National Park
- Guiana Highlands
- [8]
- Pico da Neblina
- BRAZIL
- Equato
- Amazon Basin
- Negro River
- [11]
- Pacific Ocean
- Andes
- BOLIVIA
- SOUTH AMERICA

Scale:
0 — 200 miles
0 — 200 — 400 km

1. Andes mountains
This chain of mountains on the west of South America marks the western limit of the llanos.

2. Caribbean coast
Grassland gives way to hilly shrubland and tropical dry forest along the northern coast of Venezuela. Moist forest flourishes on the mountains.

3. Llanos de Apure
An almost tree-less flooded savanna in the centre of the llanos, home to roseate spoonbills, anacondas and many other wetland animals.

4. Aguaro-Guariquito National Park
A 0.6-million-hectare (about 1.5-million-acre) protected area of savanna and wetland, inhabited by pumas, jaguars, giant anteaters and capybaras.

5. Orinoco River
The main river draining the llanos. Its western tributaries include the Guaviare, Meta and Apure Rivers.

6. Orinoco Delta
A complex mosaic of swamp forest, mangroves and grassland. In the dry season, agoutis and pacas comb the forest floor for seeds; in the wet season, crocodiles and otters take their place when the delta floods.

7. Embalse de Guri
A gigantic reservoir formed in 1986 by construction of a hydroelectric plant on the Caroní River.

8. Guiana Highlands
A wild area of highlands, formed from very ancient crystalline rock and covered with savanna and rainforest. Famous for flat-topped mountains called tepuis.

9. Angel Falls
The world's highest waterfall, at 979 metres (3212 ft) tall. The water plunges down the side of a tepui called Devil's Mountain, barely making contact with the sheer face as it falls.

10. Rupununi savanna
Distinct from the llanos, this remote area of tropical grassland is surrounded by rainforest. The dominant plant here is grass because the sandy soil and high ground cannot hold enough water for trees.

11. Amazon Basin
The world's largest river basin, mostly filled with dense tropical rainforest.

Fact file

▲ The llanos lie between the Andes mountains, the Caribbean Sea and the Guiana Highlands. Their total area is about 570,000 square km (220,000 sq miles) – bigger than all of France.

▲ The land is mostly savanna, but dense forest borders the rivers. Treeless areas of swamp grasses and sedges are common in low-lying areas.

▲ The llanos receive more rain than most tropical grasslands. Rainfall varies from 1000 mm (39 in) in the east to 4570 mm (180 in) near the Andes. The dry season lasts 5–6 months in the east but only 1–2 months in the south-west.

▲ The Amazon Basin contains islands of savanna, called campos, where the soil is too sandy, stony or marshy for trees to grow.

East Africa

East Africa's savannas are famous for their astonishing diversity of large mammals and for the spectacular mass migrations of wildebeest, zebras and other herbivores.

Mount Kilimanjaro's snowcapped peak dominates the skyline over Kenya's Amboseli National Park.

Ngorongoro Crater

Ngorongoro Crater is one of the wonders of the natural world – visitors sometimes compare it to Noah's ark. Packed into this 20-km-wide (12-mile-wide) volcanic crater is just about every large mammal species to be found in East Africa's savannas, including lions, hyenas, elephants, wildebeest, zebras and rhinos. The crater even has hippo-filled water holes and its own soda lake,

complete with thousands of pink flamingos. Many of the animals stay year round, but others come only in the dry season, attracted by permanent water on the crater floor. Even without wildlife, Ngorongoro would be amazing. Surrounding the central grassy plain is a 600-metre-high (2000-ft-high) crater wall, covered in cloud forest. Visitors drive up and over the jungly rim before descending into the sun-baked interior.

Fact file

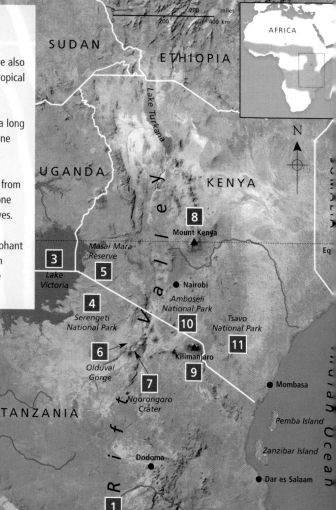

▲ Most of East Africa is savanna, but there are also large areas of treeless grassland, shrubland, tropical forest, mountains and lakes.

▲ There are two rainy seasons in East Africa: a long one between March and June, and a shorter one between October and December.

▲ Kenya and Tanzania rely heavily on income from tourists visiting their national parks. Kenya alone has more than thirty national parks and reserves.

▲ Poaching nearly wiped out East Africa's elephant and rhino populations in the 20th century. Even today, anti-poaching patrols in some parks are authorized to shoot and kill poachers.

---

1. Great Rift Valley
A massive depression in the Earth's surface, formed by gradual separation of the African and Arabian landmasses. It extends from Jordan in the Middle East to Mozambique in Africa, where its east and west branches average 45–65 km (30–40 miles) wide.

2. Lake Tanganyika
In the western branch of the Great Rift Valley is the world's longest freshwater lake. It is also the world's second deepest lake, after Lake Baikal in Russia.

3. Lake Victoria
The world's second largest lake, and Africa's largest, occupies a shallow basin between the two branches of the Great Rift Valley. The region around Lake Victoria is one of the most densely populated parts of Africa.

4. Serengeti National Park
Tanzania's most famous national park, some 15,000 sq km (6000 sq miles) in area. Its almost treeless grassy plains are inhabited by millions of wildebeest and zebras.

5. Masai Mara National Reserve
This Kenyan reserve is joined to Tanzania's Serengeti. Packed with lions, it is one of Africa's top tourist attractions.

6. Olduvai Gorge
An archaeological site in the Serengeti plains where footprints and fossils of ancient hominids (ancestors of the human race) have been found.

7. Ngorongoro Crater
A massive volcanic crater in Tanzania, rich in savanna wildlife and rimmed by cloud forest. Protected as a world heritage site, a biosphere reserve and a Tanzanian national park.

8. Mount Kenya
An extinct volcano in the Kenyan highlands, 5199 metres (17,058 ft) high, where giant lobelias, groundsel trees and other unusual plants grow.

9. Kilimanjaro
At 5895 metres (19,340 ft), this extinct volcano is Africa's highest mountain and one of the only places in Africa that gets snow.

10. Amboseli National Park
Kenya's second most popular park after the Masai Mara. Huge herds of elephants survive here, but poachers have wiped out all the rhinos.

11. Tsavo National Park
Kenya's largest national park, at around 20,000 sq km (8000 sq miles) in area, or the size of Wales. The region was once home to the 'Tsavo man eaters', a pair of male lions that ate dozens of railway workers in 1898.

Tropical forests of the world

Tropical forests are dark and humid, filled with tall trees and amazing animals. They grow only in parts of the world that are warm all year: the tropics.

Unspoilt cloud forests still exist in Central America's mountains.

The best-known type of **tropical forest** is tropical rainforest, which flourishes in places that are both warm and rainy throughout the year. This kind of weather is perfect for plants, allowing them to keep their leaves and grow continuously, instead of dying or shedding their leaves in winter. Tropical rainforests are home to more plant **species** than any other biome – and they contain so many animal species that no one has even tried to count them. The biggest areas of tropical rainforest are in northern South America, central Africa and Southeast Asia. There are also small patches of rainforest on rainy mountains, islands and coasts throughout the tropics.

Most parts of the tropics have one or more wet seasons followed by a period of weeks or months when it hardly rains. Rainforests do not usually grow in places with a long dry season, but other types of tropical forest do. There are fewer tree species in these seasonal tropical forests, but the wildlife is still very rich. In some places the trees are **deciduous** – they shed their leaves for part of the year.

Not all rainforests grow in the tropics. Some forests in **temperate** (cool) countries are also called rainforests. There are temperate rainforests in very rainy parts

of Australia, New Zealand, South America and North America. You can find out more about these forests in Taiga and Temperate Forests (pages 40–75 and 76–113).

Tropical forests have existed for more than 100 million years. Because they are so ancient, millions of species of plants and animals have evolved within them, and these species rely on each other in complex ways. As a result, tropical forests are fragile places. Since people started cutting down trees and introducing new species from elsewhere, the forests have begun to change, and many of their original inhabitants are dying out.

Tropical forest climate

Tropical forests grow in parts of the world that are warm all year round and get lots of rain.

Tropical forests are warm because of their position on the Earth's surface. They grow in the region around the **equator** – the imaginary line that divides the Earth into northern and southern halves. In places close to the equator, the sun shines down from high overhead in the middle of the sky for most of the day. However, in places far to the north and south of the equator, the sun stays closer to the horizon (where the ground meets the sky), especially in the winter. You might notice this when you make a long

Rolling hills in the south-eastern part of the Amazon rainforest trap banks of fog in the early mornings. The air here is humid for most of the year.

Small patches of tropical forest flourish on islands throughout the tropics, like this one in the Pacific. The warm sea makes the air humid (moist), creating frequent rain.

Driven by the sun's heat, the humid air over the tropics rises high into the atmosphere. As the rising air cools, the moisture it carries condenses and forms clouds.

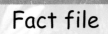
Fact file

▲ Enough rain falls on the Amazon rainforest in a year to fill 2000 million Olympic swimming pools.

▲ Tropical forest can soak up heavy rain, preventing floods. In Bangladesh, people have cut down so much forest for fuel or to make money that the country suffers devastating floods every few years.

▲ Scientists have found that during droughts smoke from forest fires stops rain clouds from forming, making the land even drier.

journey from north to south. For example, the Mediterranean is usually sunnier and warmer than Scotland!

To the north and south of the equator are two more imaginary lines: the **tropic of Cancer** to the north and the **tropic of Capricorn** to the south. These lines mark the limit of the region around the equator in which the sun is high in the sky all year round. The area between the two lines is described as the tropics, and things that live there are tropical. In the tropics, the days are more or less the same length all year around, while away from these areas, days are long in summer and short in winter

Invisible water
The effect of the sun being high in the sky is that more heat reaches tropical regions than cooler areas to the north and south. The sun beating down warms the land, the air and

Right: Hurricane Fran closes in on the USA in 1996. Also called typhoons, hurricanes form over the oceans during the wet season in many parts of the tropics.

Main image: Seen from a space shuttle, vast storm clouds (cumulonimbus) form over southern Brazil. Thunderstorms are very common in the wet tropics.

FLORIDA (USA)

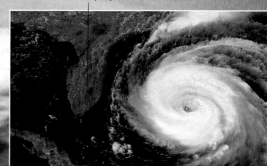

the oceans. When water warms up, it begins to **evaporate** – it turns into an invisible gas, or vapour, that mixes with the air.

When air contains a lot of water vapour, we say it is humid. During a hot bath, the air in a bathroom gets very humid because the hot water produces lots of vapour. The air in tropical rainforests is as humid as that in a bathroom for much of the day. The warmth and humidity can be uncomfortable, making people feel sweaty, hot and tired.

Warm air rises. At the equator, warm air is rising nearly all the time, carrying water vapour high into the sky. As the humid air gets higher, it cools down, which makes the vapour turn back into liquid water. The water forms towering rain clouds and falls to the ground as heavy rain. Often the rain comes in violent storms, followed by periods of calm, sweaty conditions.

Tropical seasons

On average, the Earth's equator gets more strong sunlight than anywhere else, so it is the warmest and most humid part of the planet – and therefore the rainiest. A belt of rainy weather roughly encircles the equator, as the maps on this page show (right).

This rain belt changes position slightly during the year. It moves because the Earth is tilted, which causes the amount of sunlight falling on the tropics to vary during the year. In July the North Pole tilts towards the sun, so the tropic of Cancer gets stronger sunlight than the equator. As a result, the belt of rainy weather moves north a bit. In January the opposite happens: the

South Pole tilts towards the sun, and the tropic of Capricorn gets more sunlight than the equator. So the rain belt moves south.

Places very near the equator stay under the rain belt for most of the year, though there might be a 'dry' season when it rains less

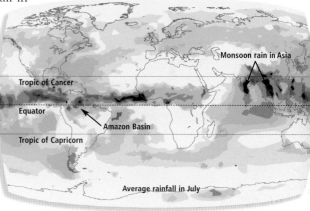

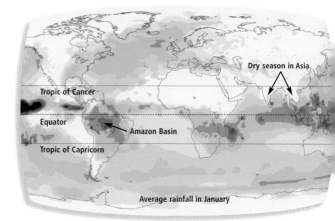

A belt of rainy weather (blue) surrounds the equator. It moves north in summer (above) and south in winter (below), creating wet and dry seasons.

often. These places, such as the Amazon Basin, are where rainforests flourish. As much as 2500 mm (100 in) of rain can fall on a rainforest in an average year – that's five times as much rain as London gets.

271

Wildfires

In many parts of the tropics, the rainy season is unreliable. Every few years, the rains fail to fall in large enough quantities, causing a drought. As the forest dries out, the risk of a raging wildfire gets greater and greater. Forest fires can sweep through dry areas of the USA and Australia and burn for weeks on end. In the tropics, they are even worse. In 1998, fire destroyed about 130,000 sq km (50,000 sq miles) of tropical forest worldwide. The smoke blocked out sunlight, and ash covered cities hundreds of kilometres away from the fires.

In contrast, other parts of the tropics move in and out of the rain belt. These places have a significant dry season each year, which has a huge influence on the wildlife.

Places with a very long dry season don't get enough rain for forests. Instead, grass takes over, forming **savanna** (tropical grassland with scattered trees). Places with a shorter dry season have seasonal tropical forests, which are different from rainforests. The trees are shorter, less tightly packed, and many are deciduous – they shed their leaves and stop growing for part of the year.

Monsoons

The biggest area of seasonal tropical forest is in southern Asia. The forest there is called **monsoon** forest because of an unusually intense rainy season termed the monsoon.

The monsoon is caused by a wind that blows in one direction during summer and the opposite way in winter. The summer wind blows north from the Indian Ocean, bringing lots of humidity and rain. This wet season lasts from May to the end of September. The winter wind blows south off Asia and is much drier.

The wind itself is caused by a difference in the way the Earth's land and sea warm up during the year. Land warms up quickly when the summer sun shines on it, but it cools down just as quickly in winter. In contrast, the oceans warm up and cool down slowly.

During summer the vast landmass of Asia warms up enormously because of its size. As a result, air starts rising over it. Moister air from the ocean – the monsoon wind – rushes inland to take the place of the rising air. As it crosses the land, it dumps its moisture as heavy rain. In India it can pour down every day for weeks during the monsoon.

The temple of Angkor Wat in Cambodia, South-east Asia, is surrounded by seasonal tropical forest. The trees are not as tall or densely packed as in a rainforest.

Climographs

Each place in the world has its own pattern of weather. The typical pattern of weather that happens in one place during a year is called climate. We can sum up a place's climate on a climograph, such as the one shown here for St Louis in the USA. The letters along the bottom are the months of the year. The numbers on the left and the small bars show rainfall, and the numbers on the right and the curvy line show temperature. You can see at a glance that St Louis is hottest in July, but December is the driest month.

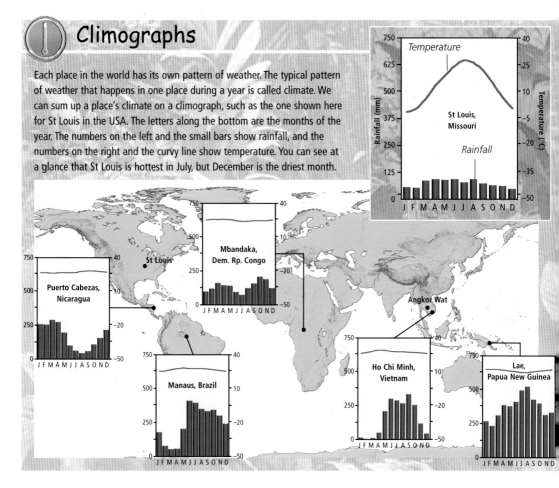

In winter the landmass of Asia cools, and the air above it starts sinking. The sinking air spreads outwards, causing a dry wind to blow south from Asia towards the Indian Ocean. During the dry season, there may be no rain at all for months.

Winds that change direction between seasons in other parts of the world are also called monsoons. The rains that fall on Arizona in the USA in summer are carried by a monsoon wind, for example.

Microclimates

Inside a tropical forest, temperature and humidity vary from place to place. The treetops, for instance, are sunnier and warmer than the forest floor. Scientists call the different conditions found in various parts of the forest 'microclimates'.

Microclimates include more than just temperature and humidity. Light levels, wind speeds and the amounts of the gases **oxygen** and **carbon dioxide** also vary from place to place in the forest. The large range of microhabitats in tropical forests is one of the reasons there are so many species.

Tropical forests do not have summers and winters, but the change in conditions from day to night is almost as great as the change between these two seasons. During the day, it is warm and bright. This is when the plants grow fastest, just as they would in summer.

By contrast, the nights are cooler and darker, and most plants do not grow very much, as if it were winter. The difference between the temperatures at night and during the day is larger than the difference between the average temperatures in January and July.

Cloud forests

The weather on mountains is always different from weather in the lowlands. In the tropics, the lowlands are often hot and humid, with little breeze. Mountains are usually cooler and windier, making the air feel fresher. On a single mountain, the weather can vary a great deal – one side might be wet and rainy, while the other is as dry as a desert.

Some tropical mountains always seem to be shrouded in mist, even when the weather below is dry and clear. Strange

Right: Floods are a frequent problem in Chittagong, Bangladesh, during the monsoon season. Deforestation in recent years has made the problem worse.

Under the waterfall

In the heart of southern Africa, the mighty Zambezi River plunges into a gigantic chasm in the ground, forming one of the biggest and most spectacular waterfalls on Earth: Victoria Falls. This breathtaking waterfall is twice as wide and twice as deep as Niagara Falls in North America. Although the land around the waterfall is savanna, patches of rainforest grow on the cliffs around the falls. The forest is watered not by rain but by the constant spray thrown up as the river thunders over the edge.

Many of the animals and plants in this unique microclimate are the same as those found in central Africa's rainforests hundreds of kilometres to the north. There are palms, ebony trees and strangler figs, for example, as well as the magnificent trumpeter hornbill, a fruit-eating bird that also lives in the Congo forests.

and enchanting forests grow in such places, their plants thriving on the moisture-laden air. They are called **cloud forests**.

Cloud forests are as lush and green as lowland rainforests, but the plants are different. The trees are shorter and often crooked. Smaller plants called **epiphytes**, which hang from the trees' branches and cling to their trunks, are much more conspicuous in cloud forests than in lowland rainforests. The epiphytes grow so thickly that the whole forest appears to be dripping with plant life. One of the world's biggest areas of cloud forest is on the Virunga and Ruwenzori mountains of central Africa – home to the endangered mountain gorilla.

At 1430 metres (4700 ft) above sea level, Monteverde cloud forest in Costa Rica is often wrapped in clouds. This reserve is home to more than 400 orchid species.

Plants of the forest

The tropical climate is ideal for plants, but life is still tough. Forest plants are crowded together and battle with each other to survive.

The number of plants in a tropical rainforest is staggering. Plants don't just grow from the soil – they also grow on the trees, and a few tiny ones even grow on the plants that are growing on the trees. Most plants grow well when they have plenty of sunlight, lots of water and a warm climate. Tropical rainforests are like this all year round – that's why so many plants grow in them.

Epiphytes are plants that grow on other plants. They get all their moisture from the air or rain.

Getting light

Trees are the kings of the forest, and other plants have to live in their shadow. Many rainforest trees are among the tallest plants in the world – the klinki pine of New Guinea grows to 100 metres (300 ft), almost as tall as St Paul's Cathedral. Trees win the battle for light by growing above the other plants. Unlike the trees you might see in your park, rainforest

Right: Sunlight breaks through the canopy of a tropical rainforest in northern Australia. Rainforest plants grow so densely that little light reaches the forest floor.

trees typically have tall trunks with few low branches. At the top, a mass of branches spreads out into a broad crown. Together, all the crowns form a thick layer of leaves called the **canopy**, which soaks up the sun's rays. A few giant trees, called emergents, are taller than the canopy and poke out of the top. Like many rainforest trees, emergents often have buttress roots – huge, spreading roots that grow out from the base of the trunk and support the tree's weight (*see* page 281).

Underneath the canopy it is much darker, but many plants manage to survive in this shady world. Some, like ferns, simply make do with the weak, greenish light that filters through the canopy. Others are cheats – they hitch a ride on other plants.

Hitching a ride

Plants that grow on other plants are called **epiphytes**. They sprout and take root in nooks and crannies on the trunks and branches of trees, where they are much closer to the light than plants of the forest floor are.

Some epiphytes sprout in the canopy, but others climb to get there. The roots of such epiphytes stick to bark, and the plant grows steadily toward the light. As the ends of the roots die away, the whole plant creeps gradually up the tree, like a very slow snail.

Other climbers, such as lianas, start from the ground but lean on a tree for support. With no need to produce a trunk of their own, their wiry stems quickly shoot up to the canopy. Once there, they grow a crown that can be as big as that of the supporting tree, throwing it into shade and weakening it.

Lianas can grow hundreds of metres long in tropical rainforests. As they tangle their way through the canopy, they tie lots of trees

Number of plant
species per 100 km
(62 miles) square

- less than 100
- 100–200
- 200–500
- 500–1000
- 1000–1500
- 1500–2000
- 2000–3000
- 3000–4000
- 4000–5000
- more than 5000

NORTH
AMERICA

SOUTH
AMERICA

Andes

EUROPE

Sahara Desert

AFRICA

ASIA

Himalayas

New Guinea

AUSTRALIA

Forest hot spots

The colours on this map show how many plant
species there are in different parts of the world.
Red and pink places have the most plant
species, while yellow areas have the fewest.

You can see at a glance that tropical forests
contain some of the richest areas of plant life
on Earth, with far more species than deserts or
the forests of Europe or North America. The
areas with the greatest diversity of plants are
where tropical forests meet mountains, such as
the Andes in South America, the Himalayas in
Asia or the mountains of New Guinea.

Mountains are very diverse habitats, with
complex weather and different plants and
animals living at varying heights. That's why
they support such a variety of species.

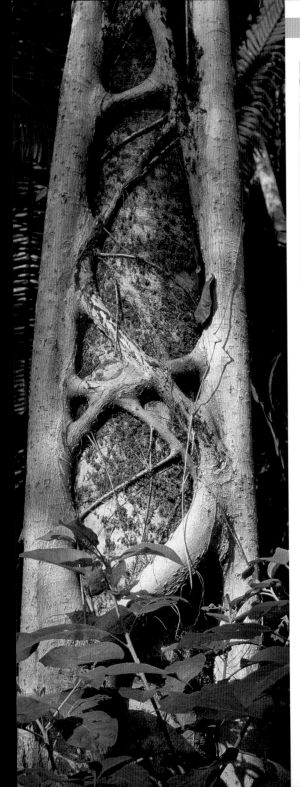

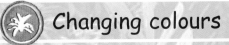

Changing colours

In autumn in Europe, forests turn gold and red as the leaves die. In some tropical forests, the opposite happens: leaves start off red and turn greener as they age. The reasons for the colour changes are similar. Young tropical leaves are often red because they don't have chlorophyll – the green substance that plants use to trap light energy for photosynthesis (making food). Chlorophyll is valuable to plants, but young leaves are the favourite food of many animals and likely to be eaten. So chlorophyll enters the leaves only when they begin to mature. In Europe, forests turn red because the trees extract the chlorophyll before letting the leaves die and fall.

together. They are especially common in open areas, such as riverbanks. People sometimes use lianas as a source of water – they chop them open with a machete and drink the clear water that dribbles out.

Stranglehold

Strangler figs are climbing plants that kill the trees they grow on. They start life as epiphytes growing from seeds left high in the branches by an animal. As a strangler's leaves climb up toward the light, its roots grow down to the ground and wrap around the tree's trunk. As the strangler gets bigger, more roots twist around the trunk, surrounding it with a lattice of roots that appears to be strangling the tree within. Meanwhile, the strangler's crown grows so big that it casts a shadow over the tree, killing it. The tree's trunk eventually rots away, but the strangler stays standing. Its network of roots now form a hollow trunk that is strong enough to hold up the mature crown.

A strangler fig chokes its victim in a Belize rainforest. The tree inside will die and rot away, leaving a hollow.

Lianas provide a handy means of getting around the rainforests of Sumatra. Despite their agility, orangutans suffer many falls from the trees.

Water, water everywhere

For plants in many biomes, getting water is often a challenge. But for the trees in a rainforest, the problem is sometimes the opposite – they have to cope with frequent downpours. If too much water collects on the leaves, it weighs down the branches or causes mould to grow. So, many rainforest trees have smooth leaves that repel water and pointed leaf tips that help water dribble off.

Plants get water through their roots. Though rainforest trees are huge, their roots are mostly less than 60 cm (2 ft) deep – much shallower than the roots of temperate-forest trees. Because of the shallow roots, rainforest trees are prone to fall over in storms, so some have stilt-like roots that prop them up. The buttress roots of emergents also help them withstand storms. Although shallow, the roots of rainforest trees often spread very widely from the base of the tree.

Up in the air

Epiphytes don't start life on the ground, so they have to get their water elsewhere. Many have roots that collect rain dribbling down the tree, and many can absorb water from the humid air. Most epiphytes have thick, leathery leaves or swollen stems that store water. Some, called tank bromeliads, collect water in a tiny pond. Tank bromeliads have a rosette of spiky leaves like the cluster of leaves on a pineapple. The leaf bases overlap, forming a bowl that traps rainwater. Some frogs lay their eggs in these bromeliad ponds, and the tadpoles develop inside them.

Some epiphytes are **parasites** – they steal food and water from another plant. Parasitic epiphytes drive their roots into the host tree to tap into its veins. Some parasites have their own leaves for making food, as well.

Getting nutrients

Plants don't just need water and light to survive – they also need chemicals called **nutrients**, which they get from rotting animal and plant remains in the soil. The soil in a tropical forest forms from animal droppings, dead leaves, fragments of wood and dead animals. Fungi, bacteria and insects

This tropical mistletoe is a parasite. It grows on trees and has roots that burrow into its host to steal water and nutrients.

279

break this mixture down, turning it into a damp compost and releasing the nutrients. Because tropical forests are often warm and wet, the rotting matter breaks down very quickly, and the trees absorb the nutrients almost as soon as they are released. As a result, the soil in a tropical forest is surprisingly shallow and low in nutrients – temperate forests have much thicker, richer soil. If rotting matter was not constantly replacing nutrients, the soil would soon run out of them and nothing would grow.

Epiphytes somehow have to get nutrients from high in the trees. Some collect falling bits of debris, which slowly build up into a thin layer of soil. Those that steal water from their host tree get a free supply of nutrients dissolved in the water.

Buttress roots give rainforest trees extra support. Because rainforests have shallow soil, most trees have wide, spreading roots rather than deep ones.

Chemical war

If you think a rainforest is living banquet, full of tasty leaves for plant-eating animals, then think again. Many of the leaves contain deadly poisons or foul-tasting chemicals that stop animals from eating them. Leaf-eating monkeys get around this problem, but it takes effort. They choose only the youngest, most tender leaves, and they eat leaves from lots of different tree species. By varying their diet, they prevent any single poison from building up too much.

Flower power

Flowers are not just for decoration – they enable plants to reproduce sexually. Flowers produce male cells and female cells. When a male cell from one flower joins with a female cell from another flower, the united cells grow into an embryo (the beginning of a new plant), and a **seed** forms around this.

This might sound straightforward, but there's a snag: unlike animals, plants can't move around to find a mate. They have other ways of making sure that male and female cells from different plants join together. The most common solution is to make **pollen**, a dust-like substance that carries the male cells from one flower to another. When pollen lands on the female part of a flower, it sprouts and grows down into the flower to deliver the male cell. This process is termed **pollination**.

Finding a partner

Pollination is tricky in tropical forests because there are so many different species. A plant can reproduce only with other members of its species, but the nearest mate may be miles away. Among many of the tall tree species, the wind carries pollen. The trees' flowers release vast amounts of tiny pollen grains into the air. Most blow away and get lost, but a few grains settle on exactly the right flowers somewhere else in the forest.

Beneath the canopy, the air is too still for wind pollination. Instead, flying animals carry the pollen between flowers. In return for this service, the animals receive **nectar**, a sugary liquid produced by flowers. A few animals also eat some of the pollen.

Red-eyed tree frogs clamber over a Heliconia *plant in Belize.* Heliconia *flowers are usually pollinated by hummingbirds.*

Getting noticed

Flying insects, such as bees, beetles, butterflies and moths, are the most common animal pollinators. Many flowers have a specific shape that suits a certain type of pollinator. For example, flowers that beetles pollinate are broad and dish-shaped, allowing these large insects to scramble about as they gather nectar. As they do so, pollen sticks to them, ready to rub off on the next flower.

Bee flowers open during the day, when bees are busiest. Such flowers are often brightly coloured, with lines that direct the bee towards the pollen. Butterfly flowers are usually funnel-shaped. To reach the nectar at the base of the funnel, a butterfly uses a very long mouthpart that works like a straw. When the butterfly isn't feeding, the mouthpart coils up under its head. Moths feed like butterflies, but at night. Their flowers are often white and scented so they are easy to find in the dark.

Some flowers are pollinated by birds and bats. Bird flowers are usually red and are tough because birds are much larger than

Banana flowers are pollinated by bats. Wild banana plants produce fruit and seeds after pollination, but cultivated banana plants (right) produce seedless fruit.

insects. Hummingbirds hover beside their flowers, flapping their wings up to seventy times a second to keep perfectly still while they probe for nectar with their bills. Bats feed at night, so their flowers are often pale, with a musty scent. Most bat flowers look a little like brushes – when a bat pays a visit, the brush gives its chest a dusting of pollen.

Many birds and bats are too big to fly into the middle of a plant, so their flowers are usually positioned on the outside of the plant. Banana flowers are like this and are usually pollinated by bats.

Spreading out

Once a plant has produced its seeds, it can't just drop them onto the ground. If they sprouted there and started growing, the young plants would end up crowded together, competing with each other and their parent for light, nutrients and water. Most plants, therefore, have ways of dispersing their seeds. Although many go to waste in the crowded forest, a few stand a good chance of finding just the right place to start life.

A snowcap hummingbird hovers over a wild poinsettia flower to sip nectar. This tiny bird from Central America is a mere 6 cm (2.5 in) long – people often mistake it for an insect.

Many of the tallest trees produce seeds with wings, which make the seeds spin around in the air, slowing their fall. When such seeds are released from the high treetops, they can travel a long way on the breeze. However, most tropical forest plants have a different strategy to spread their seeds: they bribe animals to carry the seeds away.

The usual way of doing this is by enclosing the seed in an edible fruit. Animals eat the fruit, swallow the seeds and move off into the forest. When the seeds eventually pass out of the animal's body, they are far from the parent plant. They land on the ground in a heap of droppings – a perfect fertilizer for the young plants.

Biggest flower in the world

The world's biggest flower belongs to a peculiar plant called *Rafflesia arnoldii*, which grows only in the rainforests of Sumatra. In some ways *Rafflesia* is more like a fungus than a plant. It has no true roots, stems or leaves, and it cannot make its own food. Instead, it lives as a parasite, sending fine, thread-like growths into vines to steal water and nutrients. The only part of *Rafflesia arnoldii* that you can see is its gigantic red and white flower, which grows to 1 metre (3 ft) wide on the forest floor. Even the flower is weird. It smells of rotting flesh, attracting flies that normally lay eggs on dead animals. Tricked by the foul stench, the flies unwittingly pollinate the flower.

sucking
mouthpart

*Above: With its slender mouthpart unrolled, a postman
butterfly sucks nectar from a flower in Costa Rica.*

In temperate climates, plants that produce
fruit or nuts all tend to do so at the end of
summer. In a tropical rainforest, different
types of fruit come into season at different
times of the year. Because fruit and nuts are
usually available somewhere in the forest,
many animals specialize in eating little else.
They include fruit bats, many monkeys and
birds such as parrots, toucans and hornbills.
Such animals usually move around a lot as
they search for the few trees with ripe fruit.

Stinky fruit

Durians are large, spiky fruits that look like
giant horse chestnuts. Although the flesh
inside a durian is sweet, the fruit has such a
disgusting, rotten smell that it is banned from
many restaurants in South-east Asia, where
durian trees grow. However, in the forest, the
powerful smell attracts orangutans, tigers and
many other animals, all of which eagerly
devour the custard-like flesh.

Above: Durians smell revolting to us, but many animals, from orangutans to tigers, find them delicious.

Awaiting the gap

Once a seed has been carried across the forest, dropped in a perfect patch of soil and sprouted into a sapling (baby tree), it faces a new challenge: lack of light. The floor of a tropical forest is usually dark and gloomy, so how can a sapling get the light it needs to grow all the way to the canopy?

For many trees, the answer is to wait. After reaching a few metres tall, the saplings stop growing. They can wait for years like this, absorbing just enough energy from the dim light to keep themselves alive. Their big chance comes when a large tree falls down, creating a gap in the canopy that lets sunlight flood onto the forest floor.

Once a gap opens, the saplings race upwards in a fierce contest to fill the empty space. Eventually, one wins, and the gap disappears. Some small plants grow only in gaps. They flower and set seed quickly, before the forest closes in again, and their seeds lie ready in the soil for the next gap to form.

Banyan trees

Producing seeds enables trees to spread to new places, but some tropical trees can spread where they stand – by growing sideways. The banyan tree, a native of tropical Asia, produces aerial roots that grow down from its branches. When they reach the ground, they become new trunks. A single banyan tree can spread indefinitely this way, turning into a thicket or even a small forest. One banyan tree in Hawaii covers nearly half a hectare (about an acre).

Animals of the forest

Tropical forests teem with an amazing number of weird and wonderful animals, from flying frogs and birds of paradise to giant millipedes and midget hippos. They are also home to some of the most colourful animals on Earth.

Nobody knows how many animal species live on Earth, but one thing's certain: a lot of them live in tropical forests. One scientist collected beetles from just nineteen trees in the rainforest of Panama. He counted nearly 1000 species, so the total number of tropical beetles worldwide could be millions. Beetles probably outnumber most other animal species, but tropical forests are still home to countless other insects and spiders, not to mention snakes, monkeys, bats, birds, frogs, cats, anteaters and all sorts of animals you've probably never heard of.

Blue-and-yellow macaws are a common sight in the Amazon rainforest. These birds form very strong bonds with each other and are often seen in pairs.

Grasping toes and flexible ankle joints allow kinkajous to hang by their feet while searching for food. They live in Central and South America.

Animal niches

You might wonder how so many species could survive in such a crowded place – surely they'd end up eating each other's food and getting in each other's way? They avoid such problems because each animal species has its own particular way of life, or **niche**. It eats certain foods, lives in a particular part of the forest and uses unique skills to survive.

A niche is not just the animal's home in the forest, such as the canopy or a rotting log. It is a combination of habitat, behaviour and time. For example, an animal that feeds at night has a different niche from one that feeds during the day. Likewise, two species of bats might fly around the same sorts of plants in search of insects to eat, but one might prefer large moths while the other eats flies. Each bat, therefore, has its own niche.

Toucans (above) live in South America, while hornbills (right) live in Africa. They have evolved into species that fill similar niches in forests thousands of miles apart.

 Forest midgets

Many of the mammals that live in tropical forests are smaller than their relatives from more open country. These small animals are often called pygmies.

Africa's Congo rainforest is home to pygmy elephants and pygmy hippos, for example. Pygmy elephants are about half the weight of their savanna cousins, while pygmy hippos are one-tenth the weight of other hippos (but still three times heavier than a person). Rhinoceroses in Asian forests are also much smaller than their grassland relatives in Africa, and deer in some rainforests are as small as rabbits.

One reason forest mammals are small is that it helps them move through undergrowth. Another is that there is more high-energy food, such as fruit, in forests. Small mammals need a constant supply of energy, but larger mammals digest and use their food more slowly. Savanna elephants grow to a huge size while eating large quantities of poor-quality food.

Tropical forests are complex places, with millions of different niches. This is why so many animal species can coexist in them.

Similar but different

Tropical forests in different parts of the world have very different sets of animals, but they often have similar niches. As a result, unrelated animals have become similar through evolution. Scientists call this process convergent evolution.

One example is the similarity of South America's toucans to the hornbills of Africa and Asia. Both types of birds have spectacularly long bills, which they use to break open nuts and fruits.

Another pair of animals that look and behave the same way but live on the opposite sides of the world are the pudu and mouse deer. Pudus live in the forests of South America, where they feed on fruit. They are only 30 cm (1 ft) long – about the same size as rabbits. They share the title of world's smallest deer with mouse deer, which live in the forests of Malaysia. They, too, are no bigger than rabbits and feed on fruit. These

South-east Asia's slow lorises come out at night to look for insects and fruit, using their large eyes to see in the gloom. To avoid being spotted by predators, they do everything in slow motion.

deer species have evolved in similar ways because they occupy similar niches in the rainforest.

Sometimes a niche is filled by a completely different type of animal. For example, there are no monkeys or lemurs in the tropical forests of Australia, so the fruit-eating niche is filled mainly by birds, especially parrots and pigeons.

Monkey business

Monkeys are perhaps the most familiar of forest animals. These agile creatures live all over the forest from the highest branches in the treetops to the forest floor and along the edges of rivers. Monkeys belong to a larger group of animals called **primates**, nearly all of which live in tropical forests. Besides

monkeys, the primate group includes apes, lemurs and smaller animals called bushbabies, tarsiers and lorises. Apes are generally bigger than monkeys, with longer arms and no tails. Gorillas, chimpanzees, orangutans, gibbons and humans are all apes. Lemurs are easy to tell apart from monkeys because they have cat-like faces with long snouts. They live only on the island of Madagascar, where there are no monkeys. Bushbabies, lorises and tarsiers are small, **nocturnal** (night-active) primates with huge eyes for seeing in the dark. While monkeys,

 ## Tree kangaroo

Although there are no monkeys in the forests of Australia and New Guinea, other mammals have taken to the trees. One of the most surprising is the tree kangaroo, a relative of the more familiar kangaroos that hop around on the ground. The tree kangaroo has more muscular arms and wider feet than its ground-dwelling cousins. It uses the claws on its hands to grip branches, and it can 'walk' by moving its back legs alternately – something other kangaroos cannot do. It can also hop along the ground when it needs to.

In Central and South America, many of the monkeys have a tail that is prehensile – it can wrap around things and be used as a fifth limb. Spider monkeys (left) have tails strong enough to support their whole body weight. Their prehensile tails help them move, but spider monkeys can also swing from branch to branch like gibbons, using their thumbless hands as hooks.

High-ranking male mandrills have very bright blue and red marks on their face as a display of status. These marks grow darker when a male is spoiling for a fight.

The world's smallest monkey – the pygmy marmoset – weighs a mere 90 g (3 oz) and could sit on your hand. This diminutive primate lives in the northern parts of the Amazon rainforest. While large monkeys swing through the trees, pygmy marmosets are small enough to perch on blades of grass.

apes and lemurs tend to live in social groups, most of the nocturnal primates live on their own or with their offspring.

Large and small

The world's largest monkey is the mandrill, which lives on the floor of Africa's Congo rainforest. A fully grown male mandrill weighs about as much as an eight-year-old child, while females are half the weight of males. Male monkeys are often larger than females because they have to fight with each other to win mates.

Like many primates, mandrills live in social groups with a ranking system. The top-ranking male usually gets more mating opportunities than his rivals in the group.

Only adult males sport the bright markings for which mandrills are famous. Blue and crimson patches of skin on the buttocks complement those on the face.

Above: Lemurs spends most of their time in the trees. Sifakas are lemurs that make spectacular leaps from tree to tree, but their jumping style of movement seems clumsy on the ground.

Below: Pygmy marmosets are the world's smallest monkeys. They are nervous animals and move in a quick, jerky manner. Unlike most monkeys, they have claw-like nails that help them cling to tree trunks.

In all, there are nearly two hundred species of monkeys, the majority of which live in tropical forests. Most eat either fruit or leaves, but a few species, such as capuchins, feed on all sorts of food, from shellfish to insects and small frogs.

Aping about

Many people think apes are large monkeys, but they are different in lots of ways. Apes don't have tails, and while monkeys usually have long back legs and shorter arms, most apes have arms longer than their legs. Monkeys are good at scampering along branches and jumping from tree to tree, but apes climb more slowly, using their strong arms to grip the tree trunk. Gibbons are an exception, though – these apes use their long arms to swing below the branches.

Orangutans are red-haired apes that live on only two islands in South-east Asia. These gentle giants spend their whole lives in the

Getting around

Most mammals get around by walking on all fours, but that's not the best way to travel in a dense rainforest – especially if all the best food is up in the canopy. As a result, all sorts of unusual ways of moving have evolved in forest animals. In a South-east Asian forest, for instance, fruit bats fly, colugos glide, siamang gibbons swing, orangutans clamber lazily through the branches, slow lorises creep very slowly to avoid being seen, squirrels scuttle up and down trunks and langur monkeys make bold leaps between treetops.

Gibbons can move at tremendous speed through the canopy by swinging underhand from branch to branch. Their wrists and shoulders are so flexible that, while hanging from one arm, they can turn up to 360 degrees without having to let go of the branch.

trees – they find it hard to walk on the ground because their feet are turned inwards for holding branches. At night, orangutans weave beds out of twigs and branches high in the trees. The other apes – chimpanzees and gorillas – live in large groups in the forests of Central Africa. They spend most of their time on the ground, though

Gorillas are the largest of the primates. They are highly endangered due to poaching and loss of forest.

they also often sleep in beds woven out of tree branches. Only one species of ape lives outside tropical forests: humans.

Fellow travellers

Primates are by no means the only mammals in tropical forests. Like most other types of forest, tropical forests are also home to all sorts of rodents – animals like mice, rats and squirrels. Most rodents are small, but in South American forests a few species have evolved into giants. The agouti is a shy, secretive rodent that searches the forest floor for fallen fruit. At 0.6 metres (2 ft) long, it is so big

Agoutis are attracted to the sound of ripe fruit falling on the forest floor. Like squirrels, they bury food in secret stores, helping spread the trees' seeds.

that many people mistake it for a small deer. Its relative the capybara is even bigger – it grows to more than 1.2 metres (4 ft) long and can weigh as much as a person, making it the biggest rodent in the world. Capybaras are good swimmers and usually live close to rivers, lakes or marshes. Local people call them water pigs, but they are more closely related to rats than pigs.

Other forest mammals include bears and hoofed animals, such as deer and cattle. Tropical bears are much smaller than the giant hunters of colder areas. Sun bears live in South-east Asian forests; honey bears, named for their favourite food, live in India and Sri Lanka; while spectacled bears live in cool forests in the

highlands around the Amazon Basin. Unlike their fiercer cousins, tropical bears do not hunt large animals. Instead, they eat a mixed diet of fruit, roots, leaves and insects.

The top **predators** of the forest are the cats. The most famous forest cat is the tiger, which once lived throughout Asia. This wonderful animal is now very rare and survives only in small, protected pockets of forest. Tigers are so big and powerful that they will prey on anything they can catch, even small elephants and rhinoceroses. A few develop a taste for human flesh and become maneaters.

Other forest-dwelling cats include leopards and ocelots, both of which have spots that help them hide in the dappled shade. Leopards are the success story of the cat

Jaguars are often heard but seldom seen in the tropical forests of Latin America. They are solitary animals and often become aggressive when they meet each other.

Few parrots are as colourful as the rainbow lorikeet of eastern and northern Australia. Lorikeets are small parrots with brush-tipped tongues for sipping nectar.

Hello, Polly

Tropical forests can seem like unbroken stretches of green, but there are occasional splashes of colour. Among the most colourful inhabitants are parrots – large, noisy birds that generally have curved beaks for cracking nuts and cutting fruits. Some parrots have magnificent long tails. The largest parrot of all is the hyacinth macaw of Brazil, which measures 1 metre (40 in) from head to tail.

Parrots are often known by different names. Macaws, cockatoos, lorikeets and parakeets are all different types of parrots, for example. Unlike most birds, parrots have two forwards-pointing toes and two backwards-pointing ones. This allows a parrot to lift food to its mouth with one foot while clinging to a branch with the other.

Birds are especially common in the forests of New Guinea and Australia, where there are fewer mammals to compete with.

world. While most big cats have declined in number because of environmental damage, leopards are still relatively common in Africa and Asia. When they make a kill, leopards haul the victim's mutilated body into a tree to hide it from other animals. There are no leopards in South America, but the stockier jaguar fills a similar niche.

 ## Elephant bird

The island of Madagascar used to have some of the most amazing animals in the world – before people arrived and started cutting down the forests. One was the elephant bird, a gigantic, flightless bird nearly twice as tall as a person and weighing 450 kg (1000 lbs). Even the egg of an elephant bird was enormous, as 1000-year-old specimens (right) found buried in sand have proved. Scientists think the elephant bird fed on the bodies of dead animals, and it may have survived on Madagascar until as recently as 1100 years ago. Some Arabic and Persian myths describe a terrifying,

giant bird called the roc. Perhaps these stories were based on reports from merchants who once sailed from Arabia to the waters around Madagascar.

The emerald tree boa hangs from branches in the Amazon, impersonating vines. It kills small animals by wrapping around them and squeezing until they suffocate; then it swallows them whole.

Wriggling reptiles

The largest snakes in the world live in tropical forests. The green anaconda is the heaviest and lives in swampy parts of South America, including the Amazon. The longest snake is the reticulated python, which can reach nearly 10 metres (32 ft). These snakes are just two of thousands of **reptile** species, including geckos, chameleons, monitor lizards, rattlesnakes, vipers, tree pythons and boa constrictors, that live in tropical forests. Snakes that live in trees tend to have long, slender bodies that can drape across flimsy branches without falling through. Geckos have sticky feet that let them run up vertical trunks or even along the bottom of branches. And chameleons have strange, pincer-like feet for gripping branches as they creep along.

The Komodo dragon – a huge, flesh-eating monitor lizard – holds the record for the world's heaviest lizard. It reaches 135 kg (300 lbs) in weight and lives only on several islands in South-east Asia.

New Guinea is home to the birds of paradise. Male birds of paradise are brightly coloured and adorned with wild headdresses and long tails – all to impress the females.

One of the strangest birds in the world lives in the flooded forests of Ecuador and Peru. The hoatzin is known by local people as the stink bird because of its disgusting smell. It looks a little like a turkey, but it has a bright blue face and a punk hairstyle of feathers. What makes this bird unique is that the young chicks have claws on their growing wings, which they use for clinging to trees. This prehistoric feature is probably a leftover from the distant reptilian ancestors that birds evolved from: dinosaurs.

The mangrove snake lives in the forests and swamps of South-east Asia. It sniffs out prey with its tongue and kills with a venomous bite.

Left: The strawberry poison-dart frogs of Central America are tiny, growing to only 2.5 cm (1 in) long. To attract females, males inflate their throats and make a trilling sound. The tadpoles develop in puddles or pools of water in bromeliad plants.

Wet and wild

Amphibians are animals such as frogs, toads and salamanders that live partly in water and partly on land. They need to keep their skin moist when they are out of water, so the damp climate of a rainforest is perfect for them. The many pools, puddles and slow-flowing rivers provide countless sites for the tadpoles to develop.

Below: Yellow-banded poison frogs live in Colombia and Venezuela. Their skin contains a potent nerve toxin derived from the ants they eat.

Frogs are so common in rainforests that their strange calls, which range from croaks to bleeps, often fill the air at night. Some tropical frogs have beautiful skin colours and patterns that warn predators that they are poisonous. The poison-dart frogs of the Amazon

Right: Red-eyed tree frogs hide in the trees of Central America during daylight hours, using sticky toe tips to hold on. Their amazing eyes perhaps serve to startle any predators that wake them.

Wallace's flying frogs use their webbed feet and skin flaps between their legs to glide up to 15 metres (50 ft) between trees in the forests of Borneo.

have the most spectacular colours, but also the most deadly poison. The most dangerous species is the terrible poison-dart frog of western Colombia – a single lick of its skin can kill you. Forest people use the skin of this frog to poison their arrow tips for hunting.

Other amazing forest frogs include the tree frogs, which have sticky disks on their toes that help them cling to leaves and branches. Some tree

frogs lay their eggs in trees, gluing them to the undersides of leaves overhanging water. When the tadpoles have developed, they drop into the water below. Flying frogs are tree frogs with webbed feet and skin flaps that act like wings, enabling them to glide great distances after leaping from a tree.

Right: Blue poison frogs live only in southern Surinam. They are ravenous eaters, preying on fruit flies, termites, crickets and ants. Their striking colour has made them popular pets – many are now bred in captivity.

Leaf-cutter ants use leaf cuttings to grow an edible fungus inside their nests. The ants consume more plant matter than any other group of animals in the forests of Central and South America.

Insects and spiders

Large animals might be exciting to spot, but they are insignificant in number compared to the insects and other **invertebrates** that teem over every surface in a tropical forest.

Forest insects range from huge, spike-covered crickets to shiny beetles that appear to be made of metal. There are tiny wasps that live inside plants, butterflies bigger than your hand and all sorts of insects disguised as twigs, leaves, thorns or flecks of dirt. The wandering spiders of Brazil are perhaps the world's most dangerous spiders. These aggressive creatures wander into houses and attack people with little provocation – and a single bite can kill.

Tropical forests are home to the world's biggest insects. Top prize for the heaviest insect goes to the goliath beetle of Africa's Congo rainforest. It grows to 11 cm (4.3 in) long and reaches 100 g (3.5 oz) in weight. The longest insect is *Pharnacia*

Below: Goliath beetles of Africa are the world's heaviest insects. When they are in flight they sound like miniature helicopters.

Each leg ends in a pair of claws, or tarsi, used for gripping tree trunks or other surfaces.

Male goliaths have horns for fighting.

ACTUAL SIZE

wing case

When the wings are not in use, they fold away under protective wing cases.

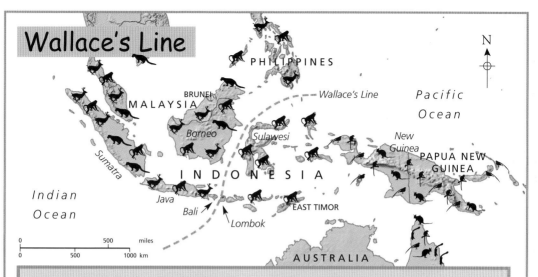

Wallace's Line

PHILIPPINES

BRUNEI
MALAYSIA

Borneo

Sulawesi

-- Wallace's Line

Pacific Ocean

New Guinea

PAPUA NEW GUINEA

INDONESIA

Indian Ocean

Java

Bali

Lombok

EAST TIMOR

Sumatra

| 0 | 500 | miles |
| 0 | 500 | 1000 km |

AUSTRALIA

N

If you walked in the footsteps of the explorers and naturalists of the 19th century, through the forests of Malaysia and across to the islands of Indonesia, you might notice changes in the animals around you. You would leave behind the familiar animals such as deer, monkeys and cats as you left the shores of Bali or Borneo. In Sulawesi and Lombok you would see a mixture of animals from Asia and Australia, but eventually, if you reached New Guinea and Australia, you would see mainly the marsupial mammals that live there, such as tree kangaroos, possums and pademelons, a type of wallaby. The famous naturalist Alfred Russel Wallace (1823–1913) drew an imaginary line that divided these characteristic animals of Asia and Australia.

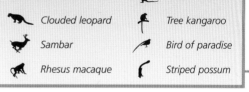

     Clouded leopard   Pademelon

     Sambar   Tree kangaroo

     Rhesus macaque   Bird of paradise

     Striped possum

---

serratipes, a stick insect from Malaysia that reaches 55.5 cm (22 in) in length – as long as a man's arm.

The leaf litter on the forest floor is alive with tiny animals. Industrious termites and ants play a largely unseen role breaking down dead wood and plants, while scorpions and centipedes patrol in search of food. Without these tiny invertebrates keeping nutrients cycling through the forest, the plants and large animals would not survive for long.

The spiny katydid of the Amazon rainforest is a prickly relative of crickets. Its spiny legs can discourage predators as large as bats and monkeys.

Amazon rainforest

The Amazon rainforest is as large as all of the USA from the Rockies to the Atlantic Ocean. It occupies a vast, flat river basin filled with branches of the mighty Amazon River.

The mighty rivers of the Amazon Basin flood an area of forest the size of England every rainy season. Birds, monkeys and insects continue life in the canopy, while river dolphins, fish and caimans swim among the tree roots.

Fact file

▲ With few roads, much of the endless Amazon rainforest is inaccessible and unexplored.

▲ Early explorers described it as an area where water and land had swapped places – the wide, smooth rivers are easy to move along, while the dense forest is mostly impassable.

▲ Pico da Neblina, a mountain on the northern edge of the Amazon Basin, is Brazil's highest mountain at 3014 metres (9888 ft) high. It was discovered as recently as 1962.

Slowly but surely

Sloths hang from the branches of trees in the Amazon. They move so slowly that algae (simple plants) grow in their fur, giving the sloths a greenish tinge. Sloths rarely venture to the ground, even giving birth up trees. Their diet of leaves and twigs contains very few nutrients, so they conserve energy by moving very slowly; they spend most of their time hanging motionless while digesting their food. Their hook-like claws are so effective that sloths may stay hanging for weeks after they have died.

Caribbean Sea
Atlantic Ocean
PANAMA
Caracas
TRINIDAD AND TOBAGO
VENEZUELA
Orinoco River
Llanos (grassland)
Mount Roraima
Georgetown
Paramaribo
Bogotá
Canaima National Park
GUYANA
SURINAM
Cayenne
FRENCH GUIANA
COLOMBIA
Guiana Highlands
Savanna
Angel Falls
Amazon
Pico da Neblina
Central Surinam Nature Reserve
Quito
ECUADOR
Putumayo River
Japurá River
Negro River
Jaú National Park
Marajó Island
Belém
Equator
Fortale
Sangay National Park
Napo River
Manaus
Amazon River
Guayaquil
Iquitos
Flooded forest
Rio Abiseo National Park
Ucayali River
Juruá River
Flooded forest
Madeira River
Tapajós River
Basin
Xingu River
Araguaia River
Tocantins River
São Francisco River
Brazilian Highlands
Trujillo
Purus River
PERU
Manu National Park
Madidi National Park
BRAZIL
Cerrado (grassland)
Atlantic Forest
Salv
Lima
BOLIVIA
Mato Grosso Plateau
Brasília
Goiânia
Andes
La Paz
Noel Kempff Mercado National Park
Pacific Ocean
Pantanal (wetland)

NORTH AMERICA
SOUTH AMERICA

0   500 miles
0   500   1000 km

1. Andes
Many of the region's rivers begin in the Andes mountains and flow east into the vast Amazon Basin.

2. Rio Abiseo National Park, Peru
These rugged, forested river valleys in the Andean foothills are the last refuge of the yellow-tailed woolly monkey, previously thought extinct, and the tiny mouse opossum.

3. Flooded forest
On the flat bottom of the Amazon Basin, the rivers flood huge areas of nearby forest to a depth of up to 10 m (30 ft).

4. Madidi National Park
The local people take tourists through the forest here to see monkeys and macaws.

5. Angel Falls
The world's highest waterfall tumbles off the sheer side of a table mountain and plummets into the jungle below.

6. Manaus
A large city in the centre of the Amazon rainforest. Manaus was originally the centre of the Brazilian rubber industry.

7. Amazon River
Earth's largest river flows through the heart of the forest.

8. Guiana Highlands
The forests on these low mountains remain pristine, safe from loggers because the area is so difficult to get to.

9. Central Surinam Nature Reserve
An undeveloped hilly area where animals such as jaguars, giant armadillos, tapirs and sloths are protected, as well as 400 species of birds and 8 species of monkeys.

10. Belém
A large port at the mouth of the Amazon, where the river meets the ocean, 6400 km (4000 miles) from the source.

Congo rainforest

The Congo rainforest lies in a vast river basin straddling the equator in central Africa. The heart of the forest is a largely unspoiled wilderness, where only rivers and occasional clearings break the canopy.

The swampy clearings, or bais, of the Congo region are like magnets to wildlife. Animals such as forest elephants and lowland gorillas visit them to eat roots, grass and minerals. The bais allow scientists to study the animals before they melt back into the forest.

Congo facts

▲ Most of Africa's rainforest is in or around the Congo basin, but there is also rainforest in parts of west Africa, including Liberia and Ivory Coast.

▲ The central part of the Congo rainforest is so swampy and difficult to reach that it remains almost untouched by loggers and farmers.

▲ One of the main threats to the forest wildlife is poaching. Poachers hunt elephants for ivory and gorillas and other animals for meat.

▲ Deforestation by farmers and loggers is a growing problem in outer parts of the Congo basin.

▲ The Bronx Zoo in New York in the USA houses a 2-hectare (about 6 acres) reconstruction of Congo rainforest, complete with 22 gorillas, 11 waterfalls and 15,000 plants of nearly 400 species.

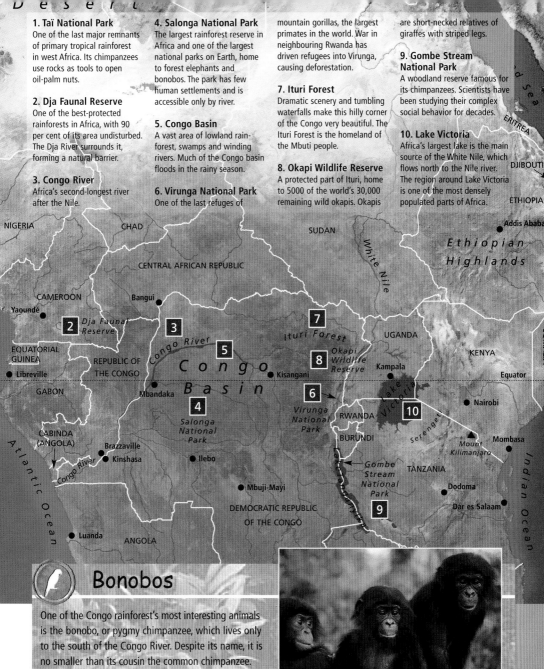

1. Taï National Park
One of the last major remnants of primary tropical rainforest in west Africa. Its chimpanzees use rocks as tools to open oil-palm nuts.

2. Dja Faunal Reserve
One of the best-protected rainforests in Africa, with 90 per cent of its area undisturbed. The Dja River surrounds it, forming a natural barrier.

3. Congo River
Africa's second-longest river after the Nile.

4. Salonga National Park
The largest rainforest reserve in Africa and one of the largest national parks on Earth, home to forest elephants and bonobos. The park has few human settlements and is accessible only by river.

5. Congo Basin
A vast area of lowland rainforest, swamps and winding rivers. Much of the Congo basin floods in the rainy season.

6. Virunga National Park
One of the last refuges of mountain gorillas, the largest primates in the world. War in neighbouring Rwanda has driven refugees into Virunga, causing deforestation.

7. Ituri Forest
Dramatic scenery and tumbling waterfalls make this hilly corner of the Congo very beautiful. The Ituri Forest is the homeland of the Mbuti people.

8. Okapi Wildlife Reserve
A protected part of Ituri, home to 5000 of the world's 30,000 remaining wild okapis. Okapis are short-necked relatives of giraffes with striped legs.

9. Gombe Stream National Park
A woodland reserve famous for its chimpanzees. Scientists have been studying their complex social behavior for decades.

10. Lake Victoria
Africa's largest lake is the main source of the White Nile, which flows north to the Nile river. The region around Lake Victoria is one of the most densely populated parts of Africa.

Bonobos

One of the Congo rainforest's most interesting animals is the bonobo, or pygmy chimpanzee, which lives only to the south of the Congo River. Despite its name, it is no smaller than its cousin the common chimpanzee.

Scientists think bonobos (right) are descended from a group of chimpanzees that crossed the Congo River from north to south about 1.5 million years ago. Isolated by the river and its swamps, they evolved separately. Common chimpanzees live in aggressive, male-dominated societies. The males form gangs and sometimes wage war on rival groups. In contrast, bonobos live in more peaceful, female-dominated societies. In addition to grooming each other regularly (as most primates do), bonobos use sexual behavior to forge and strengthen social bonds.

Mountains of the world

On an expedition in one of the world's great mountain ranges, you would see changes in the conditions, plants and animals as you climbed from the lower slopes to the highest peaks.

In northwestern Wyoming, USA, Grand Teton peak reaches 4,198 m (13,770 feet) high. Grand Teton National Park protects this spectacular mountain scenery and its diverse wildlife.

Earth's great mountain ranges are so large that they are clearly visible to astronauts orbiting hundreds of kilometres above us. Some rise far above sea level – Mount Everest, for instance, is over seven times higher than Ben Nevis. High, mountainous regions can continue without a break over wide areas without rising into sharp peaks, in which case they are called highlands.

There are mountains and highlands on all parts of the Earth, so their conditions, their plants and their animals vary widely. Mount McKinley in Alaska, for instance, rises impressively straight from the Arctic **tundra** at its base, but many giant peaks in the tropics have lower slopes swathed in rainforest. **Temperate** forest, **shrubland**, taiga and grassland cover other mountains, and one of the Earth's driest deserts, the Atacama, extends into the mighty Andes mountain range in South America.

So what do mountains have in common? For one thing, their summits poke up into the upper **atmosphere** where the air is thin and winds are very strong. Air temperature also decreases as you go higher – everywhere. **Climate**, plant life and animal life all change as you climb or descend a mountain.

At the top of the Earth's highest mountains, the Himalayas, you would need to wear breathing apparatus because the **air pressure** is so low. No animals or plants live here; conditions are too cold for all but the very simplest life-forms. Lower on the mountainsides are grassy slopes, bright with flowers in spring. Lower still, you would find yourself in forest, with birds, mammals and other forms of animal life. Yet you would still be thousands of metres above sea level, on the same mountain but in different conditions. Each mountain is not so much a biome as a complex mixture of different biomes.

Mountain climates

Mountains are places of extremes. Some of the wettest, coldest and windiest places are on mountains, but some mountains are sunny and dry. The weather on a mountain can change drastically in minutes.

Most high mountains, particularly those far from the **equator**, are cold places. Anywhere on Earth, as you climb higher above sea level, the air temperature falls. For every 100 metres (330 ft) you climb up a mountain, the temperature gets about 0.6°C (1°F) cooler. At the top of the Earth's highest mountain, Mount Everest, the temperature is 55°C (100°F) colder than it would be at sea

Fact file

▲ In 1998, Hurricane Mitch dropped up to 1900 mm (75 in) of rain on mountains in northern Honduras in just 60 hours – that's twice as much rain as the country's capital city gets in a year.

▲ Mountains experience the highest winds. In 1934, instruments on Mount Washington in the USA recorded a wind of 372 km/h (231 mph).

▲ Mountains in Alaska average over 24 metres (900 in) of snowfall a year – enough to bury a church!

level. The summits of all the very highest mountains, even those in the tropics, are permanently covered with snow and ice. Meteorologists (weather experts) use a variety of instruments to measure the weather, but it is difficult to maintain weather stations on high mountains since they are often very remote. As a result, there is still much to learn about mountain climates.

Cold comfort

Generally, the top of a mountain is colder than halfway up, and halfway up is cooler than the base. However, **altitude** (height above sea level) is not the only thing that

On mountain peaks, the wind is often so fierce that it blows away clouds of fallen snow. This is the volcano Cotopaxi, which, although situated near the equator in Ecuador, is so high that it is always covered in snow and ice.

controls temperature. If a mountain is in the tropics it is likely to be warmer than a mountain in a temperate or polar region, because the tropics receive stronger sunshine than the poles. For example, average afternoon temperatures at tropical Bogotá, which is near the equator in the Colombian Andes, reach 19°C (67°F); at the South Pole, which is about as high as Bogotá, summer temperatures peak at around –26°C (–15°F). In London, afternoon temperatures in June can often be 27°C (80°F), the same as Kathmandu in the Himalayan foothills. Kathmandu is much higher than London, but also much closer to the equator.

The direction the mountain slope faces (its aspect) is also important. Slopes facing the sun during the hottest part of the day are much warmer than those in the shade. In the

Downslope winds

Winds blowing over mountain ranges can produce very unusual weather. As air climbs a mountain, it cools and drops its moisture as rain or snow. By the time it reaches the top, the air is drier and colder. Then, as it descends the far side of the mountain, it becomes squeezed and warms up. This flow of warm, dry air – called a downslope wind – brings clear blue skies and sunny weather. It can also cause unusually hot weather. In June 1995, in the US states of Washington and Oregon, a downslope wind from the Cascade Mountains created a heat wave. As it flowed west down the mountains, the air became warmer, ensuring clear skies. Temperatures between the mountains and the Pacific Ocean were much warmer than forecast, reaching 35°C (95°F) at Portland, Oregon – a good 12°C (22°F) above the usual afternoon peak for that time of year.

northern **hemisphere**, south-west-facing slopes are the warmest; in the southern hemisphere, north-west-facing slopes are the warmest. Some steep-sided mountain valleys rarely receive any direct sunshine, and they stay cold most of the time. The amount of sunshine that shines on a mountain slope has a big influence on the plants that grow there, since plants require warmth and light to grow. Plants on sunny slopes grow bigger than those on cool, shady slopes.

At night, temperatures fall but they do not fall evenly. Cold air is heavier than warm air and flows downhill, collecting in hollows or valleys. Overnight, mountain valleys can become colder than mountain tops, the opposite of conditions during the day. This situation is called a temperature

Being enshrouded in cloud nearly all the time is an unusual kind of climate not often experienced outside mountains. In the highlands of southern Venezuela (below), cloud forests grow in the perpetual moisture.

inversion and is why valleys in mountain areas can become frosty or filled with mist in the mornings.

Catching the rain

Mountains and highland areas are usually wetter than lowlands. There is a simple explanation for this. Since mountains form an obstacle to the winds blowing around big weather systems, the only way the wind can get past is to blow over the top. Air is like a sponge and can hold large quantities of water **vapour** (a gas formed when water **evaporates**) that it picks up as it passes over the oceans. Warm air is a better sponge than cool air; it can hold more water vapour. As the air rises, it cools, and the water vapour condenses into cloud droplets. Eventually, the water droplets become large enough to fall as raindrops or snow. That is why mountain slopes facing into the prevailing wind (the most common wind direction) tend to be wet, particularly if the wind has blown over an ocean.

Mountain deserts

The Chilean Altiplano, a highland part of the Atacama Desert in Chile, is probably the driest area on the Earth. Although the town of Calama is more than 2450 metres (8000 ft) above sea level, it never rains there. One explanation for the Altiplano climate is the warm, wet winds that blow west across southern South America. These winds drop almost all their moisture as they climb the Andes mountain range. As the winds descend on the Chilean side of the mountains, the air becomes warmer so it holds onto the little remaining water vapour. The Atacama Desert is said to be in the rain shadow of the southern Andes.

If you look at an atlas showing mountains and prevailing wind direction, you can predict where the wettest places will be. A combination of high mountains near an ocean, with onshore winds, is almost guaranteed to produce a lot of rain over the mountains. Three of the wettest places on Earth are in highland areas of Colombia, Hawaii and north-east India. From April to October, warm and very wet south-westerly winds blow from the Bay of Bengal over Bangladesh. These winds are known as the south-west **monsoon** and, since the air is so warm, it absorbs millions of tonnes of water from the ocean. When the air is pushed up the southern slopes of the Himalayas over places such as Cherrapunji, it cools, releasing the water in torrents of rain. Something similar happens in western Colombia and on Mount Waialeale, on Kauai, Hawaii, where very warm, moist air that has blown over the Pacific is forced upwards by mountains.

So does it get wetter the higher you climb up a mountain? No – rainfall reaches a maximum at a certain height and then starts to decline, because the air has released most of its water vapour. The height at which this happens varies from mountain to mountain, but, generally, rainfall begins to decline above 3050 metres (10,000 ft). Mountains that are higher than that are often shrouded in cloud, but rainfall tends to be less.

Rain shadows

Mountains are not always wet. On the side of a mountain range facing away from the prevailing wind, conditions tend to be drier; the onshore wind has lost most of its moisture on the climb up the mountains, so there is little water to deposit as it descends. Also, as the air descends, it warms up, so its ability to hold on to water vapour increases. It is as if the sponge is getting bigger again. The drier area behind a mountain range is called the **rain shadow**. The Sierra Nevada in the US state of California casts a huge rain shadow, creating semi-desert conditions in the mountains and valleys of the Great Basin.

Mountains are also less rainy if the prevailing wind blows across land rather than sea – there are less opportunities for the air to soak up water vapour – or if the wind is cool before it reaches the mountains. This may happen if it has blown over a cold ocean, for example. Since it is cool, it won't be a very effective sponge. The weather station at the South Pole records less than 2.5 cm (1 in) of snow a year, despite being about 3000 metres (10,000 ft) above sea level in the middle of the very high Antarctic ice cap.

In the teeth of the gale
In lowland areas and on the low slopes of mountains, winds tend to be slowed by rubbing against the ground. Higher up, they blast into mountains with their full force. In a storm, a mountain top is a scary place to be. In many cases, people can be blown over by the force of the wind. Mountain valleys can

Seen from a space shuttle, the rain shadow cast by the Himalayas is very obvious. The south side of the mountains (top) is covered with dark forest, but the north side (bottom) looks almost as dry as a desert.

Much more snow falls on some cold mountains than in the cold polar regions. In Yellowstone National Park in the USA (right), the snow builds up into huge drifts.

channel and concentrate winds, making them even more powerful. While the side of a mountain facing the wind tends to get lots of rough weather, the lee side (the side facing away from the wind) is relatively sheltered. Trees and shrubs grow taller on the lee side of mountains, animals find more shelter and people are more likely to live there.

Avalanches
Snowfall is greater in some mountains than in any of Earth's biomes, but it does not snow on all mountains, and even some of the highest mountains have snow only near the summit. For snow to fall, the air must be cold, and there has to be moisture in the air. If the air is too warm, it will rain instead of

Mount Everest

N

Rainy record breakers

The windward slopes (above) of the island of Kauai, Hawaii, are drenched with rain. Mount Waialeale, a 1588-metre (5208-ft) peak on the island, is a strong contender for the rainiest place on Earth. It averages 11,700 mm (460 in) of rain every year, but is eclipsed by Cherrapunji, a village in north-east India. Cherrapunji is over 1300 metres (4000 ft) high on the southern slopes of the Himalayas. Average rainfall is 12,700 mm (500 in), with a world record 26,400 mm (1042 in) in one very wet year. In the rainy season, more rain falls in one month in Cherrapunji than falls in a year in lowland tropical rainforest. There are two reasons why Cherrapunji is so wet: for six months of the year it is drenched by the monsoon rains that sweep up from the Bay of Bengal; and since it is on a mountain, the winds are forced to drop their moisture there.

snow; if the air is too dry, there will be neither rain nor snow. The line above which snow remains on the ground all year is called the **snowline**; this level is higher in the tropics than in temperate latitudes.

Snow can be great fun; thousands of people travel to mountains each year to ski, toboggan or snowboard. But snow can also create problems by blocking mountain roads and preventing people from reaching their homes. There are more serious problems, too.

In spring, when the snow starts to melt, huge slabs of it sometimes break away without warning. They slide down the mountain at speeds of up to 160 km/h (100 mph) and flatten everything in their path – even trees and houses. These big snow slides are called avalanches, and they kill people every year. If the weather warms up very quickly in spring, the run-off from melting snow can cause catastrophic floods as it cascades down narrow mountain valleys.

Factor 50

There are places in mountains where rainfall is not that great but where the sun rarely shines. Some mountain valleys and peaks lie at the height where clouds usually form. These mountain slopes remain shrouded in cloud for much of the year, and the type of plant life that grows there is called **cloud forest**. Cloud forest is very lush, and it is easy to understand why. Water droplets in the cloud do not fall as rain but are deposited directly on the leaves of plants. This is called horizontal precipitation or cloud stripping, because the moisture is stripped from the clouds as it condenses on the plants. Measured rainfall may be lower in cloud forest than at sites further down the mountain, but cloud forest is always wet.

At higher altitudes still, mountains poke out above the clouds for most of the time. There, it is sunny throughout the day, and – because the air is thin and free from pollution and water vapour – the sun's radiation is very powerful. Climbers have to cover exposed parts of their bodies with strong sunscreen of up to factor 50 to prevent sunburn, even though the air may be very cold.

Clues to the past

Mountain areas hold many clues to how the Earth's climate has changed over the millennia. By measuring and dating the piles of rubble (moraines) that build up around glaciers, scientists can figure out when the climate was colder or warmer. Cores of ice are sometimes drilled out of glacial ice. These cores provide a frozen record that shows past rates of ice build-up, concentrations of gases in the atmosphere and layers of volcanic dust – evidence of past eruptions. All these measurements can give an idea of what the weather was like in the past.

Mountains such as Grand Teton in the USA (below), are so tall that their peaks are often above the clouds. On such sunny mountain tops, sunglasses (inset) are vital to protect eyes from the brilliant glare of the snow.

Mountain plants

Plants can survive in some of the harshest mountain habitats, from smouldering volcanoes to the windswept peaks of Alaska. There are even plants clinging to life high in the Himalayas – the tallest mountains on the Earth.

In winter, North America's Rocky Mountains look inhospitable. Deep snow carpets the ground, howling gales blast the jagged rock outcrops and temperatures are cold enough to kill a person in minutes. That is what many mountain regions are like for much of the year. The harsh weather is too severe for human settlement, and even the hardiest animals are forced to retreat to the lower slopes. Surely no plant could survive in such an extreme environment.

Yet return to the same place in spring and you would witness an entirely different spectacle. Gone is the carpet of snow, and in its place is a flower-filled meadow. Amazingly, there are many plants that can grow and flourish in places that are covered in snow for

As soon as the snow disappears from the slopes of the Rockies in Colorado, the USA, alpine plants burst into bloom. Similar displays occur in the Alps of Europe.

most of the year and where temperatures remain freezing for months on end. In the Himalayas, plants grow on mountainsides as high as 7000 metres (22,000 ft).

Four essentials

Plants need light, water, warmth and **nutrients** to grow and to reproduce. On mountains, one or more of these essentials

314

is usually in short supply, at least for part of the year. Most plants get nutrients from the soil, but on rocky mountain peaks there is little or no soil. Plants receive light and warmth from sunshine, but many mountain ranges are bathed in cloud, which cuts out sunlight for much of the time. While some parts of a mountain range might receive a regular dousing of rain, others are in rain shadows and are very dry. Sometimes, even when there is water, the plants cannot use it because it is frozen.

Mountain plants face other problems, too. Many plants need insects to pollinate their flowers, but there are fewer insects on cold mountainsides than there are lower down. And the wind that blows so strongly on high mountains stops trees from growing tall.

Fact file

▲ The oldest bristlecone pines in the White Mountains of California in the USA are 4600 years old. They were already ancient when the Mayan civilization was at its height in Central America.

▲ Microscopic plant-like organisms thrive in the boiling waters of volcanic lakes; the scalding water is so acidic that it dissolves the seams of boats.

▲ The highest forest on Earth is on the slopes of Sajama Volcano, Bolivia. It is 5100 metres (16,700 ft) above sea level, higher than any town.

▲ The *Rafflesia* plant of Mount Kinabalu, Borneo, has flowers 1 metre (3 ft) wide.

Mountain zones

WEST   *rain-bearing winds* →   EAST

Ice and snow

Alpine tundra and grassland

Coniferous forest

Broad-leaved forest

Chaparral shrubland

Ice and snow

Alpine tundra and grassland

Coniferous forest

Dry sagebrush shrubland

Different types of plants grow at particular heights on mountains, forming zones of plant life that are like biomes in miniature. Walking across California's Sierra Nevada mountains is a bit like taking a trip to the Arctic and back. As you climb, shrubland gives way to broad-leaved forest, followed by conifer forest, alpine tundra and then barren snow and ice. The plants of the western and eastern slopes differ because the west side gets more rain.

Creosote bush   Red fir

Evergreen oak   Dwarf willow

                   Grass

Giant redwood   Sagebrush
(or sequoia)

The treeline

Generally, plants become smaller the higher up a mountain you go. At lower levels, many mountain ranges are cloaked in forest. The trees tend to get smaller higher up the mountain. Above a certain height on the mountainside, no trees grow at all, and small shrubs and grasses grow in their place. This point, called the treeline, is often clearly visible from a distance as the dividing line between dark green forest and paler grassland above. The treeline is higher in tropical regions than in cooler, temperate parts of the world. That is because the growing season – the time during which temperatures are warm enough for plant growth – gets longer as you move from the poles toward the equator. In the Rocky Mountains of British Columbia, the treeline is about 1900 metres (6000 ft) high. Further south in Nevada, where the climate is warmer, it is almost 3300 metres (11,000 ft) high. Further still, on the Mexican volcano Popocatépetl, pine forests flourish up to 4000 metres (13,000 ft) above sea level.

Above the treeline are zones of heath and moor before the permanent snowline. Beyond this, plant life stops and snow lies on the ground all year round. Like the treeline, the snowline gets lower the further from the equator you go. In the very far north of North America, Europe and

Asia, the treeline is at sea level, meaning there are no trees at all and the landscape is covered only with Arctic tundra or barren expanses of snow and ice.

The greenest forest

On the lower slopes of tropical mountain ranges, such as the northern Andes, there is a bewildering array of big trees, forming tropical forest. The same is true in the Himalayas and many of the mountains of South-east Asia. Under the umbrella of the tropical forest **canopy** is an **understorey** of young trees and smaller plants fighting for what little light penetrates to the forest floor.

A little higher up the slopes of many of these tropical mountains is a zone that becomes engulfed in cloud from late morning

Cloud forest and elfin forest

At Monteverde in Costa Rica (below), cloud forest grows between about 1370 metres (4500 ft) and 1500 metres (5000 ft) above sea level. An amazing variety of plants thrive in this lush jungle, including nearly 900 species of epiphytes (plants that grow on other plants) and some 450 orchids. The forest is constantly dripping, and mosses and epiphytes grow on every tree. Higher up the mountain, trees have to contend with cooler air and stronger wind – when fully grown, they reach only about 5 metres (16 feet) tall. Because the trees are so small, such forest is called elfin forest.

✳ Getting a leg-up

Very little sunlight reaches the floor of a conifer forest, such as the forest in the Rocky Mountains. What light does penetrate the dense canopy is often blocked out by a lower layer of ferns. So how do young trees get the light they need to grow? The seeds get a leg-up on their fallen neighbours. When one of the huge conifers falls, perhaps after a storm, the top of the horizontal trunk is above the height of the ferns, so any seeds falling onto it can begin to grow and stand a reasonable chance of getting the light they need. In effect, the dead tree supports and nurtures the young saplings, so people call it a nurse log. Sometimes, trees of the same age can be seen growing in a straight line – the line of the fallen nurse log.

nearly every day. The forest that grows in such places is called cloud forest. It is an environment so lush that even the tree trunks are covered with greenery.

Small plants trying to grow in a forest of massive trees face a hard struggle. In cloud forest it is even more difficult for them since the supply of light from the sun is reduced by cloud every afternoon. Even small plants need to reach the light of the forest canopy, but how? Plants called **epiphytes** turn the tables on the big trees by using them as platforms. Birds eat epiphyte fruits, carry them up to their favourite perch on a large tree then expel the seeds in their droppings. The seeds begin to grow, and their roots take hold in cracks in the tree's trunk. Epiphytic plants include orchids, and there are even cacti that grow on forest trees. Bromeliads are epiphytes whose leaves grow in a rosette shape. The rosettes collect rainwater and moisture from the cloud. Birds, frogs, lizards and snakes drink the water, leaving their droppings before they move on. The animals' droppings provide the plants with nutrients, and the bromeliad receives far more light than it would on the forest floor. Epiphytes get all the water they need from the dampness in the clouds that sweep past daily, and they help make mountain cloud forests the greenest of all forests.

Needles for leaves

Trees need to draw water through their roots, up their trunk and into their leaves. In colder regions, far from the equator – and especially high on a mountain – many trees cannot draw water all year round. The water might be frozen in the ground, but even when it is liquid, the trees run the risk that it might later freeze in their leaves. Many trees simply shut down from autumn to spring. Such trees have broad leaves and live

The Indian paintbrush plant is often seen clinging to rocky crevices in the mountains of eastern USA. Its scarlet leaves are often mistaken for flowers.

Thanks to their springy, downward-sloping branches, conifer trees shake off snow easily and suffer little damage after a heavy snowfall.

in regions that are temperate – neither very hot in summer nor very cold in winter. Every autumn, the broad leaves of these trees dry out and lose their green colour before falling to the ground. Thousands of people visit the Appalachian Mountains in North America each autumn to witness the myriad colours – reds, yellows, oranges and browns – that the leaves take on before they drop. Not until the following spring do the tiny green buds of a new year's growth of leaves appear.

The slopes of the Rocky Mountains are generally colder than the Appalachians. Even in summer, temperatures may drop below freezing at night. Broad-leaved trees could only stay in leaf for a small part of the year, but another type of tree – the conifer – can survive in these conditions. Conifers avoid dropping their leaves, so their leaves can continue the work of capturing sunlight and pumping water for longer. In the Rocky Mountains and other cold mountain areas, conifers such as sitka spruce, hemlock and Douglas fir are the dominant types of trees. Their needle-shaped leaves have a protective waxy covering and only a tiny amount of freezable sap, allowing them to survive the winter freeze. The leaves do not work as efficiently as those of broad-leaved trees but do not have to be shed in autumn.

Trees on the mid-slopes of the Rocky Mountains and other mountain ranges also have to deal with big falls of snow in winter. The snow's weight would break the branches of many types of trees, but mountain conifers have branches that slope downwards and so let the snow slide off.

Mountain zones

In most mountains, there are several zones of plant life, with different trees dominant at different heights. In the Rockies, spruce trees are most common at lower levels. Higher up the mountain slopes, larches and pines dominate, towering over an undergrowth of shrubs, mosses and lichens. Higher still, the large trees are replaced by dwarf pines, birch, willow, alder and shrubs.

Above the treeline, mountains are less hospitable. Temperatures are warm enough for plant growth during only a short part of the year. There may be more exposed rocks and less soil, strong winds blow on many days and the ground may be covered in a blanket of snow. Although trees can't survive these conditions, many small plants occupy this zone. In some ways, the landscape above the treeline in mountains looks like the tree-less wastes of the Arctic tundra.

Alpine tundra

People sometimes call the tree-less zone of mountains 'alpine tundra', though it is different from Arctic tundra. For one thing, the Arctic gets much less rain and snow than most mountains. Its seasons are also much more severe, the long, freezing winters, when the sun hardly rises, contrasting with the short, sunny summers, when the sun hardly

✿ Giant sequoias

The mountains of Sequoia National Park in California are home to forests of giant sequoias, the biggest trees on Earth. Some of the trees are so famous that they have been given their own names. The largest, General Sherman, is 88 metres (290 ft) tall – well over one-third the height of the Canary Wharf Tower. Its trunk has a circumference of 24 metres (80 ft) – the girth of a small house. If its trunk, roots, branches and leaves could be put on a giant weighing scale, they would register more than 6000 tonnes.

Another one of these huge conifer trees, General Grant, is about 2500 years old, and the top of its highest branch stands 81 metres (267 ft) above the ground. Giant sequoias are not good trees to climb; you would need a ladder 39 metres (129 feet) high to reach the lowest branch of General Grant.

Plants of the Andes

The plant life of the Andes changes along the mountain range as the warm, wet climate of the tropics merges into the cooler, more temperate south. Running along the spine of the mountains are high, windswept grasslands, known as puna. Cloud forests and rainforests flourish on the eastern slopes near the equator, where the air is misty and humid. Further south, gnarled queñoa trees – the world's highest growing trees – survive among the dry, dusty valleys of Bolivia. Further still, forests of southern beeches and monkey puzzles hug the slopes of the Chilean Andes, sustained by moist winds blowing off the Pacific.

Cloud forest, featuring epiphytes

Temperate, broad-leaved forest, featuring southern beeches

Dry mountain forest, featuring queñoa trees

Grasslands

sets. Another difference is that Arctic tundra has permafrost – a layer of permanently frozen ground just below the surface.

In the alpine tundra of Austria and Switzerland, plants such as the alpine snowbell lie dormant under the snow. When spring sunshine begins to penetrate the snow, the dark surface of snowbell buds absorbs the heat and helps melt the snow. This gives the plant an advantage: it becomes snow-free, and so can start to grow before its neighbours. Its beautiful mauve flowers, like those of many other plants that grow on high mountains, are large relative to the plant itself. They need to be large to attract the insects that will pollinate them, since there are fewer insects in high mountains than in the valleys and plains below. In the alpine tundra of the Rocky Mountains, there is a continuous blanket of grasses and small plants with large, brilliant flowers in spring.

Other mountain plants are pollinated by birds, notably hummingbirds in North and South America. In Costa Rica, the bright red flowers of fuschias attract one called the magnificent hummingbird, which comes to drink nectar; in so doing it pollinates the flowers. In the Rockies, calliope hummingbirds pollinate gooseberries, currants, red columbine and Indian paintbrush.

Cushion plants (foreground) are among the few plants that can survive high in the Chilean Andes. Their low, rounded shape gives protection from wind and cold.

Cushions and jackets

Mountain plants risk freezing at night, even in summer. In every mountain range on Earth, there are plants with antifreeze mechanisms. In the Alps, edelweiss has a

 Fly trap

Some plants reward their pollinators with an energy-rich drink of nectar, but not all plants are quite so generous. Rothschild's slipper orchid (right) grows on Mount Kinabalu in Borneo. Its flower is an amazing construction, with two long, twisted wings stretching on either side of a slipper-shaped cup. The wings have dark marks that look like a swarm of aphids. Some flies lay

their eggs among aphids so that the fly grubs can use the aphids for food. The orchid's disguise clearly works since flies enter the cup to lay their eggs and, having done so, find themselves trapped inside. The only escape for the unfortunate fly is by completing a complicated manoeuvre to get out of the flower – which results in a bundle of pollen sticking to the fly's back.

Tough at the top

The climate gets harsher the higher you climb up mountains, and trees find it increasingly difficult to survive. In some places, the winter wind turns trees into shrubs, creating a strange, flattened type of shrubland called krummholz (a German word that means 'twisted wood'). Krummholz forms in places where plants survive the winter under a shallow blanket of snow. Although snow is cold, it acts like a quilt, protecting plants from the much colder air above. But if trees grow too tall in the summer, their branches stick out of the snow, and winter frosts soon cut them back. The result, after many years, is a high-altitude shrubland made up of stunted trees that creep along the ground.

coat of woolly hairs that protects its buds from killer frosts. In the Himalayas, *Saussurea* is completely surrounded by a protective jacket of hairs. The jacket has a hole in the top, through which insects fly to pollinate the mauve flowers. Sometimes, the insects stay the night inside the plant's shelter.

Cushion plants are protected from the cold by their shape. Their stems are packed very tightly together, forming a kind of cushion that retains warmth. The shape also preserves moisture, protecting the plants from dehydrating mountain winds. When the leaves die, they stay inside the cushion as they decay, allowing the living parts of the plant to recycle precious nutrients.

Bristlecone pines grow on the arid mountains of western North America and are thought to be the oldest trees on Earth. One of them is nearly 5000 years old.

Bristlecone pines, which grow high in the mountains of North America's Great Basin region, also have to survive extreme conditions. From a distance these peculiar trees look dead, with gnarled and battered trunks. However, clusters of green pine needles on some of the branches show that they are alive. In fact, they are the oldest trees on Earth and can reach thousands of years old. These tough survivors live through bitterly cold winters when there is snow on the ground, and arid summers when very

A lost world

Some of the strangest mountains are in South America. Standing thousands of metres above the rainforests of southern Venezuela are flat-topped mountains called tepuis. The vertical walls of the tepuis form some of the tallest cliffs on Earth. These mountains are nearly always shrouded in cloud, and rain falls so frequently and heavily that big puddles only rarely dry out. The rocks at the top of Roraima (above), the highest of the tepuis, look black but are really pinkish-white; their true colour is hidden under a skin of algae (tiny plant-like organisms that can grow even where there is no soil). On top of the tepuis, the boggy soil contains few of the nutrients that plants need. Pitcher plants and sundews solve this problem by trapping and digesting insects, releasing extra nutrients. The plants on Venezuelan tepuis (inset) have been isolated from the forest below for millions of years. Over this time, the plants have evolved (changed gradually) and become well suited to life in cool and very wet conditions. The mountains are home to almost 1000 types of orchids that live nowhere else on Earth. In all, half the plants that live on these mountain tops live in no other place.

little rain falls. Such extremes mean that the pines grow very slowly – in some years they may not grow at all. Few bristlecone pines are more than 9.5 metres (30 ft) tall, and many are much shorter, despite their great age.

Mountains and highlands are often plagued by strong winds that limit the growth of plants. However, in some parts of the tropics, strong winds are rare, and plants can grow relatively tall even on high mountains.

At 4000 metres (13,000 ft) in the Andes, espeletias grow taller than a basketball player. When their yellow flowers brighten the grassy mountainsides in October and November, bearded helmetcrest hummingbirds flit from flower to flower, pollinating the plants as they go. Groundsels and giant lobelias in the mountains of East Africa grow even taller, some to more than 10 metres (30 ft). Like other mountain plants, they run the risk of

freezing at night – and if a plant's water supply freezes, the ice can kill it. Groundsels, espeletias and giant lobelias protect themselves from ice in a similar way. Each year they grow a new rosette of leaves around the main stem. The leaves remain in place after they die, building up to form a protective jacket that keeps out the cold.

Groundsels (lower left, green) and lobelias (below, grey-green) grow into giants on the mountains of East Africa.

Mountain animals

Mountain animals have to contend with hazardous terrain, freezing temperatures and ferocious gales. But for those tough enough to survive, mountains are full of rich pickings, with more breeding sites than lowland areas and less competition for food.

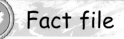 **Fact file**

▲ The heart of a hummingbird in the Andes beats up to 1260 times a minute.

▲ Even though they are cold-blooded animals, some iguanas live at 4000 metres (12,500 ft) in the Andes – higher than any other reptiles.

▲ A chough (a relative of the crow) once accompanied a climbing expedition up Everest to a height of 7925 metres (26,000 ft) – that's almost as high as aeroplanes fly when crossing the Atlantic.

▲ Snow leopards have larger lungs than other big cats because they live at very high altitudes, where there is not so much oxygen in the air.

Mountains are cooler than the lowlands around them, and the very highest peaks are usually extremely cold – even those in tropical Asia and Africa. Animals that live on mountains need ways of surviving freezing winters and bitter nights. Some have a coat of fur or feathers to keep them warm. Others can go into a deep sleep called **hibernation**, allowing their body temperature to fall without doing harm to themselves. Still more animals simply move to warmer places lower down the mountain.

Guanacos live in the high grasslands of the Andes, ranging from Peru and Bolivia to the southern tip of South America. They are wild animals but are very close relatives of llamas and alpacas – the domestic animals that people of the Andes keep for wool, meat or carrying goods. This group lives in the Torres del Paine National Park in the mountains of Chile.

The snow leopard (below) can endure freezing Tibetan winters thanks to its luxuriously thick fur, stocky build and bushy tail, which serves as a portable blanket.

Fur coats

The Tibetan **Plateau** is so high that it is always cold, but it is too vast in area for animals to escape to warmer lowland regions. The larger animals that live there, such as snow leopards and yaks, protect themselves with a thick furry coat. The snow leopard's tail is as long as its body and much bushier than most cats' tails. When lying down, the leopard wraps the tail around its body and face for extra protection from the cold.

The snow leopard's smoky-grey colour helps **camouflage** it against snow and rocks as it hunts for food. It preys on **mammals** large and small, including young yaks. But yaks have more problems to contend with than prowling snow leopards. These massive, grass-eating mammals – adult males weigh as

White-tailed prairie dogs live higher up than their black-tailed cousins of the prairies. In late summer, they begin fattening themselves up, ready for hibernation in winter.

A long sleep

To deal with the terrible winter, some animals go into a state of inactivity called hibernation. When food becomes scarce and the weather is cold, they save energy by hibernating in a warm burrow for months on end. In the forests of the North American Rocky Mountains, black bears hibernate for five to seven months of the year. These magnificent animals make a good living in the forest for half the year, feeding mostly on much as a small car – endure temperatures that sometimes plunge to –40°C (–40°F); yaks need every hair of their shaggy coat to keep out the cold.

Feathers trap warm air in much the same way as fur does. The black-tailed ptarmigan survives even the bitterest winters in the mountains of Alaska and the Alps thanks to its insulating plumage. Like snow leopards, ptarmigan are camouflaged – in winter, their feathers turn white to blend in with the snow. Unlike snow leopards, however, their camouflage is to hide them from **predators**, not prey. Ptarmigan and snow leopards have something else in common: snowshoes. Snow leopards have large paws and ptarmigan have feathered feet to help them walk on snow.

Bamboo munchers

The giant pandas that live in the bamboo forests of south-western China have enormous appetites. Large adults munch more than 4.5 tonnes (10,000 lbs) of bamboo a year; that's the weight of four cars. Pandas have large, strong jaw muscles that enable them to crush the tough bamboo. It is these big jaw muscles that give pandas their rounded faces. Pandas eat young bamboo stems from November to March, old stems from April to June, and bamboo leaves from July to October. Below a height of 2600 metres (8500 ft) most of the bamboo forest has been cut down by people, and above about 3500 metres (11,500 feet) bamboo does not grow naturally, so giant pandas have to live between these heights. That is partly why they are so rare; fewer than 1000 now survive in the wild. The forests where they live are cold and wet for much of the year, but pandas do not hibernate. Instead, they have very thick, dense fur that is slightly oily; this fur protects them from the rain and cold.

berries, grass, roots, flowers and nuts, but also eating carrion (dead animals), small mammals and fish. When the weather gets colder in autumn, the bears search for a good place to spend the winter months. They may select a cave or hollow tree or dig a den. Before hibernating, they feed as much as possible to put on weight – even though they use very little energy while in hibernation, they may still lose one-third of their body weight before coming out of hibernation the following April or May.

During the long winter, a black bear's heart slows to just eight to twelve beats a minute, and its body temperature falls by several

Above: In spring, calliope hummingbirds migrate to the Rockies from their wintering grounds in Mexico. They are North America's smallest birds – adults grow to only 8 cm (3.1 in) and weigh less than a five pence piece.

degrees. At that temperature and heart rate, the bear uses much less energy and can survive on its reserves of body fat.

Many other mountain mammals hibernate, including ground squirrels and prairie dogs. In the USA, white-tailed prairie dogs live in mountain country more than 2000 metres (6550 ft) above sea level from Montana to Arizona and New Mexico – areas where the mountains become frozen wastes in winter. The prairie dogs feed well in autumn to put on a layer of fat ready for winter. Then, in late autumn, they disappear into their burrows and go to sleep. They burn off the fat bit by bit while hibernating, keeping their body temperature above freezing. In spring, when they emerge into the outside world, they are thin and feed quickly on the new plant growth to get back to a healthy weight.

A few types of birds can also slow down their body to save energy. The Andes get cold at night, even close to the equator, where many hummingbirds live.

329

Cave Dwellers

Wherever there are mountains, there are likely to be caves as well. Though cold, dark, and wet, caves provide many animals with a refuge from enemies and inhospitable weather. Bats (right) roost in caves during the day and emerge at night to hunt insects. Bears sometimes hibernate in caves, and pumas, or mountain lions, (below) use them as lairs—gruesome feeding sites where they drag their mutilated victims.

Hummingbirds need to eat lots of sugary nectar to stay active, but they cannot feed at night when the flowers they feed from are closed. The hummingbirds' way around the problem is to go into a state called torpor – for a few hours every night, their heartbeat slows down and their body temperature drops by as much as 19°C (34°F).

Blue-spotted salamanders live in the northern Appalachian Mountains in the USA, which get very cold in winter. These **amphibians** survive the winter by hibernating underground but emerge early in the year when there is often still snow on the ground. They do this so they can try to be first at the breeding sites. Blue-spotted salamanders

migrate across snow and ice to reach the lakes where they breed. Even when they reach the water and dive in, they have to survive near-freezing conditions that would kill most other amphibians – some individuals even freeze. As long as there is plenty of moisture when they thaw, however, they just get up and walk away as if nothing has happened. No one knows how they survive being frozen.

Exodus

Some animals simply leave the higher slopes of mountains when the weather gets colder in autumn. This way of escaping the cold is called **migration** and is a common strategy among birds – it is easier for them since they can fly. Migration is more difficult for mammals, reptiles and amphibians, which have to walk. In the Himalayas, seed-eating birds such as Brandt's mountain finches eke out an existence over 6000 metres (19,700 ft) up – more than one and a half times as high as most Alpine peaks. It makes sense for

The resplendent quetzal

Resplendent quetzals are brightly coloured birds of mountain cloud forests in Central America. The males are famous for their incredibly long tails. Quetzals eat, among other things, the fruits of wild avocados. In fact, there are not many birds with a mouth wide enough to swallow an avocado. Flying to a favoured perch, the quetzal swallows the avocado and strips the soft outer layers from the fruit before regurgitating (coughing up) the stone. Female quetzals probably use nutrients gained from eating avocado flesh to produce their eggs. So important is this fruit to quetzals that the birds often nest close to an avocado tree.

spend much of their lives in underground burrows. They sleep in their burrows at night, hibernate in them in winter and raise their young in them. At night, pikas in the Himalayas and Tibet share their burrows with birds named snowfinches, which also need shelter. The birds sometimes take more advantage of the hospitality of their pika

them to do so because there is little competition for food at that height. They can breed and rear their young in the summer when food is plentiful, then migrate to lower levels of the mountain in winter when the upper levels are blanketed with snow. Birds called longspurs make a similar annual migration in the Rocky Mountains.

Instead of hibernating, pikas collect plants in autumn and dry them to make hay, providing a store of food to last through the winter.

Snug down under

Mountains are often very windy places, and the chilling effect of wind can make animals lose heat quickly. This is not a problem for an active adult animal, but it can kill an inactive or young animal. Ground squirrels and prairie dogs in the Rocky Mountains, pikas on the Tibetan Plateau and giant mole-rats in the Bale Mountains of Ethiopia all

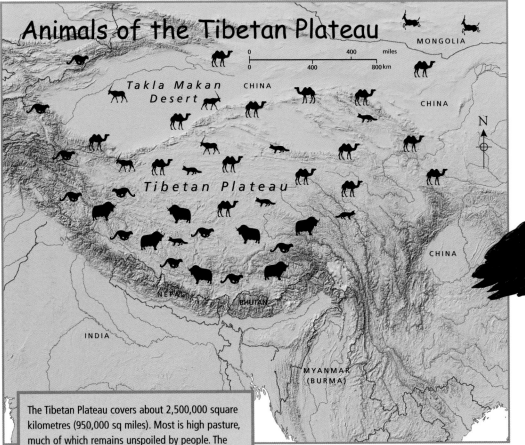

Animals of the Tibetan Plateau

Takla Makan Desert

Tibetan Plateau

MONGOLIA

CHINA

CHINA

CHINA

N

NEPAL

BHUTAN

INDIA

MYANMAR
(BURMA)

The Tibetan Plateau covers about 2,500,000 square kilometres (950,000 sq miles). Most is high pasture, much of which remains unspoiled by people. The north especially is a desolate, arid wilderness, where only wild animals and occasional nomads set foot. Rare Tibetan antelopes and wild Bactrian (two-humped) camels live on the sparse grass of the plateau and deserts to the north. They share the area with snow leopards, Tibetan foxes, Mongolian gazelles and yaks – both wild and domestic.

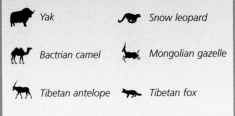

Yak

Bactrian camel

Tibetan antelope

Snow leopard

Mongolian gazelle

Tibetan fox

hosts and build their nests in the burrows. The mammals and birds seem to live together without any problems.

Visitors move in

Mountains are places of extremes. In winter, the mountain landscape may be covered in snow, and food may be very difficult to find. Even if it does not snow, there is little food in winter. Yaks and other plant-eating animals on the Tibetan Plateau are forced to exist on a diet of dry, dead plants for most of the year – green shoots are available for only three months or so.

A bone clutched in its claws, a lammergeier soars over the Drakensberg mountains of South Africa. These huge vultures nest on rocky ledges among mountains. They feed on carrion (dead animals) and break open bones by dropping them from a great height.

Bone breakers

Vultures and other birds of prey soar high on spirals of warm air called thermals. From their vantage points high in the sky, the birds can search for dead animals lying on the mountainside. One type of vulture, found in the mountains of Europe, Asia and Africa, has an ingenious method of increasing its intake of protein: the lammergeier picks up a bone from a dead animal and then soars very high. Once high enough, it drops the bone, which usually breaks into pieces on the rocks below. The lammergeier then flies down to feed on the nutritious marrow. Although it is a large and impressive vulture, it is dwarfed by a vulture in the Andes. The Andean condor is the largest flying bird on Earth; its wings span the length of a small car. Like the lammergeier, it feeds mostly on dead animals.

In summer, however, when the snow has gone, the mountainside may be clothed in flowers, with their attendant insects. For those animals able to take advantage of it, the mountain then becomes a place of plenty, even if only for a few short months. Visitors make incredible journeys to take advantage of the insects and other invertebrates that appear on the slopes. The northern wheatear is an insect-eating bird that spends the winter months in Africa. Each spring, many thousands of these birds desert their winter quarters. Some fly thousands of kilometres to the high-altitude meadows of the Alps, but others go much further: to the mountains and highlands of Scandinavia, Central Asia, Greenland and even Alaska. The birds nest in their summer home, and in late summer they and their offspring make the epic return journey – across land and sea – to Africa.

Sure-footed and agile, mountain goats can negotiate even the most treacherous cliffs and glaciers with effortless confidence. They shed their woolly coats each summer.

Gentle giants

High in the mountains of south-western Uganda, Rwanda and the Democratic Republic of the Congo live about 600 of our closest relatives – mountain gorillas. In the past, gorillas gained a fearsome reputation because of their size and our lack of understanding about how they live. Films such as King Kong encouraged the view that gorillas are aggressive monsters, liable to attack and kill people without provocation – but nothing could be further from the truth. They are, in fact, gentle giants.

Mountain gorillas certainly make an impressive sight. A fully grown male has a wide chest and powerful legs and arms. He may weigh 180 kg (400 lbs) – two and a half times the average weight of a man – but a female may be half this size. Despite their appearance, gorillas are shy animals that feed on plants and fruit, supplemented with termites. They have few enemies except people. Relentless hunting and destruction of mountain forests by people have brought mountain gorillas to the brink of extinction. If the mountain forests disappear, the last gorillas will disappear with them.

Mountaineers

Mountain animals have to get around in difficult terrain. Two animals that live in the Alps and Pyrenees of Europe – the ibex (right) and chamois – are masters of the art of climbing and jumping. Both species make leaping from rock to rock and climbing near-vertical slopes look easy. In the summer, ibex feed in meadows and on rocky ground up to 3050 metres (10,000 ft) high in the Alps, but they descend to lower levels when the weather turns colder in autumn.

Timed for success

Animals are most vulnerable to cold and hunger when they are young. Mammals and birds that breed in harsh mountain environments time their courtship and breeding so that the young are born or hatch when conditions are most favourable. Every June, female Tibetan antelopes hurry north across the very high Tibetan Plateau, following an ancient migration route north to sites in the Kunlun Mountains (no one knows exactly where) to give birth. Two months later, the mothers return on their long trek south to meet with the male antelopes, this time accompanied by their offspring. Even in midsummer, blizzards often sweep across the vast plateau; when they do, many young antelopes die.

Blizzards are not the only hazard the antelopes have to contend with. Predatory snow leopards with their own young to feed prowl the plateau in search of weak antelope to prey upon. Female snow leopards give birth to two or three cubs in late March

or April. The cubs remain dependent on their mother for almost two years, and during this time the mother is constantly on the lookout for a meal. A good-sized kill – an ibex or blue sheep, for example – will last for several days.

Mountain butterflies (right) emerge from pupae in summer to feed in the flower-filled alpine meadows.

Rocky Mountains

Pine forests, flower meadows, deserts, glaciers and temperate rainforests are just a few of the diverse landscapes that exist in the Rocky Mountains of North America.

Mount Rainier in the USA is a dormant volcano surrounded by glaciers and wildflower meadows. It last erupted 2000 years ago.

Brooks Range

ALASKA
(USA)

Denali National Park

Mount McKinley

Mount Foraker

Alaska Range

1

2

In hot water

Yellowstone is the oldest national park in the world. Established in 1872, this big protected area straddles a colossal volcano. Although dormant, the volcano generates enough heat to boil undergound water and blast it into the air in geysers (such as Castle Geyser, above). The biggest is the Steamboat Geyser, which sometimes rises 90 metres (300 ft) and showers viewers with mineral-rich water. The Steamboat is not the most famous geyser; that award goes to Old Faithful. There are more geysers in Yellowstone than anywhere else on the Earth.

Yellowstone National Park is also famed for its animals, which include bison strong enough to toss an adult into a tree, and grizzly bears that should be avoided at all costs. People have lived in the Yellowstone area for at least 12,000 years.

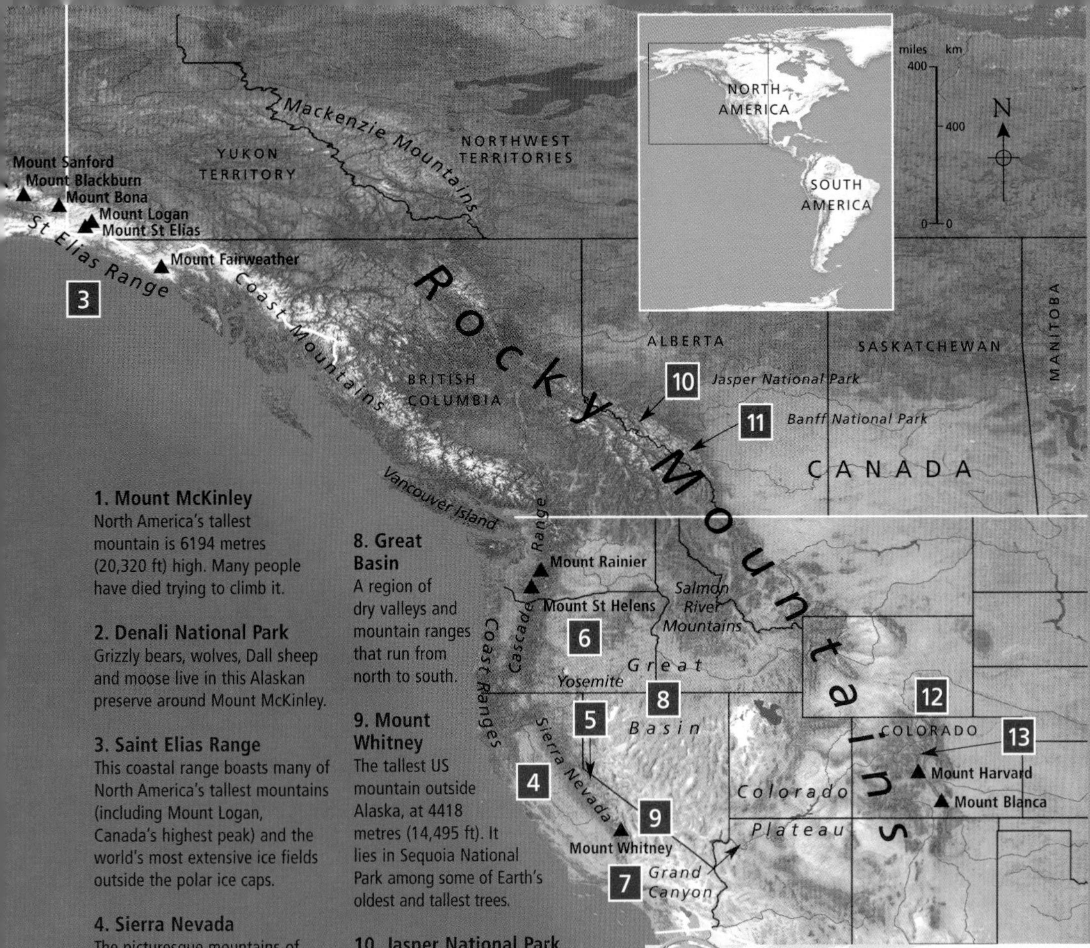
Mount Sanford
Mount Blackburn
Mount Bona
Mount Logan
Mount St Elias
St Elias Range
Mount Fairweather
3
Coast Mountains
Mackenzie Mountains
YUKON TERRITORY
NORTHWEST TERRITORIES
NORTH AMERICA
SOUTH AMERICA
miles km
400
400
0 0
N
Rocky Mountains
ALBERTA
SASKATCHEWAN
MANITOBA
BRITISH COLUMBIA
10 Jasper National Park
11 Banff National Park
CANADA
Vancouver Island
Cascade Range
Mount Rainier
Mount St Helens
Salmon River Mountains
6
Coast Ranges
Great Basin
Yosemite
8
5
Sierra Nevada
4
9
Mount Whitney
7
Grand Canyon
Colorado Plateau
12
COLORADO
13
Mount Harvard
Mount Blanca

1. Mount McKinley
North America's tallest mountain is 6194 metres (20,320 ft) high. Many people have died trying to climb it.

2. Denali National Park
Grizzly bears, wolves, Dall sheep and moose live in this Alaskan preserve around Mount McKinley.

3. Saint Elias Range
This coastal range boasts many of North America's tallest mountains (including Mount Logan, Canada's highest peak) and the world's most extensive ice fields outside the polar ice caps.

4. Sierra Nevada
The picturesque mountains of this California range cast a rain shadow over Nevada, giving the Great Basin a very dry climate.

5. Yosemite National Park
A beautifully scenic valley in the Sierra Nevada range, featuring dramatic cliffs, waterfalls and sequoia groves.

6. Mount Saint Helens
A huge volcano that erupted explosively on 18 May 1980.

7. Grand Canyon
This breathtaking chasm formed over thousands of years as the Colorado River slowly wore its way down into the rising Colorado Plateau.

8. Great Basin
A region of dry valleys and mountain ranges that run from north to south.

9. Mount Whitney
The tallest US mountain outside Alaska, at 4418 metres (14,495 ft). It lies in Sequoia National Park among some of Earth's oldest and tallest trees.

10. Jasper National Park
Visitors to this Canadian reserve can see cougars (mountain lions), black bears, coyotes, moose and elk.

11. Banff National Park
Rockclimbing, hiking, skiing and birdwatching are all popular with visitors to this mountain park.

12. Colorado
This state has many of the USA's tallest mountains outside Alaska. It also has some of North America's best ski resorts.

13. White River National Forest
A hikers' paradise in the heart of the Colorado Rockies.

Fact file

▲ The Rockies run all the way from Alaska to New Mexico, forming the backbone of the Western Cordillera, a vast system of mountains and highlands in western North America.

▲ The Western Cordillera began to form about 80 million years ago as the bed of the Pacific collided with North America, making the land crumple.

▲ There are more protected areas in the Rocky Mountains than in any other mountain range.

▲ Some parts of the Rockies receive very little rain, but the coastal ranges in Alaska and British Columbia are extremely wet.

Himalayas

The soaring peaks of the Earth's tallest mountains formed as the Indian landmass collided with Asia, squashing and folding the land over millions of years. The mountains are still rising today.

Fact file

▲ The Himalayas include our planet's fifteen highest mountains. Mount Everest is the tallest.

▲ Every year, Mount Everest grows in height by about the thickness of a one pound coin.

▲ Tibetan people carry out 'sky burials' when someone dies. Instead of putting the body in a grave, they chop it up and let vultures eat it.

Because it's there

People have always been fascinated by the challenge of climbing mountains. Mount Everest (below), the greatest of them all, is no exception. The first seven recorded attempts on the summit ended in failure, but in 1953, Edmund Hillary and Tenzing Norgay reached the top. Since then, more than 600 climbers from twenty countries have scaled Everest. Milestone climbs include those by Junko Tabei, the first woman, in 1975; Tom Whittaker (right), the first disabled climber, who climbed Everest in 1998 with an artificial leg; and Reinhold Messner, the first to reach the summit without oxygen. Having climbed it once, would anyone want to go back to the top? Yes! A sherpa (guide) named Ang Rita has performed the climb ten times so far. There have been many sad endings, too: at least 100 climbers have died in pursuit of the ultimate climbing glory.

route to summit

Mount Naptse

Mount Lhotse

Glacier

Mount Everest

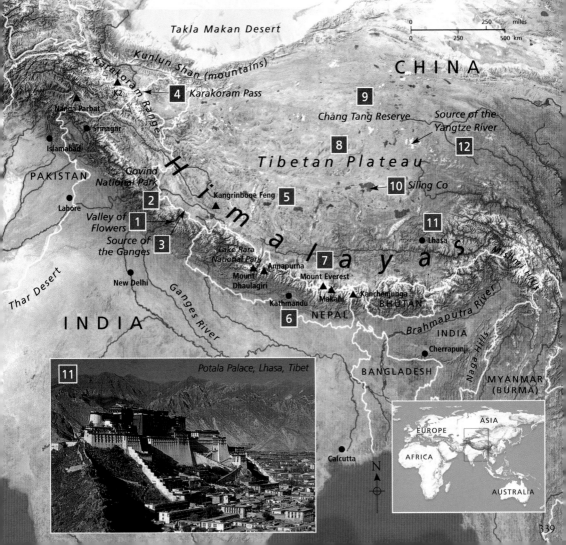

1. Valley of Flowers National Park
Hundreds of different wild-flower species carpet the meadows of this small reserve.

2. Govind National Park
The rare snow leopard lives in the higher parts of this Indian Himalayan reserve.

3. Source of the Ganges
The Ganges River is sacred to Hindus. It flows through India and Bangladesh, where it empties into the Indian Ocean.

4. Karakoram Pass
One of the highest trade routes on Earth, this pass links India with China.

5. Kangrinboqe Feng
Pilgrims from Nepal, India and China consider this round-topped mountain sacred.

6. Kathmandu
Nepal's capital lies in the foothills of the Himalayas. Its temples are overrun by monkeys, which the local people consider sacred.

7. Mount Everest
The highest mountain on Earth at 8850 metres (29,035 ft).

8. Tibetan Plateau
A huge area of highlands to the north of the Himalayas. The mountains block rain-bearing wind, giving Tibet a much drier climate than India.

9. Chang Tang Reserve
Antelope, yaks and pikas live in this vast reserve, which is dotted with salt lakes. Chang Tang is as big as the UK.

10. Siling Co
Fed by glacial meltwater, this is the biggest lake on the Tibetan Plateau. Tibet has the highest concentration of lakes in China.

11. Lhasa
The capital of Tibet has some beautiful buildings, including magnificent Potala Palace, with more than 1000 rooms.

12. Source of the Yangtze
From its source in Tibet, the Yangtze River flows all the way through China to Shanghai.

Takla Makan Desert

Kunlun Shan (mountains)

CHINA

Karakoram Range

K2

Nanga Parbat

Srinagar

Islamabad

PAKISTAN

Lahore

Govind National Park

Valley of Flowers

Source of the Ganges

Thar Desert

New Delhi

INDIA

Ganges River

Kangrinboqe Feng

Lake Rara National Park

Annapurna

Mount Dhaulagiri

Kathmandu

Chang Tang Reserve

Source of the Yangtze River

Tibetan Plateau

Siling Co

Lhasa

Himalayas

Mount Everest

Makalu

Kanchenjunga

NEPAL

BHUTAN

Brahmaputra River

Mishmi Hills

INDIA

Cherrapunji

Naga Hills

BANGLADESH

MYANMAR (BURMA)

Calcutta

Potala Palace, Lhasa, Tibet

N

EUROPE

ASIA

AFRICA

AUSTRALIA

0   250   miles
0   250   500 km

Oceans & beaches

Oceans cover more than two-thirds of the Earth's surface, making the ocean biome the biggest biome of all. Under the waves, there are a multitude of habitats, from the beach to the deep-ocean floor.

A boater enjoys a sunset off the coast of Florida in the Gulf of Mexico.

The oceans are one gigantic body of water, but we give different names to different parts. The four major oceans are the Pacific Ocean, Atlantic Ocean, Indian Ocean and Arctic Ocean. Each lies in a huge hollow in Earth's crust, called a **basin**.

The oceans are not really one habitat, but a collection of habitats, many of which overlap. Most ocean plants and animals live near the coast, where the water is rich in **nutrients** from rivers, and where the shallow seafloor gets plenty of sunlight. Coastal habitats include forests of giant seaweeds, meadows of sea grass and some coral reefs.

Where sea meets land, another habitat exists: the intertidal zone. It can be a violent place, where savage waves continually crash into rocky cliffs. In other places, there are calm, sandy beaches that slope gently into the water. The animals and plants of the intertidal zone lead double lives, having to cope with being exposed to air and then being covered with water, at least once a day.

Most of the open ocean has far less wildlife than the coast. Even so, the sea surface in places teems with microscopic creatures called **plankton**, which flourish in the sunlit water. Deep below the plankton is a zone of dark, cold water less rich in life but with some very unusual inhabitants.

The ocean floor is home to all sorts of animals. Many feed on dead matter raining from the waters above. Most seem to live near land, or on the summits of underwater mountains. Most of the seafloor has not been explored, so there could be many creatures far from land that we don't know about.

You might think the deepest parts of the ocean would be devoid of life, but they are home to some of the weirdest animals of all. While most life on Earth depends on the sun for energy, some of the strange creatures living on the deep-sea floor get their energy from chemicals gushing from hot-water **vents**.

Oceans and climate

Oceans have a huge influence on the Earth's weather. They also have their own underwater climates, which depend on ocean currents, depth below the water surface and the way sunlight travels through water.

Seawater absorbs sunlight. Even in the clearest water, only about 1 per cent of the light reaches a depth of 100 metres (330 ft), and only the surface of the ocean receives as much light as land. Sunlight is a mixture of different colours, which together appear white. The sea absorbs the different colours in differing amounts, screening some out but letting others pass. If you go scuba diving in a tropical sea, you soon notice that the spectacular coral reef colours get less vivid the deeper you go. Red and yellow get filtered out, making everything look blue-green.

Beyond the twilight zone
Scientists divide the ocean into layers, or zones, based on depth. The top zone is the sunlit zone. As you sink through it, the light fades, the water gets cooler and the pressure increases. At a depth of 200 metres (660 ft), there is barely any light left, and the pressure is twenty times higher than at the surface. This is the bottom of the sunlit zone.

Conditions on the coast are dominated by the tides and the force of the waves. Over time, waves can carve bare rock into towering sculptures called sea stacks, like these at Cannon Beach in Oregon in the USA.

Beneath the sunlit zone, down to 1000 metres (3300 ft), lies the twilight zone. The creatures of the twilight zone are often red or black, making them almost invisible in the gloom. But there are flashes of light because many animals, including twilight-zone fish and squid, produce their own light by a process called **bioluminescence**. They use this light to dazzle **predators**, to attract prey or to signal to other members of their **species**.

Beyond 1000 metres (3300 ft) deep is the dark zone – a world of total blackness, except for occasional flashes of bioluminescent light. This zone extends to the deep plains that make up most of the ocean floor. Pressures in the dark zone are more than 100 times greater than at the surface – enough to crush your lungs completely – and the water is bitterly cold, hovering between freezing point and 4°C (39°F). Some of the animals here are

Ocean facts

▲ Oceans cover 71 per cent of Earth's surface.

▲ The seas and oceans are slowly changing shape and size. The Pacific Ocean is shrinking, but the Red Sea is getting wider.

▲ If all the continents were scraped off to sea level and dumped into the Pacific basin, they wouldn't come close to filling it in.

Ocean zones

Right: Air-breathing divers usually stay less than 50 metres (160 ft) from the surface. Even at these depths, sea water filters out most red light, leaving only blue and green.

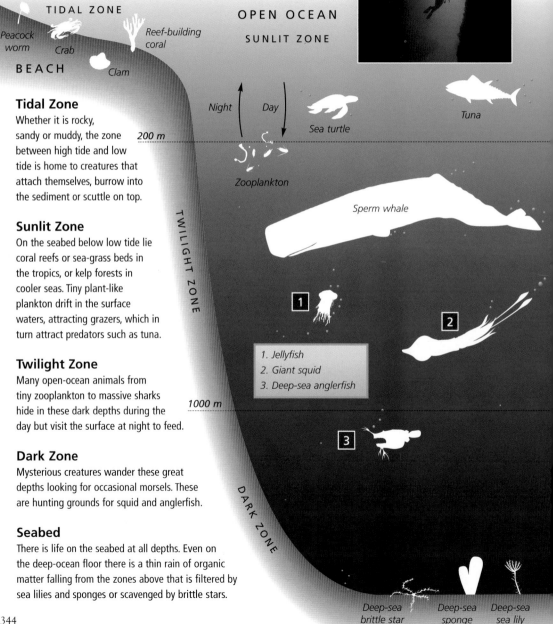

TIDAL ZONE

OPEN OCEAN

SUNLIT ZONE

Peacock worm

Crab

Reef-building coral

BEACH

Clam

Night   Day

200 m

Sea turtle

Tuna

Zooplankton

TWILIGHT ZONE

Sperm whale

1

2

1. Jellyfish
2. Giant squid
3. Deep-sea anglerfish

1000 m

3

DARK ZONE

Deep-sea brittle star

Deep-sea sponge

Deep-sea sea lily

Tidal Zone

Whether it is rocky, sandy or muddy, the zone between high tide and low tide is home to creatures that attach themselves, burrow into the sediment or scuttle on top.

Sunlit Zone

On the seabed below low tide lie coral reefs or sea-grass beds in the tropics, or kelp forests in cooler seas. Tiny plant-like plankton drift in the surface waters, attracting grazers, which in turn attract predators such as tuna.

Twilight Zone

Many open-ocean animals from tiny zooplankton to massive sharks hide in these dark depths during the day but visit the surface at night to feed.

Dark Zone

Mysterious creatures wander these great depths looking for occasional morsels. These are hunting grounds for squid and anglerfish.

Seabed

There is life on the seabed at all depths. Even on the deep-ocean floor there is a thin rain of organic matter falling from the zones above that is filtered by sea lilies and sponges or scavenged by brittle stars.

Oceans play a central role in Earth's climate. Water escapes from the ocean surface as water vapour. It rises, cools and turns to droplets, which form clouds.

deep trenches, reaching depths of 10 km (6 miles) or more. Life in the abyssal zone is similar to that in the dark zone, but pressures here are even more extreme. Only a handful of people in the deepest-diving submersibles have ever entered this world.

Heat sink

Compared to land, oceans warm up and cool down very slowly. As a result, they act as a gigantic heat store, able to absorb vast amounts of energy from the sun in warm weather, and then release the heat slowly during cold weather. The oceans therefore have a huge influence on the Earth's **climate**.

In warm, sunny parts of the world, the oceans pick up heat from the sun. Ocean currents then carry this heat away and release it in cooler areas. Warm sea water flowing towards the North Pole, for example, keeps the Arctic Ocean warmer than it would otherwise be. Besides carrying heat around

miniature monsters: grotesque fish with swollen heads, gaping mouths and scrawny bodies. Food is so scarce that these fish try to eat everything they come across, dead or alive. It is an eat-or-be-eaten world.

There is another zone below the dark zone: the abyssal zone. This is the deepest part of the ocean, where the sea floor plunges into

Origins of life

Life on the Earth probably began in the sea around 4 billion years ago. There are several reasons why scientists think this. First, organisms are at least 70 per cent water, and the concentration of salt and other chemicals in their body liquids is similar to that of sea water. Second, the oldest fossils known are stromatolites – stony formations built up by mats of sea-living bacteria 3.8 billion years ago. Bacteria still build stromatolites in parts of the ocean today (right).

The first life might have arisen in shallow coastal waters warmed by the sun, where stromatolites grow. However, some scientists suspect that life may have begun on the deep-ocean floor, powered not by the sun but by chemical energy.

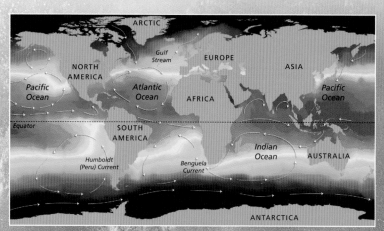

Right: Sea surface temperatures range from below 4°C (40°F), shown in black on this map, to above 27°C (80°F), shown in red. The warmest waters are near the equator, but where there are strong currents (white arrows), the ocean can be warmer or cooler than expected. The cold Humboldt (Peru) Current off the west coast of South America, for instance, causes a tongue of cool water to extend hundreds of kilometres towards the equator.

Rogue waves

In the days of sail, it was vital that seafarers knew the courses of major ocean currents. Sailing against a current could add many days to a journey, and sailing across a current could deflect a ship from its course. Even today, seafarers have to understand ocean currents. If waves from a storm meet an oncoming current, the colliding waves can add together to form 'rogue waves' big enough to swamp ships. Such rogue waves, some of which sailors claim are more than 30 metres (100 ft) high, sometimes form off the south-east coast of Africa – a notorious danger spot where even giant tankers have been known to sink.

the planet, the oceans release water vapour into the air, producing the clouds and rain on which life on land depends.

NORTH AMERICA

Rivers in the sea

There are several reasons why ocean currents exist. One is simply that winds blowing on the ocean surface push the water along.

Winds exist because Earth's air is in constant motion, driven by the sun's energy and stirred around by our planet's rotation. Air is continually circulating, travelling up and down in great circular patterns called circulation cells. The bottoms of these cells, where air moves along the planet's surface, form global winds. These, in turn, produce global currents in the ocean surface. One such current is the Gulf Stream, which flows across the Atlantic from the Gulf of Mexico to western Europe. The Gulf Stream transports nearly 500 million bathtubs full of water every second – several times the water passing through all the world's rivers put together. All that water carries a lot of heat, which keeps the climate of north-west Europe much milder than it would be otherwise.

warm water

PERU

Pacific Ocean

Merry-go-round

The major ocean currents flow in huge circles called gyres (shown on the map opposite), which are set spinning by Earth's rotation. Earth's rotation also makes the gyres turn in specific directions. In the northern hemisphere, the gyres turn clockwise. In the southern hemisphere, they turn counterclockwise. One consequence of

El Niño

In most years, strong winds blow from east to west across the middle of the Pacific Ocean, driving the ocean current west. As warm surface water moves west, cool water wells up from deep below to take its place, bringing nutrients to the surface off the coast of Peru. The upwelling supports such vast shoals of anchovies that it forms one of the world's most important fishing sites. But in some years (left), the winds are weak. The upwelling does not develop, the anchovies don't come and the fishing is disastrous. The cool, nutrient-rich water is replaced by warm water from the western Pacific (white and red in the image). This is called an El Niño event. The El Niño event alters wind patterns around the world, causing unusual and extreme weather. It also makes the sea surface warmer in some places, killing the organisms that build coral reefs.

this is that in the southern Atlantic and Pacific, cold water from the poles extends along west coasts, while warm water from the **equator** usually travels along east coasts.

Upwelling and downwelling

Life in the oceans is richest where there is plenty of light, warmth and nutrients. The microscopic plants that live in surface waters – **phytoplankton** – need these to grow. But many parts of the open sea are like deserts because of a lack of nutrients. Where there are few nutrients, there are few phytoplankton. And without phytoplankton, there are few of the animals that eat them.

There are oases in this desert. In certain places, a current of cold water from deep below, a process called **upwelling**, brings nutrients to the surface. Plankton grow in abundance at these places, providing food for fish and other animals. People also benefit from regions of upwelling – many of the world's fish are caught in these places.

Upwelling tends to happen on the eastern side of the great oceans. They are caused by offshore winds, which blow the surface waters out to sea. Deep waters full of nutrients well up from below to replace the surface waters.

What goes up must come down. Where ocean surface currents from opposite directions collide, some of the water is forced downwards in a process called **downwelling**. The downwelling water is usually clear because it has few nutrients and not very much plankton. The clear waters let plenty of light through, which is ideal for coral reefs. Some of the world's largest coral reef systems – those of the Caribbean and the Great Barrier Reef of Australia, for example – grow in regions of downwelling on the western side of oceans.

Oceanic conveyor belt

Downwelling and upwelling areas are linked by deep currents flowing sluggishly through the oceans many thousands of feet down. These currents form what scientists call the oceanic conveyor belt – a continuous current of water that carries heat energy around the planet. The conveyor belt carries huge volumes of water and probably has a great effect on the Earth's climate.

One downwelling region that feeds the oceanic conveyor belt is where the Atlantic Ocean meets the Arctic. Surface currents carry warm water from the Atlantic to the Arctic, where the water cools, freezes and floats. Salt is left behind when sea water freezes, so the remaining water is cold and salty, which makes it heavy. This cold water sinks and begins its long voyage southward along the oceanic conveyor belt.

Between the tides

A rocky shore can be packed with all kinds of life, from seaweeds to crabs and sea anemones (right). A beach seems like a good place to live. But compared to the many thousands of different organisms that live in shallow water close to the shore, fewer species thrive on the beach. Why? Because life on a beach is tough.

A rocky beach is a frontier between land and sea. When the tide is out, the beach is exposed to the air – which can be far hotter or colder than the sea water. Marine organisms can dry out. If it is raining, animals are drenched in fresh water rather than salt water. And when beach animals are exposed to air, they can be attacked by land predators.

Life is still tough when the tide returns. Animals are battered by waves, and marine predators can then attack them. A barnacle or mussel fixed to a rock

cannot run away when conditions change – it has to stay there and put up with the changes. Sea anemones are also stranded. They choose hollows that become rock pools at low tide, or attach themselves in crevices that stay moist, withdrawing their tentacles to protect them from drying out. For those who can ride it out, the sea brings a fresh supply of food with each rising tide, and for seaweeds there is plenty of sunlight.

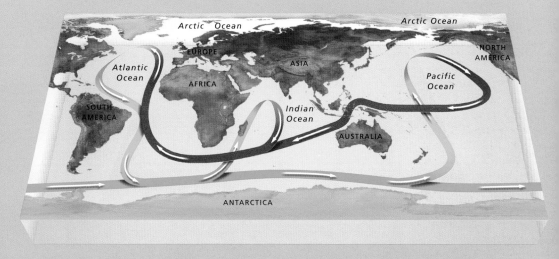

Warm surface currents (red) and cold, deep-sea currents (blue) are connected in a continuous stream of moving water called the oceanic conveyor belt.

Global warming could disrupt this process. If ice stops forming in the far North Atlantic, the oceanic conveyor belt would be interrupted, with consequent climatic effects occurring across the globe.

Hot or cold

Temperature is one of the major factors that affects where sea creatures live. Birds and mammals are warm-blooded – they keep their bodies at a constant warm temperature, no matter whether the surroundings are warm or cool. Warm-blooded animals such as whales can travel between warm and cold areas and still survive. The grey whale, for instance, spends summers in the chilly waters of the Arctic, but swims to much warmer waters off Baja California in winter. Most sea animals, however, are cold-blooded, which means their body temperature is greatly affected by their surroundings. Such species are less flexible about where they can live. Tropical fish would die in cold water, for instance, and cold-water fish cannot survive in tropical water.

The Bay of Fundy, Nova Scotia, Canada, has the largest tidal range in the world. During the maximum high tide, the water is 16 metres (52 ft) higher than at low tide.

Ocean plants

Most ocean plants are not true plants at all. They are algae – simple, plant-like organisms that lack proper stems, leaves or roots. But like the true plants on land, they trap sunlight and use it to make food.

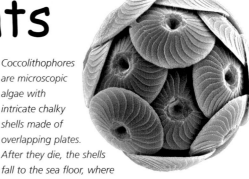

Coccolithophores are microscopic algae with intricate chalky shells made of overlapping plates. After they die, the shells fall to the sea floor, where they build up and gradually turn into chalk or limestone. These coloured microscope images show coccolithophores at 2000 times their actual size.

Plants on land are obvious – just take a look at the trees and grasses around you. But where are the plants in the oceans?

On some beaches you can find seaweeds – usually visible as brown, leathery ribbons washed back and forth by the waves. In some shallow waters, you can spot meadows of **sea grass**. But out at sea, you can't see any plants at all. They are there, but they are microscopic. They are single-celled marine **algae**. In a cupful of sea water there are tens of millions of them.

Over the course of a year, the growth of these microscopic marine algae is greater than that of all the grasses and trees on land. Marine algae are really important – it's just that most of them are too small to see without using a microscope.

Plankton

Most marine algae are plankton – organisms that drift along with ocean currents. Those plankton, including algae, that can trap sunlight and use it to make food are called phytoplankton (*phyto* means 'plant').

When phytoplankton make food they also release **oxygen**, as do land plants. The whole process, called **photosynthesis**, is vital to most life-forms, because they rely on the food and oxygen that plants produce. **Zooplankton** (animal-like plankton) eat phytoplankton, and larger animals such as fish and squid eat the zooplankton. The vast majority of marine animals' food comes from phytoplankton.

The smallest phytoplankton are incredibly tiny – hundreds would fit on a pinhead. Many are not algae but a kind of **bacteria**, although they are only distantly related to the bacteria that cause disease in people. Because of their small size, these bacterial plankton slipped through scientists' nets, so nobody realized how common and important they were until recently. We now know that the tiniest

SCOTLAND

Plankton blooms

Every spring, there is an explosion in the number of phytoplankton in the surface of the North Atlantic, brought on by warm, sunny weather. At its height, this 'plankton bloom' is so intense that the plankton are clearly visible from space. The bright blue-green patch of plankton in the picture lies off the coasts of England and France. The bloom fades in summer, and the dead plankton sink, forming a sludge that settles on the ocean floor.

All manner of worms, crabs and sea cucumbers feed on the fresh sludge. It also attracts swimming scavengers, from fish to small, shrimp-like creatures called amphipods.

IRELAND

ENGLAND

plankton bloom

FRANCE

Diatoms are minute algae that multiply in all the world's oceans. Their many complex shapes are formed by glassy skeletons.

phytoplankton can produce more than three-quarters of the food and oxygen in any particular part of the sea.

Small but beautiful

The medium and large phytoplankton are tiny, too. The largest are about the size of the full stop at the end of this sentence. Some, called coccolithophores, look like a tiny ball covered in round, chalky plates. When these plankton die and fall to the sea floor, their remains build up over millions of years to form a chalky carpet that can be hundreds of metres thick. England's famous White Cliffs of Dover formed this way from countless billions of coccolithophores.

Many phytoplankton have fascinating shapes. Diatoms, for instance, have beautifully intricate skeletons made of silica (the main chemical in glass). Others, called dinoflagellates, have thinner skeletons shaped like leaves or cones. Many dinoflagellates are bioluminescent – they produce their own light when the water is disturbed. In some parts of the world, the sea surface sparkles at night with the green light of dinoflagellates when waves break or when a person swims.

Red tides

Sometimes phytoplankton grow so quickly, and in such huge numbers, that they colour the water. As they die and become trapped on the surface, they form a scum. This is called a red tide. Despite the name, it can be any colour from yellow to blue.

Red tides can remove so much oxygen from the water that sea animals suffocate. And some red tides are poisonous. Shellfish, such as clams and oysters, can feed on the poisonous phytoplankton unharmed, but fish or other animals that eat the shellfish may die. Worldwide, red tides caused by a phytoplankton called *Alexandrium* kill nearly 200 people every year this way.

Left: This is not a river of pollution but a red tide – a mass of tiny dinoflagellates. Under certain conditions, these tiny algae multiply so quickly that they stain the sea and can poison creatures that feed on them.

Kelp forests are full of dark corners for sea life to hide, so they are good places for divers to visit. This diver is filming in a California kelp forest in the USA.

Seaweeds

You can often find seaweeds attached to rocks in cool, shallow water. There are three different types – red, green and brown – depending on the coloured chemical used to trap light in photosynthesis. The biggest seaweeds are of the brown type and are called giant kelp. They are like underwater trees, towering up from the sea floor to the surface with fronds as long as 100 metres (330 ft). The smallest seaweeds, such as the bright green sea lettuce, are paper-thin. Other seaweeds form a tufted or crusty covering on rocks.

Large seaweeds have a tough time. Growing in shallow water, they have to resist the battering of waves and strong currents. They have to stay anchored to stop being swept out to sea. At the same time, they have to reach towards the surface to trap sunlight.

Below: There are many types of kelp, but they all live in cool seas. They grow nearer the equator only where cold currents bring water from cooler regions. This happens on the west coasts of South America and Africa.

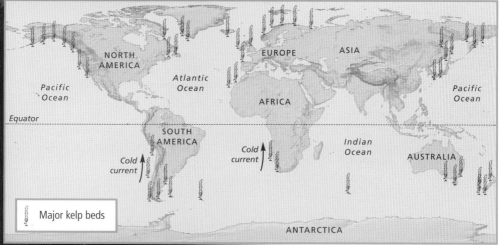

NORTH AMERICA
EUROPE
ASIA
Pacific Ocean
Atlantic Ocean
Pacific Ocean
AFRICA
Equator
SOUTH AMERICA
Cold current
Cold current
Indian Ocean
AUSTRALIA
Major kelp beds
ANTARCTICA

353

A large seaweed is mostly three parts: a stem, fronds or blades (like leaves) and a holdfast. The stem and fronds are flexible so they can bend with the currents and waves. If they were rigid, they would easily snap. The holdfast, which looks a bit like a tangle of roots, anchors the seaweed to rocks on the sea floor. The fronds and the stem often contain air sacs, or bladders, that make the seaweed's fronds float.

Kelp and otters

Lots of animals live among seaweed or attached to it, although few animals eat live seaweed. Many more feed on the thin covering of green algae that grows on the seaweed's surface.

In the North Pacific, there is a strange relationship between kelp and sea otters. Where sea otters live among the kelp, the kelp usually thrives, unless the water is polluted. But where sea otters are absent (perhaps removed by hunting), the kelp seems to go through a boom-and-bust cycle. Sometimes it is abundant, but at other times

Above: After being laid out to dry, this seaweed harvested in California might end up being used as a strengthener in ceramics or as thickener in jelly.

Below: In parts of California in the USA, sea otter numbers are slowly recovering and healthy kelp forests are returning. The sea otter is so important to the kelp habitat that it is called a keystone species.

it almost disappears. Sea urchins – spine-covered animals related to starfish – seem to be responsible. Where sea otters are present, they feed on sea urchins and keep their numbers in check. Where otters are missing, sea urchins multiply and eat the kelp until there is almost none left. Without food, the sea urchins then die, and the kelp re-grows.

Kelp and yoghurt

What has kelp got to do with yoghurt? Seaweeds – raw, cooked or dried – can make delicious food. They are also rich in vitamins and materials. Not only this, seaweeds contain chemicals called alginates that are used in the food, medical and cosmetics industries. Alginates form thickeners, binders and stabilizers for all sorts of items: drug capsules, lipsticks, shampoos, toothpaste, low-fat mayonnaise and yoghurts. Brewers even add them to beer to make the foamy head last longer.

Sea grass

Sea grasses are the only flowering plants that live underwater in the sea. They are true grasses, with proper stems, roots, leaves and flowers. They grow best in clear, shallow water that has a soft bottom of nutrient-rich mud or sand. Where they grow well, they form large meadows that support many animals.

Few animals can eat the tough leaves of sea grass, but many use the leaves as a floating platform. If you examine a sea-grass leaf closely, you'll see green slime on the surface – a layer of microscopic algae. Snails, fish and other animals graze on the algae. Many more creatures – tubeworms and sea squirts among them – attach themselves to sea-grass leaves and filter the passing water for the plankton on which they feed. These small animals, in turn, are eaten by crabs, fish and other large animals.

In tropical waters, some sea urchins and parrot fish eat sea-grass leaves, as do some endangered animals, such as green turtles, manatees and dugongs. Manatees and dugongs are also called sea cows. They are large mammals that look a bit like friendly walruses, though they are more closely related to elephants. They munch through energy-rich sea-grass roots as well as leaves.

Knotted wrack, a type of kelp, holds itself afloat with tiny air bladders, which act like water wings.

Fact file

▲ The largest giant kelp can grow 30 cm (12 in) a day.

▲ The total amount of kelp harvested every year in the USA for human use weighs 60,000 tonnes (65,000 tons), or as much as 10,000 African elephants.

▲ There are more than 6000 types of seaweeds.

355

Under threat

Sea grasses are under serious attack – from us.
In some places, industries pollute seawater
with oil or with heavy metals such as lead
and zinc. All these pollutants kill sea grasses.
Sewage also kills sea grass because it is very
rich in nutrients – the nutrients make
microscopic algae in the water multiply so
much that they turn the water cloudy,
depriving the sea grass of light. Fishing boats
that dredge the sea floor for shellfish or drag
fishing nets through sea-grass meadows also
make the water cloudy.

*Left: Look closer at this delicate frond of seaweed and
you'll discover it is in fact one of the world's most
bizarre fish, called a weedy sea dragon. Its long, green
fins camouflage it among kelp and sea grass.*

A mysterious disease sometimes destroys
sea grass. Scientists disagree on the exact
cause of the disease, but some think it might
be brought on by an increase in ocean
temperatures caused by **global warming**. If
sea-grass plants are already weakened by
pollution, rising temperatures might be
enough to finish them off.

In some parts of the USA, bays have lost
more than half their sea-grass meadows in
the last 40 years. Marine biologists are trying
to reintroduce sea grasses into areas where
they were once abundant, but if global
warming is causing the decline, the new
plants are unlikely to survive.

Sea-grass meadows are not only important
for wildlife. They also bind together mud and
sand, and so help protect coastlines from
being slowly worn
away by the sea.

*The dugong is one of the
few animals that can eat
the tough leaves
of sea grasses.*

The bright blue flecks on the lips of this giant clam are algae. They produce food from sunlight, and pass some food to the clam. In return, the clam provides protection.

Strange homes

Coral reefs – those dazzling, multicoloured, fish-rich havens of tropical waters – would not be there but for microscopic algae. But where are the algae on the reef? They are inside the animals. Each coral **polyp** (*see* page 362) contains microscopic algae called zooxanthellae – these can make up more than half the mass of coral polyps on a reef. The polyps give the algae a safe home in the sunlight, and in return, the algae give the polyps a supply of food, produced by photosynthesis. The algae also help the polyps produce their chalky armour. This close relationship, where both partners benefit, is a form of **symbiosis** (a close partnership between different species). The zooxanthellae are symbiotic algae. Without them, coral reefs would not exist.

The alga–polyp partners build their biggest reefs in clear, shallow waters in tropical seas, where the zooxanthellae can collect the most sunlight. Clear waters are found in downwelling regions where surface waters are poor in nutrients. Here, coral reefs grow particularly well.

Coral polyps are not the only sea creatures with plants inside them. Animals called sponges do the same thing. Giant clams – those that look as though they could grab your leg (but do not) – sport brightly coloured bands of algae in their lips, where the two halves of the shell come together.

Life without plants

Scientists once thought that all life depended on energy from the sun. Plants and algae absorb the sun's energy to make food, and animals eat them (or one another) to obtain the food. But another way of life is possible.

In 1977, scientists in a submersible on the floor of the Pacific Ocean, more than a mile below the surface, were looking for hydrothermal vents – places on the sea floor where volcanically heated water gushes into the ocean. They found something much more exciting. On the dark sea floor near a vent they came across huge, pale clams and dozens of giant worms – 1.2 metres (4 ft) long with bright red, feathery gills (right).

Scientists discovered that creatures living close to hydrothermal vents do not need sunlight or plants at all. They get all their food from bacteria that use energy from the chemicals in the vent water to make food. The giant worms and clams have bacteria inside their bodies. They give the bacteria a home and get food in return. The worms and clams grow much faster and larger than their relatives in shallow water.

Ocean animals

Animals live at all depths in the oceans, from the surface to the sea floor 10 km (6 miles) down. They range in size from the microscopic to the largest animal that has ever lived on the Earth – the blue whale.

The oceans contain a vast amount of living space. They cover nearly three times as much of the Earth's surface as does land, but they are more three-dimensional (3D), with animals able to live at any depth. As a result, there is 6000 times more living space in the oceans than on land.

A drifting life

Animals that live floating near the ocean surface, among the plankton, are called zooplankton. Many are microscopic, but the largest, such as the biggest jellyfish, can be more than 1 metre (3 ft) wide, with tentacles 9 metres (30 ft) long.

Small and medium-sized zooplankton eat plant plankton (phytoplankton), which they catch in a variety of ways. Animals called **salps** and **larvaceans** pump sea water through their bodies, catching the phytoplankton in gel-like nets. Tiny, shrimp-like animals called **copepods** use hairy legs to waft phytoplankton towards their mouth.

Most large zooplankton eat smaller zooplankton. Arrow worms, for instance, are vicious killers, about 10 cm (4 in) long. They dart after almost any prey smaller than themselves. Jellyfish capture fish and large zooplankton with their stinging tentacles. Not all large zooplankton are predators, though. Among the exceptions are krill – shrimp-like animals about 2.5 cm (1 in) long that feed on phytoplankton. Krill are very common in Antarctic waters, where they are the main source of food for many fish, birds and whales.

Water babies

Many ocean animals live in the plankton only when young, as **larvae**, and settle on the sea floor or seashore to grow into adults. Most larvae look completely different from the adults they will become. Barnacle larvae

 ## How to float

The trick in living among the plankton is to avoid sinking. Plankton use various techniques to stay afloat. One is to have lots of body projections, such as spines or hairs, to give the body a larger surface area. Another technique is to use droplets of oil or bubbles of gas to buoy up the body. Jelly-like animals, such as salps and comb jellies, get rid of heavy chemicals and replace them with lighter ones.

With water to support their bodies, ocean animals have less need for a skeleton than do land animals. Octopuses have no bones whatsoever, allowing them to form their flexible bodies into endless different shapes and squeeze through tiny crevices. They use their suckered tentacles to grasp and smother prey.

Insects of the sea

The most common animals on Earth are not ants, flies or any other kind of insect, but tiny shrimp-like sea creatures called copepods, which also live in fresh water and wet places on land. Copepods outnumber all other animals on the planet. In their countless trillions, they probably outweigh any other type of animal, too. In the

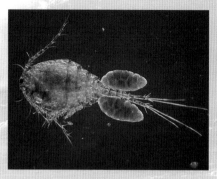

oceans, they are one of the main sources of food for fish, making them of great ecological importance.

Copepods are members of a group of animals called crustaceans, which also includes shrimps, crabs and lobsters. There are almost no insects in the oceans, but crustaceans take their place.

A puffer fish, or puffer (below), wards off attackers by inflating itself like a balloon (inset) and making sharp spines stand out on its skin.

Lionfish use venom to defend themselves. If an attacker presses against one of the lionfish's spines, the spine injects a poison so strong that it can kill a person.

look like fleas, some crab larvae look like tiny spacecraft and certain sea urchin larvae look like snowflakes. For animals that spend their adult lives on the sea floor or shore, having planktonic larvae is a good way of spreading to new areas because the larvae can drift great distances on sea currents.

Near the coast, at certain times of the year, planktonic larvae outnumber the normal residents of the zooplankton. Fish and other larger creatures gather together to take advantage of this bumper harvest.

Fishy business

The true kings of the ocean are fish. More than half of all living species of vertebrates (animals with backbones) are fish, and more than two-thirds of fish species live in the sea – at least 15,000 species. Fish are amazingly successful. They come in all shapes and sizes, from gobies about 1 cm (about half an inch) long to whale sharks reaching 18 metres (60 ft) – as big as whales. Fish live at all depths to about 6000 metres (20,000 ft) down. Some can even breathe air and live on land or glide short distances over the waves.

Scientists classify fish into three main groups: those without proper jaws (lampreys and hagfishes); those with jaws and skeletons of cartilage (sharks and rays); and those with bony skeletons. The majority of fish belong to the bony group, including herring, cod, salmon, tuna and flatfish such as sole.

Though a few fish graze algae, most fish are predators – agile swimmers with sharp senses and strong jaws for snapping up food. Fish prey on everything from plankton to large sea animals, and many are skilled hunters. Some stun their prey with electricity, others hide and ambush victims and many use speed and agility to snatch prey from the water. Some of the sea's top predators are mammal- and fish-eating sharks – the most lethal fish on Earth.

Shark attack

Sharks have a bad reputation, but not all of them deserve it. Of the 400 or so species of sharks, about forty species are known to have attacked people. In 2000, there were 79 unprovoked shark attacks recorded worldwide; ten of the people involved died. In comparison, fishermen caught millions of sharks in the same year and killed nearly all of them. Sometimes, they hunt sharks on purpose, but usually the sharks are unwanted, caught among tuna or other commercial fish.

Sharks use a range of senses to track down their food. They can smell blood from nearly 2 km (1.2 miles) away but use sight to identify victims nearby. Like most fish, they can feel the vibrations that travel through water, giving them a sense of touch at a distance. And from close range, they can detect the field of electricity generated by their victim's muscles.

Three species of sharks are responsible for most recorded attacks: the great white shark, the tiger shark and the bull shark. There are several reasons why these sharks might attack people. In some cases it is a case of mistaken identity – great whites occasionally attack surfboards, probably because they mistake the outline of surfer and board for that of a seal. In other cases a shark might attack if it feels threatened. Only rarely do sharks deliberately attack people in order to eat them.

In fact, you are much more likely to be run over by a car on the way to a beach than to be killed by a shark when you get there. Nevertheless, swimming in waters where people have reported dangerous sharks is not a good idea.

Coral extravaganza

In the warm waters of the tropics are the most complex wildlife communities in the ocean: coral reefs. A single coral reef in the Pacific can contain more than 100 species of corals and several thousand species of

The great white shark's gaping jaws and jagged teeth enable it to kill seals, dolphins and other prey with a single bite.

Many corals live in large groups, sharing a skeleton and linked by sheets of tissue. The individual star-shaped animals, called polyps, emerge from the skeleton at night to catch plankton.

invertebrates (animals without a backbone), while providing a hunting ground for hundreds of fish species and other animals.

The source of this abundance is the humble coral polyp, a tiny, tentacled animal that looks a bit like a flower. Coral polyps use their mobile tentacles to strain sea water for plankton. They also obtain food from the algae that live inside their bodies (*see* page 357). Some polyps live on their own, but most clone themselves to form huge colonies in which all the individuals are joined together. Each coral species builds a colony of a particular shape – they might look like brains, antlers, mushrooms or giant plates. Corals sport

Arrowhead crabs live among the nooks and crannies of coral reefs. They use pincer-like claws to snip chunks of flesh off coral polyps and other animals.

all the colours of the rainbow – and the reef's other colourful inhabitants add to this palette, making a living reef an explosion of fascinating shapes and colours.

Many corals secrete a carbonate skeleton to protect themselves and support the colony. When the corals die, the skeletons remain in

Bright colours are often a sign of danger. The frilly skin of many sea slugs contains microscopic stings, stolen from the sea anemones on which the slugs prey.

Coral facts

▲ A barrier reef is a structure built by coral that lies parallel to the shore, on the far side of a lagoon.

▲ The largest coral reef system is the Great Barrier Reef of Australia. It is 2000 km (1250 miles) long and clearly visible from space. It is made up of more than 2500 separate reefs.

▲ The biggest coral atoll is Kwajalein in the Marshall Islands of the western Pacific. It is more than 70 km (44 miles) long and 32 km (20 miles) wide.

▲ The soft white sand of many tropical beaches forms from coral skeletons broken down by the sea.

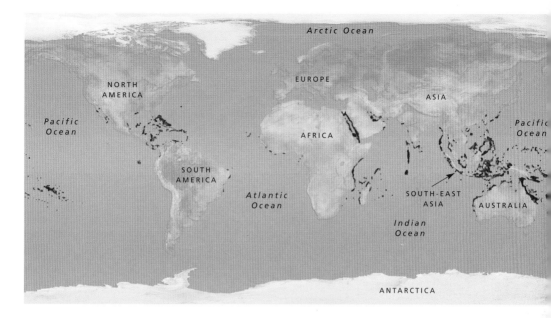

Coral reefs (red) flourish in sunny, clear, shallow water throughout the tropics, where the sea is warm. They grow near the coast and on underwater mountaintops.

place and gradually build up to form the reef. A coral reef's nooks and crannies provide havens where seaweeds and animals can settle and hide. Most reef animals graze the thin covering of algae that grows on the reef, or, like the coral polyps, they strain the water for plankton. Only a few animals, such as parrot fish and some starfish, can eat corals.

Some reef animals have their food delivered on a living plate. On many reefs there are cleaning stations where fish line up to have their skin, mouth and **gills** cleaned by fish and prawns that they might otherwise eat. The visitors seem to benefit by having parasites removed and wounds cleaned.

World without light

More than about 1000 metres (3300 ft) down, the sea is totally dark, except for light made by the animals themselves, or the headlights of submersibles carrying marine biologists.

For animals living in the dark zone, senses other than sight become important. Most scavenging deep-sea fish find food by smell.

Chemical weapons

Many coral reef animals live fixed to one spot. They can't run away when danger threatens, so they need other ways of defending themselves. A popular strategy is to make chemicals that taste repulsive or are poisonous to predators.

Some of these chemicals have proved to be useful as drugs for treating cancer and other diseases. One example is ecteinascidin-743, which is currently being tested as an anti-cancer drug. It comes from a type of sea squirt, an invertebrate, living on coral reefs in the Caribbean. Another possible drug is discodermalide, which is being tested to treat leukemia (blood cancer). Discodermalide comes from a type of sponge, also from the Caribbean.

The huge, hinged mouth and elongated body
of a deep-sea gulper eel make it look like
a creature out of a nightmare.

and viper fish can partially
dislocate their jaws to swallow
large meals. Many of these fish
have a stomach that stretches,
allowing them to swallow prey
bigger than themselves.

Those hunting live prey can
also feel the telltale ripples and
vibrations in the water that other animals
make. The long, sensitive tendrils of some
deep-sea anglerfish and the elongated fins on
tripod fish's heads are suited to this purpose.
Some fish can even detect the tiny electrical
signals produced by their victims' muscles.

Anglerfish have another trick up their
sleeve. Instead of hunting down their prey,
they use a glowing lure, attached to a long
stalk on the head, to draw victims towards
them. The lure looks like a wiggling worm –
an irresistible temptation to hungry animals.
When a victim comes into striking range, the
anglerfish snatches it in its massive jaws.

Many deep-sea creatures depend for food
on the snowfall of dead animals, body parts
and faeces from high above. Even so, food is
very scarce, and animals must conserve their
energy. Deep-sea fish move very little, and
their muscles are small and puny
compared to those of other
fish. But they make up for
this by the size of their
mouth and stomach.
Gulper eels, or deep-sea
swallowers, have vast jaws
and a snake-like body,

*Animals of the deep have to catch
whatever they find. Viper fish (far right)
have monstrous, cage-like teeth to trap
hatchet fish (above right) and other prey.*

Finding a mate

Besides being pitch-black, the deep-sea
world is enormous and mostly empty. Because
food is hard to find, animals are scattered
much further apart than in surface waters.
The darkness and emptiness can also make it
difficult for fish to find mates. Many probably
use their sense of smell to home in on scent
chemicals (pheromones) produced by a
potential mate. At close range, anglerfish can
identify suitable mates by the pattern of light
from the glowing lure, and other fish species
probably recognize light patterns, too.

Once an animal has found a mate, it is
all too easy to lose it again in the inky
blackness. Some male anglerfish have a
drastic solution to this problem: they sink
their teeth into the female's body and stay
attached for the rest of their lives. In such
species, the male is much smaller than the
female. The female's skin grows over the
male, and he becomes a parasite,
feeding on her blood.

Making light work

Many animals in the twilight zone, and some in the dark zone, can produce their own light (bioluminescence). This comb jelly, for instance, produces shimmering, rainbow-coloured lights along its transparent body. Bioluminescent light comes from a chemical reaction in special light organs and is usually blue or green. It has a variety of uses. Some deep-sea squids squirt out a cloud of shimmering

light that distracts an attacker, giving the squid a few seconds to escape. Anglerfish use a luminous lure to catch prey, and lantern fish sport complex patterns of lights that help them recognize other members of their species. Some fish of the twilight zone have lights on their underside. Seen from below, the spots of light help camouflage them against the faint glow of the sea surface.

Mysteries of the deep

Even today, there are probably many undiscovered animals in the oceans. With the ocean so difficult to study, and with so much water to search, it is not surprising that even large animals remain to be discovered.

Marine scientists only encountered the weird animal communities of deep-sea vents in 1977. In 1997, they discovered something even weirder: worms living inside frozen methane gas on the floor of the Gulf of Mexico. And one species of whale – the True's beaked whale – was only found alive at sea in July 2001. A male leaped 24 times out of the water near a ferry in the Bay of Biscay, France. Luckily, there were whale experts on board to witness and photograph the event.

For centuries, most scientists thought the giant squid was a myth. But in the 1850s, a Danish zoologist decided to examine the reports of sightings and analyze samples. He soon confirmed that the creature was real – it was a giant version of the common squid.

Now that more scientists are studying the ocean, we can expect more surprises. Despite teams of researchers searching for it, no one

has seen a giant squid alive in its midwater habitat. In the 1990s, however, scientists descended to 300 metres (1000 ft) to study another animal, called the vampire squid. They had thought it was a weak-muscled,

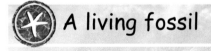
A living fossil

In 1938, fishers caught a strange, stocky fish, about 1.5 metres (5 ft) long, off eastern South Africa. The skipper took the fish to the local museum curator, Marjorie Courtenay-Latimer, who recognized it immediately. Nobody believed her when she said it might be a coelacanth – a fish believed to have been extinct for 60 million years. Luckily, she had the foresight to have the fish stuffed, and when fish expert J. L. B. Smith came to examine it, he could hardly believe his eyes. The coelacanth's internal organs had been thrown away when it was stuffed, so Professor Smith began searching for an intact specimen – a hunt that took another 14 years. In 1998, coelacanth enthusiasts discovered a second species – this time off Indonesia. Who knows what other large sea creatures remain undiscovered?

Ocean discoveries

The oceans are so vast, deep and unexplored that all sorts of mysterious creatures might lurk in their depths, awaiting discovery. The finding of animals such as giant squid, megamouth sharks and unknown whales continues to amaze experts. Some of these creatures were previously known, but only from long-dead fossils.

1. Megamouth shark
In 1976, this large-mouthed shark was found entangled in a parachute in the sea near Hawaii. It feeds on plankton near the sea surface at night, but descends to the depths during the day, which explains why it is so rarely seen.

2. Six-eyed spookfish
This fish looks like a pike but has six eyes. It was discovered in 1958, at a depth of more than 100 metres (330 ft).

3. Monoplacophoran
Scientists dredged this shelled mollusc, which looks like a giant limpet, off Mexico's west coast in 1952. Biologists thought its kind had died out 350 million years ago.

4. Vestimentiferan worm
In 1977, scientists discovered hundreds of huge tube worms, up to 2 metres (7 ft) long, among dozens of other new species of fish, clams, shrimps and crabs at deep-sea vents.

5. Ice worm
In 1997, scientists discovered this new species of worm living in methane ice on the floor of the Gulf of Mexico.

6. Lesser beaked whale
Parts of this whale's body were first found near a fish market in San Andres, Peru, in 1976. Several complete specimens were later found, and it was officially described as a new species in 1991.

7. Vampire squid
This tentacled, purple-black animal was caught in an Atlantic deep-sea sample in 1903. In 1946, scientists confirmed it is neither a true squid nor an octopus but a member of a related group thought to have been extinct.

8. Giant squid
The species that lives in the North Atlantic grows to 18 metres (60 ft) long. It has never been seen alive.

9. True's beaked whale
The first confirmed sighting of a living True's beaked whale took place in July 2001 in the Bay of Biscay, off France.

10. Deepwater stingray
The first specimen washed up on a beach at Port Elizabeth, South Africa, in 1980.

11. Coelacanth
The first live specimen known to science was caught near South Africa in 1938. At that time, the only other coelacanth specimens were fossils as old as dinosaurs.

sluggish animal, so they were amazed to see it swimming at high speed, rapidly changing shape, and turning in tight circles. The scientists had to rewrite their textbooks.

Marine migrations

Many marine animals make incredibly long journeys to find food or to breed. These epic voyages are called **migrations**.

Most migrations are seasonal. At a certain time of year, the animal migrates to a new home, where conditions are better for the next stage in its life cycle. It might migrate to breed, for instance, but then return later in the year to somewhere better for feeding.

Salmon and freshwater eels not only migrate through the sea but also travel up rivers. This is a challenge, because fresh water contains far smaller concentrations of chemicals than salt water. The move requires changes in the animal's body function.

Several species of Pacific salmon lay their eggs in the gravel-covered beds of North American rivers. When the baby fish hatch, they set off downriver, and grow into adults by the time they reach the ocean. Years later,

 ## Living in sand

At the very edge of the ocean is the shore, where conditions for animals such as this clam change drastically: the seabed is exposed twice a day by the tide. Unlike rocky shores, where hardy sea life survives attached to rocks, sandy shores often appear devoid of life. But sandy beaches can be full of animals – beneath the surface. Most sandy-beach animals burrow, especially at low tide, to avoid predators and to avoid drying out. Many clams stay buried at high tide, too, but extend their siphons (tubes) into the water. The siphons pump the water and filter out food particles.

siphons

the adults return to breed in the exact place where they hatched. To get there, they must swim upstream through rapids and leap up waterfalls. They must avoid all sorts of natural and artificial obstacles – dams, fishing nets, anglers, grizzly bears and pollution.

When they arrive at the breeding grounds, they scoop out a gravel nest. The female lays her eggs, a male fertilizes them and then both male and female die.

Atlantic eels make a reverse journey. Adults lay their eggs on the floor of the Sargasso Sea – a still patch of the Atlantic Ocean near Bermuda. The young eels rise to the surface, drift on ocean currents and swim into North American and European rivers. They mature in lakes and rivers, and then return to the Sargasso Sea to breed.

The endangered hawksbill turtle roams the tropical oceans. When it is time to mate and lay eggs, it travels to one of only a handful of nesting sites worldwide.

Many seabirds, sea mammals and turtles make journeys just as long as those of eels and salmon – or even longer. The Arctic tern flies an astonishing 32,000 km (20,000 miles) each year on its round trip between the Arctic Ocean and Antarctica. It breeds on the Arctic coast in summer, but flies south in autumn to spend the rest of the year in the ocean around Antarctica,

Spinner dolphins can swim at 40km/h (25 mph). They hunt in packs, rounding up small fish such as herring into tight shoals before moving in for the kill.

where it is summer at this time. As a result, it probably sees more hours of daylight in a year than any other animal on Earth.

The grey whale breeds in the Gulf of California in winter, away from the attentions of killer whales (orcas), which hunt in cooler waters. In summer, adults and calves swim north to the Arctic, where food is more abundant. In total, the whales swim up to 20,000 km (12,500 miles) each year – the longest migration of any mammal.

Somehow, green turtles born on Ascension Island find their way back as adults to this tiny island in the Atlantic Ocean. They travel on a 2200-km (1370-mile) journey from feeding grounds close to Brazil to mate in the waters off Ascension. The females then struggle ashore to lay their eggs.

Although sea lions need to rest, mate and give birth on beaches, they move much more easily in the ocean.

Marine mammals

Fish may be the kings of the oceans, but the biggest sea creatures are whales. Whales belong to a class of animals called mammals, which also includes dogs, bats, elephants and humans. Mammals are warm-blooded animals that breathe air and feed their young on milk. They evolved on land about 210 million years ago, but about 65 million years ago, some began living in the sea.

The first marine mammals were fierce meat eaters that looked a bit like crocodiles. Over millions of years, these crocodile-like mammals became streamlined, their stumpy legs became fins and their hair gradually disappeared. Although they still have to come to the surface to breathe, they have now mastered the oceans. They are the cetaceans: whales, dolphins and porpoises.

Some cetaceans – the toothed whales – hunt fish and squid. These cetaceans are fast and agile swimmers, and have teeth for gripping their prey. Dolphins, killer whales, porpoises and sperm whales are all toothed whales. Some toothed whales have large brains and may be highly intelligent. Bottle-nosed dolphins may even solve problems by thought, and they sometimes use tools. In the shallow seas off the coast of western Australia, bottle-nosed dolphins hold a sponge in their mouth to protect their snout while they dig for shellfish.

Other cetaceans – the baleen whales – have a giant sieve (a baleen plate) inside the mouth instead of teeth. These whales take massive gulps of sea water and squeeze it through the sieve to collect small animals, such as krill. Baleen whales are the giants of the ocean. The blue whale, which weighs up to 190 tonnes (209 tons) and reaches up to 33 metres (110 ft) long, is probably the largest animal that has ever lived on Earth.

Some baleen whales sing to one another to communicate. Humpback whales are famous for their long, haunting songs and their cooperative hunting techniques. In the breeding season, adult males sing a 20-minute song to attract females and to intimidate other males. In polar waters, groups of humpbacks blow curtains of bubbles to herd schools of fish and krill into a tight ball. Then they lunge upward through the close-packed school – a bumper harvest for a minimum amount of effort.

Humpback whales, although among the largest of animals, eat only tiny prey – krill and small fish. In one mouthful, they swallow many thousands.

Gulf of Mexico

From the sandy beaches and coral reefs of the coast to the mysterious chemical-energy communities of the deep ocean floor, the Gulf of Mexico provides varied habitats for many kinds of marine life.

Fact file

▲ Almost the entire world population of Kemp's ridley turtles – the rarest sea turtle in the world – arrives each year at Rancho Nuevo beach in Mexico. The turtles' purpose is to lay eggs together.

▲ Divers discovered the phenomenon of mass coral spawning in the Gulf of Mexico. Once a year, all the coral polyps release their eggs and sperm at once, creating an upside-down snowstorm. Scientists now study mass coral spawning the world over.

1. Rancho Nuevo
A beach where 95 per cent of the Earth's population of Kemp's ridley turtles come to nest.

2. Flower Garden Banks
This US National Marine Sanctuary protects an area of coral reefs. In 1990, divers here observed the snowstorm effect of a mass coral spawning for the first time.

3. Methane seep
Scientists found ice worms, in 1997, living in a methane seep, where methane leaks into the ocean from under the seabed.

4. Meso-American Barrier Reef System
The second largest barrier reef on the Earth lies off the coast of Belize. Countless billions of coral polyps built the reef by laying down their stony skeletons as they grew.

5. Yucatán Channel
Water flows into the Gulf of Mexico here, carrying plankton from the coral reefs of Belize.

6. Florida Keys
A long chain of low islands with coral reefs on the south side and sand and sea-grass beds on the north. Currents from the Yucatán Channel bring the young of tropical life-forms from the Caribbean Sea and deposit them on the coral reefs of the Florida Keys.

7. Florida Bay
The sea-grass beds here are among the largest on the Earth. Some of them are threatened by pollution. The beds are grazed by slow-moving manatees (sea cows).

8. Florida Strait
Water flows out of the Gulf of Mexico through the Florida Strait, forming a current that eventually flows to Europe.

9. Bahamas
Scientists take part in the Wild Dolphin Research Program in the warm, shallow waters around the Bahamas island chain. They observe the social behaviour of the dolphins.

Palm-fringed beaches with beautifully clear water are common in the Florida Keys. The main keys are connected by the Overseas Highway, one of the longest overwater roads in the world.

NORTH AMERICA
EUROPE
ASIA
AFRICA
SOUTH AMERICA
AUSTRALIA
ANTARCTICA

USA

Washington, DC

Appalachian Mountains

N

0   250   miles
0   250   500 km

Atlantic Ocean

Houston

New Orleans

Mississippi Delta

Flower Garden Banks **2**

Methane seep **3**

FLORIDA

Miami

MEXICO

Monterrey   Rancho Nuevo

1

Florida Bay **7**

Nassau

B A H A M A S

Gulf of Mexico

5

6

Florida Keys

Florida Strait

9

Havana

8

Mexico City

Guadalajara

Yucatán Peninsula

Yucatán Channel

CUBA

CAYMAN ISLANDS

Cayman Trench ▼

JAMAICA

Kingston

Belmopan

BELIZE

Meso-American Barrier Reef System **4**

Caribbean Sea

GUATEMALA

HONDURAS

Guatemala City

San Salvador

Tegucigalpa

EL SALVADOR

NICARAGUA

Pacific Ocean

Managua

COSTA RICA

San José

Barranquilla

PANAMA

Panama City

COLOMBIA

✈ Lair of the ice worm

On the deep-sea floor in the Gulf of Mexico live some of the strangest animals known to science – ice worms (left). These pinkish worms, only 2–5 cm (1–2 in) long, live in methane seeps, places where methane leaks into the ocean from deposits under the seabed. On land, methane is a gas, but in the cold and the high pressure of the seabed, it behaves strangely; it combines with water to form a kind of methane ice. It is in this unique habitat that ice worms live. They burrow in the methane ice and sculpt it into peaks like whipped cream. Scientists suspect that the worms live on bacteria. Some bacteria can use methane as a source of chemical energy to make food, just as plants use the energy in sunlight.

Arctic Ocean

At the top of the world is the Arctic Ocean, surrounded by continents on all sides. Ice formed by the freezing of sea water covers almost the entire Arctic Ocean in winter, and only powerful ice-breaking ships can pass through.

Arctic crossing

As late as the 1890s, many geographers thought that a continent lay at the North Pole, or at the very least, that the Arctic was a shallow sea. Norwegian scientist and explorer Fridtjof Nansen was one of the few who did not. Nansen designed the *Fram*, a boat that would rise up out of the ice rather than be crushed by it. Between September 1893 and August 1896, the *Fram* drifted with the Arctic ice, at one point coming to within 400 km (250 miles) of the North Pole. Nansen and a companion set out for the Pole on foot but had to turn back in severe weather and spend winter on the ice. Nansen's courageous expedition proved that there was no major continent in the Arctic, just ocean. His team made soundings through the ice and showed that the ocean was more than 2000 metres (6500 ft) deep in places.

When the great glaciers that flow off the Greenland ice cap meet the ocean, large chunks of ice, or icebergs (left), break off and float away. Once free, the icebergs drift with ocean currents and the wind, and can end up far south in the Atlantic. Some even reached Bermuda in 1907 and 1926.

Fact file

▲ Even in summer, half the Arctic Ocean is covered in sea ice, much of it over 3 metres (10 ft) thick.

▲ Every year at the North Pole, six months of darkness is followed by six months of light.

▲ In places where the Arctic Ocean is free of ice cover, winter storms cause thorough mixing of shallow waters. The mixing stirs up nutrients, which leads to blooms of phytoplankton growth from spring through to autumn.

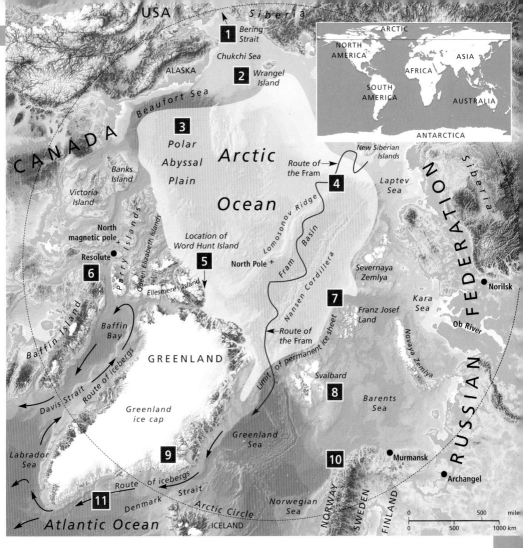

1. Bering Strait
A narrow passage between Alaska and far eastern Siberia.

2. Chukchi Sea
Walrus mothers and their calves swim from the Pacific through the Bering Strait in spring and follow the retreating ice north through the Chukchi Sea.

3. Polar Abyssal Plain
This deep plain lies 4.6 km (2.9 miles) beneath the Arctic ice. That's 20 times the height of the Canary Wharf Tower.

4. Route of the *Fram*
The route of Norwegian explorer Fridtjof Nansen's ice-bound voyage in 1893–1896.

5. Word Hunt Island
Intrepid travellers often begin their North Pole expeditions here.

6. Resolute Bay
Beluga and narwhal whales pass by on their way to their summer feeding grounds in the Arctic. The small village of Resolute stands on the shore.

7. Permanent ice sheet
The ice sheet in the middle of the ocean breaks up, at its edges, into fragments called pack ice. In winter, the pack ice reaches Canada and Siberia.

8. Svalbard
People live on this remote group of islands. Some of the inhabitants still hunt whales.

9. Greenland coast
Chilly Arctic water flows close to this coast and keeps it ice-bound for most of the year.

10. Norwegian coast
Atlantic water, warmed by the Gulf Stream and North Atlantic Drift, keeps the Norwegian coast free of ice although it is well within the Arctic Circle.

11. Greenland icebergs
The International Ice Patrol tracks Greenland icebergs that might endanger shipping. The biggest icebergs reach about 450 metres (1500 ft) high and around 1.6 km (1 mile) long, with two-thirds or more lying unseen beneath the surface.

Glossary

acacia: A type of flowering tropical tree common in savannas.

adaptation: Characteristic feature of an animal or plant developed through evolution in keeping with changes in circumstances. Adaptations can be physical, such as the long neck of a giraffe, or behavioural, such as the tool-using abilities of a sea otter.

air pressure: A force exerted by air in the atmosphere as it weighs down on Earth. Air pressure decreases with increasing altitude.

alga (plural algae): A simple, plant-like organism that makes food from sunlight like a plant but lacks proper roots and leaves. Seaweeds are types of algae, as are are many of the single-celled organisms that make up the plankton community.

alpine tundra: A tree-less zone similar to Arctic tundra above the timberline on mountains.

altitude: Height above sea level.

amphibian: An animal, such as a frog or salamander, that lives partly in water and partly on land.

amphipod: A shrimp-like animal. Some amphipods live in the ocean in polar regions.

annual: A plant that lives for only a year or less (*see also* perennial).

antarctic circle: An imaginary line drawn around the South Pole on which there is midnight sun for one day in midsummer.

antibiotic: A substance, often a drug, that kills bacteria.

aquifer: A large supply of water trapped deep underground.

Arctic Circle: An imaginary line drawn around the North Pole on which there is midnight sun for one day in midsummer.

arid: Having a very dry climate.

aromatic: Having a strong smell.

atmosphere: The layer of air around Earth.

atoll: A ring-shaped coral reef formed above a submerged volcanic island.

aurora: A colourful glow in the night sky near the poles.

bacterium (plural bacteria): A single-celled micro-organism; among the simplest forms of life.

basin: A bowl-shaped depression on land or the seabed.

bioluminescence: Light created by living organisms.

biome: A major division of the living world, distinguished by its climate and wildlife (plants, animals and other life-forms).

Tundra, desert and temperate grasslands are examples of biomes.

blizzard: A severe snowstorm with very high winds (above 51 km/h or 32 mph) and temperatures below –6.7°C (20°F) that cuts visibility to less than 152 m (500 feet).

blubber: A layer of fat under the skin of some water-living mammals, such as seals, walruses and whales.

bog: A type of wetland in which partly decayed plant matter builds up in soggy, acidic ground.

browser: A herbivore that feeds on trees and shrubs rather than grass (*see also* grazer).

bug: A type of insect with sucking mouthparts, such as a phylloxera, an aphid or an assassin bug.

bulb: A kind of fattened root used by a plant for storing food.

bush: Wild, unsettled areas of Australia and Africa.

camouflage: A natural disguise that makes animals or plants look like their surroundings.

cannibal: Animal that eats others of its own species.

canopy: A layer formed at the top of a forest by branches and leaves. Taiga and rainforests often have a dense canopy that lets by little light. Some shrublands have a broken canopy formed by shrubs.

carbon dioxide: A gas released when fossil fuels such as coal, oil or natural gas burns. Carbon dioxide is one of the main gases thought to cause global warming.

carnivore: A flesh-eating animal. *Carnivore* can also mean any member of the Carnivora, an order of mostly but not exclusively flesh-eating mammals. Members of the order Carnivora all have carnassial teeth, which are scissor-like cheek teeth shaped for slicing and shearing flesh.

chaco: A type of shrubland in South America, similar to chaparral. Also called matorral.

chaparral: Shrubland in southern California formed mainly by dense thickets of sages and evergreen oaks up to 2.5 m (8 feet) tall.

chlorophyll: A green chemical in the leaves and stems of plants and some algae that captures the energy in sunlight and helps to convert it to food.

cholesterol: A waxy chemical in the human body. When too much is present, it can block arteries, which carry blood around the body and away from the heart.

climate: The pattern of weather that happens in one place during an average year.

cloud forest: A lush, misty forest found on mountains in the tropics.

cold-blooded: Having a body temperature that depends on the surroundings.

colony: A population of animals living in the same place, such as a group of nesting seabirds.

conifer: A type of plant that does not have true fruit like flowering plants but instead produces seeds protected inside a cone. Conifers often have needle-shaped leaves.

convergent evolution: Process by which completely different species develop similar adaptations in response to similar conditions.

copepod: A tiny shrimp-like animal that forms a major part of the zooplankton of the oceans.

coppice: A woodland that people manage, to produce timber growing from the base of living trees.

deciduous: A plant that sheds all its leaves every year.

deforestation: The clearing of forest, usually carried out by cutting down or burning trees.

delta: A wide, typically triangular plain at the mouth of a river where sediment collects.

desert: A place that receives less than 250 mm (10 inches) of rain a year.

desertification: The process of becoming like a desert. It can happen naturally or because of human activity. Desertification is misleadingly described as the 'spread' of deserts, but it often occurs far from the desert edge in semi-deserts or dry grasslands.

domestic animal: An animal kept by people as a pet or farm animal.

dormant: So inactive as to appear lifeless. Plant seeds often stay dormant until their soil gets wet.

downwelling: The downwards movement of surface water to the depths of the ocean.

ecological: To do with the way organisms interact with one another and the environment.

ecosystem: A collection of living animals and plants, together with their non-living environment.

ephemeral: A plant with a very short life cycle that appears only occasionally, such as a desert poppy.

epiphyte: A plant that grows on another plant and gets its water from the air or from rain.

equator: An imaginary line around Earth, midway between the North and South poles.

ermine: A type of white weasel that lives on the Arctic tundra.

erode: To gradually wear away land by the action of wind, rain, rivers, ice or the sea.

erosion: The gradual wearing away of land by the action of wind, rain, rivers, ice or the sea.

estivation: A time of dormancy some animals such as amphibians go through in summer to help them survive drought and heat.

estuary: A place where the tide mixes with freshwater from a river, usually in an inlet of the sea at the mouth of a river.

eucalyptus: A type of plant native to Australia. Eucalyptus trees are also called gum trees. Some eucalyptuses form mallee shrublands, others make up towering rainforests.

evaporate: To turn into gas. When water evaporates, it becomes an invisible part of the air (vapour).

evergreen: A plant that keeps its leaves all year round.

evolve: To change gradually over many generations. All the world's species have formed through evolution.

excretion: The removal by animals or plants of chemical wastes from inside their cells.

fertile: Capable of sustaining plant growth. Farmers often try to make soil more fertile when growing crops.

food chain: Scientists can place animals and plants living in one place into a series that links each animal with the plant or animal that it eats. Plants are usually at the bottom of a food chain with large carnivores at the top. Food chains connect to form food webs.

fungus (plural fungi): A type of organism, neither plant nor animal, that gets its food by digesting plant or animal material, living or dead.

fynbos: Shrubland at the southern tip of South Africa formed mainly by proteas and heaths.

gallery forest: A strip of forest along a riverbank.

garigue: A sparse shrubland of the eastern Mediterranean region.

geyser: A jet of hot water or steam produced by volcanic activity.

gills: Organs that enable animals to breathe under water.

glacier: A river of ice that flows slowly off a mountain or ice sheet.

global warming: The gradual warming of Earth's climate, thought to be caused by pollution of the atmosphere, especially by carbon dioxide.

grazer: A herbivore that mainly eats grass (*see also* browser).

greasewood: Also called chamise, this low, stiff shrub grows in the California chaparral.

heath: A general name for heathers and their relatives.

heath or heathland: An area covered by low shrubs such as heathers. Heath is usually an human-made habitat in Europe.

heather: A type of shrub with small leaves and bell-like flowers.

hemisphere: One half of Earth. The northern hemisphere is the half to the north of the equator.

herbaceous plant: A plant that has no woody tissue. Many herbaceous plants die back in winter.

herbivore: A plant-eating animal.

hibernation: A time of dormancy that some animals go through during winter. In true hibernation, the heart rate and breathing slow dramatically and the body cools.

hominid: A member of the family of two-legged apes made up of humans and our fossil ancestors.

humus: Vital, dark brown organic matter in the soil created by animal dung and the rotting remains of plants and animals.

hypha (plural hyphae): The thin fibres of a fungus, usually growing underground.

ice age: A period when Earth's climate was cooler and the polar ice caps expanded. The last ice age ended 10,000 years ago.

iceberg: A huge ice block floating in the sea, having broken from a glacier or ice sheet.

ice cap: A thick layer of ice covering land near the poles. The largest ice cap is on Antarctica.

insulate: To keep warm by trapping a layer of still air.

invertebrate: An animal with no backbone, such as a worm.

irrigation: The use of channelled water by people to grow plants in dry areas.

ivory: A hard white material that forms the tusks of elephants.

lagoon: An area of shallow water sheltered by a stretch of land.

larva (plural larvae): A young form of an animal. A tadpole is the larva of a frog.

lichen: A partnership between algae and fungi.

lignotuber: A swollen, woody root storing food and water in some plants, such as mallees.

limestone: A type of rock formed over thousands of years from the shells of tiny sea creatures building up on the seabed. Chalk is a type of limestone.

loess: A wind-blown dust that forms soft soils.

mallee: A small, shrubby, fire-resistant eucalyptus that grows in south and west Australia. Also, regions covered by mallee plants.

mammal: A warm-blooded animal that feeds its young on milk.

mangrove: A tree that grows in swamps on tropical coasts. Many mangroves have prop roots that support the plant.

maquis: A type of shrubland that grows in the western Mediterranean region, formed by broad-leaved, evergreen shrubs.

marsupial: A type of mammal in which the young develop in a pouch on the mother's body.

matorral: A type of shrubland in South America, similar to chaparral. Also called chaco.

metabolism: An animal's or plant's chemical process of breaking down food to release energy.

methane: A gas that occurs naturally under the seabed. Also called natural gas, people sometimes use methane as a fuel. It can also be harvested from decaying plant matter.

micro-climate: The pattern of weather within a small area, such as a valley, treetop, or burrow.

migration: A long-distance journey by an animal to find a new home. Many animals migrate each year.

monsoon: A very rainy season in South Asia; or the wind that causes the rainy season.

mycorrhiza (plural mycorrhizae): A fungus that lives in partnership with a plant's roots.

nectar: A sugary liquid produced by a plant to attract the animals that pollinate its flowers.

niche: The particular way of life and habitat of a species.

nitrate: A mineral that helps plants grow.

nocturnal: Active at night.

nomad: A person who travels from place to place in search of food and water.

nutrient: Any chemical that nourishes plants or animals, helping them grow. Plants absorb nutrients from the soil, while animals get nutrients from food.

oasis: An area surrounded by desert where there is enough water to sustain plants.

oxygen: A gas in the air that also dissolves in water. Animals and plants, including those that live in water, need to take in oxygen so their cells can release the energy from food.

ozone: A gas that forms a layer in the upper atmosphere. The ozone layer shields Earth from some of the sun's ultraviolet radiation.

parasite: An organism that lives inside or on another organism (the host) and that causes harm to the host.

peat: Partly decayed dead plant matter that builds up in bogs.

peninsula: A narrow strip of land surrounded on three sides by water.

perennial: A plant that lives for several years (*see also* annual).

permafrost: Permanently frozen ground under the surface of some taiga.

photosynthesis: The chemical process that plants and algae use to make food from simple chemicals and the sun's energy.

phytoplankton: Tiny, plant-like organisms that float in the surface waters of oceans and lakes. Most phytoplankton are algae.

plankton: Organisms that drift along with ocean currents, mainly near the surface.

plateau: An area of relatively flat land higher than its surroundings.

podocarp: A type of conifer that grows in the temperate rainforest in the southern hemisphere.

polar desert: The main biome in Antarctica, northernmost Canada and Greenland. Polar desert gets very little rain or snow (thus, the biome is technically a desert), and the ground is usually barren or covered with ice.

pollen: Dust-like particles produced by the male parts of a flower.

pollination: The transfer of pollen from the male part of a flower to the female part of the same flower or another flower, causing the flower to produce seeds.

polyp: A coral animal. Polyps are usually tiny but live together in large colonies of various shapes.

prairie: A large area of temperate grassland, such as that in central North America.

predator: An animal that catches and eats other animals.

primate: A type of mammal that usually has grasping hands and forward-facing eyes. Most primates live in the trees of tropical forests.

protein: One of the major food groups. It is used for building and repairing plant and animal bodies.

quail: A small, ground-living wild bird similar to a small chicken.

rainforest: A lush forest that gets lots of rain. Tropical rainforests grow in the tropics; temperate rainforests grow in cool places, such as the west coast of North America.

rain shadow: An area where rainfall is low because nearby mountains provide shelter from rain-bearing winds.

rangeland: Open grassland in the Australian interior.

reptile: A cold-blooded animal such as a snake, lizard, crocodile or turtle that usually has scaly skin and moves either on its belly or on short legs.

ruminant: An animal with a complex, multi-chambered stomach. One chamber, the rumen, contains micro-organisms that help to digest tough plants.

sagebrush: A drought-resistant shrub with grey, aromatic leaves. It grows in the chaparral of North America and the Great Basin.

salp: A jelly-like, jet-propelled sea animal related to sea squirts.

saltbush: A shrub that grows on the dry Nullarbor Plain, Australia.

salt flat: A flat area covered with salt left behind by evaporation.

salt pan: A natural depression in which water collects and evaporates, leaving behind salt.

sap: The body liquid of plants.

savanna: Tropical grassland dotted with scattered trees and shrubs.

scrub or scrubland: Alternative general names for shrubland.

sea cucumber: A cigar-shaped relative of starfish. Many sea cucumbers resemble dill pickles.

sea grass: A true flowering plant that grows in meadows on seabeds just below low tidemark.

seamount: A submarine mountain rising from the seabed. Even its peak is underwater.

sediment: Particles of mud, sand or gravel carried by a river.

seed: A small, protective body containing a baby plant.

seep: A place on the seabed where chemicals such as oil and methane slowly enter the ocean.

semi-arid: Having a dry climate, but not as dry as a desert. Semi-arid areas receive about 250–510 mm (10–20 inches) of rain a year.

semi-desert: A dry area that is not as dry as a desert. Semi-desert is most common around the fringes of deserts.

short-grass prairie: Dry area of prairie where grasses such as buffalo grass and blue grama grow up to 50 cm (18 inches).

shrubland: A biome that mainly contains shrubs, such as the chaparral of California.

skink: A type of lizard, usually with very smooth scales.

snow line: the level above which snow never completely melts on a mountain.

soil erosion: Removal of soil from land by the action of wind and rain. Soil erosion often happens after deforestation.

spawn: To release lots of small eggs or sperm. Many fish and coral spawn to reproduce.

species: A particular type of organism. Cheetahs are a species, for instance, but birds are not, because there are lots of different bird species.

steppe: Vast, grassy plain in Asia and eastern Europe, often very dry.

sub-tropical: A region of Earth within the temperate zone, but near, and similar to, the tropics. Florida is often called sub-tropical.

succulent: A plant with juicy, fleshy tissue. Cacti are succulents.

swamp: A shallow wetland full of trees that can grow in water.

symbiosis: An intimate partnership between two living organisms. Both partners may benefit, or only one may benefit.

taiga: A forest biome in the north of Canada, Europe and Russia that mainly contains conifer trees. The remains of the band of taiga that once completely encircled Earth is also called the boreal forest. Taiga, or coniferous forest, also occurs at high altitudes on mountains and highlands.

tallgrass prairie: A moist area of prairie where grasses such as Indian grass and big blue stem grow up to 3 m (10 feet) tall.

temperate: Having a moderate climate. Earth's temperate zone lies between the warm, tropical regions and the cold, polar regions.

temperate forest: A biome that mainly contains broad-leaved trees. Temperate forests grow in the south of most areas of taiga.

tidal range: The difference in height between high and low tide.

timberline: The line above which no trees grow on a mountain.

tornado: Very violent funnel-shaped wind that sweeps across the land beneath a thundercloud.

trench: A canyon in the seabed.

tropic of Cancer: An imaginary line around Earth 2,600 km (1,600 miles) north of the equator. There, the sun is directly overhead at noon on 21 June.

tropic of Capricorn: An imaginary line around Earth about 2,600 km (1,600 miles) south of the equator.

tropical: Between the tropics of Cancer and Capricorn. Tropical countries are warm all year.

tropical forest: Forest in Earth's tropical zone, such as tropical rainforest or monsoon forest.

tropical grassland: A tropical biome in which grass is the main form of plant life.

tundra: A biome of the far north, made up of tree-less plains covered with small plants. Tundra begins at the northern edge of taiga forests.

understory: A layer of plants between the ground and the canopy of a forest.

ultraviolet: Invisible rays from the sun that are similar to light. Plants use ultraviolet rays to make food through a process called photosynthesis.

ungulate: A type of mammal, such as a horse, elephant or antelope, that has hooves and eats plants.

upwelling: The upwards movement of water from the depths of the ocean to the surface.

veld or veldt: A broad, high area of grassland in southern Africa. The word comes from the Dutch word for "field."

venom: A poison injected by an animal using fangs or a sting.

vent: A hole in the seabed where high-pressure hot water and minerals enter the ocean.

warm-blooded: Having a constantly warm body temperature in which heat is generated by the animal's metabolism. Mammals and birds are warm-blooded.

water vapour: Water in gas form.

wildlife corridor: A narrow strip of habitat that animals use for moving between larger patches of habitat.

zooplankton: Tiny animals and animal-like organisms that live in the surface of oceans and lakes.

Index

Page numbers in *italics* refer photographs or illustrations.

Photographic credits

Front cover, clockwise from top left:
Rocky Mountains (Photos.com); Shark (Photos.com); Red eyed tree frog (Digital Stock); Monument Valley, Arizona (Photos.com).

Ardea: 166b, Dennis Avon 69, Liz & Tony Bomford 89, John Cancalosi 165b, John Daniels 136–137, David Dixon 113b, 196–197, Hans D. Dossenbach 259b, Thomas Dressler 181, Jena-Paul Ferrero 8-9, 28, 38, 85, 200, 257t, 258tr, Bob Gibbons 128b, 239, Francois Gohier 14l, 56, 137r, 143, 159, 160–161, 167, 176b, 186, 230b, 262b, 298t, 306–307, 309, 311, 323, 327, Nick Gordon 279b, A. Greensmith 95, Martin W. Grosnick 36b, C. Clem Haagner 256b, Chris Harvey 232, Chris Knights 49, Ferrero Labat 242, 256t, 264t, Ken Lucas 174t, John Mason 97, Stefan Meyers 70–71, 100, 172–173, 336r, Colin Monteath 151b, P. Morris 244t, D. Parer & E. Parer-Cook 240–241, B 'Moose' Peterson 216t, Jamie Plaza Van Roon 79, S. Roberts 19, Graham Robertson 32, Peter Satyn 169, 215, 223b, J. E. Swedberg 48–49, 92–93, Zdenek Tunka 65r, Adrian Warren TP, 219, 228b, 324t, 334, M. Watson 154–155, Caroline Weaver 325, Alan Weaving 166t, 201, 214, Wardene Weisser 165t, Bilat Yves 254tl, Jim Zipp 145, Andrey Zvonikov 30t, 33b, 35bl; **Art Explosion:** 64b, 107t, 109t, 134l, 157t, 171t, 179t, 255b, 360c, 363b, 363t, 370b; **Bruce Coleman:** 276, Anders Blomquist 39b, Bruce Coleman Inc. 118–119, 132–133, 134–135, 138–139, 147; Bob & Clara Calhou 329, Alain Compost 283, Sarah Cook 249, Jules Cowan 160t, Gerald S. Cubitt 238, MPL Fogden 282b, Jeff Foott 171b, 320, Christer Fredriksson 238–239, 279t, HPH Photography 247tr, Carol Hughes 17t, Gunter Kohler 255t, Wayne Lankfen 148, Luis Claudio Marigo 244–245, 268–269, 324b, Joe McDonald 102, 139r, 180b, Natural Selections Inc. 43, 44, 124-125, 314–315, 359, 362–363, 364, Marie Read 142, Hans Reinhard 90t, John Shaw 28–29, Kim Taylor 98–99, 109b, 274b, Mark Taylor 277, Rinie Van Meurs 356b, Jim Watt 356t, Jorge & Petra Wegner 290t, Layer Werner 140, Staffan Widstrand 18–19, 192, 300b, Rod Williams 179b, 291b, Gunter Ziesler 213, Luis Claudio Margio 217, Pacific Stock 360b; **Corbis:** Karl Ammann 303b, Archivo Iconografico 197, Tom Bean 126bl, Tom Brakefield 287, Dean Congor 187, Ric Engenbright 202b, Michael & Patricia Fogden 174b, 176t, 202t, 218t, Frank Lane Picture Library 107b, 204, 238, Frank Lane Picture Library / Chris Mattison 216b, Stephen Frink 357t, Gallo Images 157, 208b, Raymond Gehman 20, Roger Gehman 220t, Dennis Johnson 208t, Wolfgang Kaehler 74b, 75b, Christine Kolisch 313b, George D. Lepp 331b, Buddy Mays 372, George McCarthy 104b, Joe McDonald 60, 104tr, 248tr, Kevin M. Morris 272, David Muench 121left, 126–27, Douglas Peebles 88, Robert Pickett 112b, Jeffrey L. Rotman 353, 362, Gale Rowell 338t, Kevin Schafer 196t, 278, 352b, Phil Schermeister 354t, Science Pictures Limited 105b, Karen Su 108b,

Penny Tweedie 235b, Karen Tweedy-Holmes 73b, Kennan Ward, 70l, 330b, Ralph White 357b; **Derek Hall:** 198; **Digital Stock:** World Panoramas 80–81, 190–191, 348–349; **Eberley College of Science, Penn State:** 373b; **Image Bank:** Terry Donnelly 82, Jen AEF Duboisberranger 280, Darrell Gulin 275, David W. Hamilton 24, Frans Lemmas 183, Ted Mead 284–285, Eric Meola 120–121, 254t, 259tr, G. I. Bernard 29, 296tl, 308, Mark Bowler, 296–297, Laurie Campbell 51, 90b, 96b, 326–327, James Carmichael, Jr 284, 296bl, Stephen Dalton 212–213, 297t, Manfred Danegger 101, 106, Nigel J. Dennis 163, 199, 206–207, 222, 248bl, 333t, Robert Erwin 55, Patrick Fagot 162–163, Nick Garbutt 241, 264b, Martin Harvey 234b, 237, 288tr, 292t, Hellio & Van Ingen 37b, Paul Hermansen 42–43, 54–55, Daniel Heuclin 182, 294b, Ralph & Daphne Keller 205, Rich Kirchner 11t, 328t, T. Kitchin & V. Hurst 63, 67, Stephen Krasemann 16, 132tr, 230t, Jean-Louis Le Moigne 141r, Trevor McDonald 355, David Middleton 128–129, Rod Planck 139b, 140–141, 319, Christophe Ratier 252, Andy Rouse 246–247, 258tc, 291t, Kevin Schafer 258tl, 297b, 331t, Jonathan & Angela Scott 234l, 254b, John Shaw 86–87, 111b, 119tr, 149b, 226–227, Eric Soder 335t, Mirko Stelzner 286–287, Karl Switak 46, 173, Roger Tidman 210t, Dave Watts 257b, 294t, Martin Wendler 317, Norbert Wu 293t, 366t, **NOOA:** OAR/NURP 367; **OSF:** Tony Allen 194b, Niall Benvie 318t, Ben Obsborne 21b, Paul Taylor 64–65, Steve Turner 209, Kim Westerskov 13; **Photodisc:** 266–267, Jess Alford 224–225, Neil Beer 175, Alan & Sandy Carey 146, 214–215, 292b, 295b, 333b, Don Farral 103, Alex L. Fradkin 336l, Geostock 34, 295t, 330t, Robert Glusic 4l, 164, Bruce Heinemann 5l, 313, Jack Hollinsworth 5c, Russell Illig 96, 110bl, 342–343, 348, Photolink 5r, 24–25, 27, 30b, 31tl, 33tr, 45, 53, 59, 66, 82, 92, 93, 105t, 131tr, 235t, 260–261, 269, 282r, 289t, 335b, 345t, 354b, 361, 370t, 371, 374, Kim Stele 369b, Stock Trek 270tr, 290t, Karl Weatherly 4r, 50, Jeremy Woodhouse 61, 253b; **Popperfoto:** Reuters 274–275; **Shutterstock:** Natalia Bratslavsky 76–77, Jeff Dalton 188–189, Ecoprint 184–185, Arlene Jean Gee 40–41, Jakez 152–153, Keith Levit 6–7, Gudelia Marmion 304–305, Tomasz Szymanski 114–115, Ryhor M. Zasinets 340–341; **Science Photo Library:** John Durham 236, Sinclair Stammers 299b; **Still Pictures:** Roland Birke 360t, Klein Hubert 289b, Manfred Kage 352t, Keith Kent 116–117, Luiz Claudio Marigo 319b, 300–301, Fritz Polking 240bl, Secret Sea Visions 344rt, Roland Seitre 114h, 243b, 262t, Michael Sewell 281, Dave Watts 253t, Norbert Wu 350b; **Stone:** Terry Donnelly 13, Charles Doswell III 122–123, Karen Su 328–329; **Stoll et al Phil. Trans R. Soc. Lond. A. 360 (2002):** Dr Jeremy Young 350; **USDA:** NRCS 318–319.